ADVENTURES FOR READERS

BOOK II

Adventures for

READERS, BOOK I

READERS, BOOK II

Adventures in

READING

APPRECIATION

AMERICAN LITERATURE

ENGLISH LITERATURE

MODERN LITERATURE

Adventures for READERS

BOOK II

MERCURY  EDITION

JACOB M. ROSS
PRINCIPAL, MIDWOOD HIGH SCHOOL,
BROOKLYN, NEW YORK

MARY RIVES BOWMAN
PROFESSOR OF ENGLISH, EAST TEXAS
STATE TEACHERS COLLEGE, COMMERCE, TEXAS

EGBERT W. NIEMAN
CHAIRMAN, DEPARTMENT OF ENGLISH, SHAKER
HEIGHTS JUNIOR HIGH SCHOOL, CLEVELAND, OHIO

Drawings by JOSEPH KRUSH
and ROBERT VELDE

Harcourt, Brace and Company
NEW YORK   CHICAGO

The photograph on the cover shows a group of horseback riders in Bryce Canyon National Park, Utah. Kodachrome by Mike Roberts from Shostal.

PICTURE CREDITS

Title page: Armstrong Roberts.
Facing p. 38: Forest fire (Western Pine Association); pirate (Galloway); Castle Conway, Scotland (Armstrong Roberts); sailboat (Armstrong Roberts). Facing p. 68: Airplane wing (Standard Oil Co. [N.J.]); mountain climber (Monkmeyer); swimming hole (Devaney); daffodils (Armstrong Roberts); ranch scene (Henle from Monkmeyer). Facing p. 116: Girl photographing bear (Galloway); the Aulden Griffin family of Evanston, Illinois, at dinner (*Ladies' Home Journal*); scene from "Tom Sawyer" (Culver); girl saddling horse, Texas (Standard Oil Co. [N.J.]). Facing p. 162: Hurricane devastation, Palm Beach, Florida (Galloway); Viking rocket (Devaney); ruins of Temple of Viracocha, Bolivia (Gendreau); snow crystals (General Electric Co.). Facing p. 208: Abraham Lincoln (Brown Brothers); Daniel Boone (Charles Phelps Cushing); "Old Ironsides," the *U.S.S. Constitution* (Galloway); Pony Express rider, from a painting (Library of Congress). Facing p. 260: Statue of Paul Bunyan and his Blue Ox at Bemidji, Minnesota (*The Bemidji Pioneer*); windblown tree and house (Charles Phelps Cushing); Mark Twain (drawing by Paul Callé); mouse (Black Star); magician and crystal ball (Devaney). Facing p. 312: Football player (Armstrong Roberts); stadium scene (Armstrong Roberts); basketball basket (Armstrong Roberts); boy going fishing (Gendreau); Babe Ruth (Wide World). Facing p. 366: Bear in tree (Armstrong Roberts); vulture (Armstrong Roberts); puppy dog (Armstrong Roberts); Husky dog (Galloway); white horse (Black Star). Facing p. 400: Old New Englander (Black Star); buffalo in National Bison Range, Moiese, Montana (U.S. Fish and Wildlife Service); Chinese girl playing harp (Monkmeyer); one-room schoolhouse, Bath, New York (Standard Oil Co. [N.J.]). Facing p. 444: River scene (Armstrong Roberts); American flag (Devaney); ship silhouetted against sky (Keystone); Burl Ives (United Press); Robert Burns (Culver).

Contents

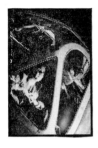

Mystery and Adventure

Outdoors

Family and Friends

The World Around Us

Exploring America's Past

Tall Tales and Fantasy

Good Sport

Animals

Americans All

Old Favorites

ADVENTURES FOR READERS

BOOK II

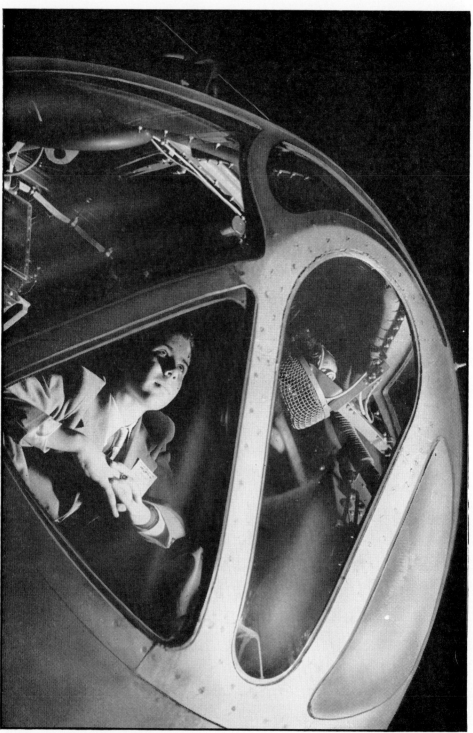

Mystery and Adventure

Red Peril

F. W. BRONSON

A forest fire roars down on the little house in a lonely clearing where a mother lies sick with pneumonia. Only her two boys stand between her and the greedy flames. Can even courage and quick wits win such a battle?

THE forest fire was closer now. Last night it had been a mere glow in the western sky. Then soon after dawn the wind had swung into the southwest. Hot blasts moaned in the tops of the pines, sweeping the flat Jersey country with smoke and ashes and torrid heat. By noon the ashes were falling like black snow over the Martin duck farm in the little clearing beside the river.

Dave waited in the kitchen to see if he could do anything for Dr. Buckley. Pretty soon the doctor came out of the front bedroom. He was shaking a thermometer and frowning.

"What time will your father be back, Dave?"

"Late this afternoon, Doctor. He started off to the market before dawn. He probably doesn't know the wind's shifted up here, so he won't hurry."

Steve, eighteen — three years older than Dave, came in from the back porch when he heard voices. Dr. Buckley turned to him.

"Steve, your mother has pneumonia. It isn't a very severe case and she'll get well, all right. But the fire's headed this way and your house isn't safe. I'd better phone for an ambu-

"Red Peril" by F. W. Bronson from *Boys' Life*, March 1945. Courtesy of the author and *Boys' Life*, published by the Boy Scouts of America.

1

lance and have her moved to the hospital."

Steve wiped the sweat from his forehead and left a smudge of ashes on the back of his wrist. " O.K., Doc."

Dr. Buckley crossed to the phone on the pantry shelf. He held the receiver against his ear for several minutes. Nothing happened. The line was dead. If the line was down it meant that the fire had cut across between Pine Center and the farm. The only way out lay eastward to the coast, three miles over a bumpy dirt road.

" Boys, you'll just have to take charge here until I can send the ambulance. I'll stop at the first house I come to that has a phone."

" Is there anything we should do for Mom? " Steve asked.

" No, just keep her quiet, that's all. And don't move her until the ambulance gets here. It ought to be here long before the fire. But you'll want to do what you can to save the house. My advice is to wet the roof and keep it wet. Twelve houses burned over in Pine County yesterday, and eleven of 'em caught fire on the roof."

Steve nodded. " O.K., Doc."

" I'll send help if I can. But the fire companies are all working their heads off to save the towns, and every farmer is looking after his own place."

" Don't worry about us," Steve said. " We'll make out. Just send the ambulance for Mom as quick as you can."

The doctor rattled off with a wave of his hand. Soon he was swallowed up by the wisps and streamers and rolling clouds of smoke. A yellowish light hung over the earth. In their pens along the river's edge the ducks were quacking restlessly. The air was dry and oven-hot; nevertheless, the moan of the wind in the trees sent a shiver along Dave's spine.

" Dad doesn't carry insurance on the house," said Steve. " We'd better keep it from burning up if we want a roof over our heads."

" What'll we do first? "

" Let's do some thinkin'. It saves time."

Together they sized up the situation. Probably the forest fire, checked here and there by roads and meadows, would not reach them for several hours. The poultry houses were all right — a cranberry bog separated them from the woods. The small, four-room, one-story house was in the greatest danger. The woods came up to within fifty feet of it on three sides. Between the house and the woods were scrub oaks, sumac, and berry bushes; they grew right up to the edge of the lawn that was Mrs. Martin's pride and joy. On the eastern side of the house were the vegetable garden, the chicken coop, and the barn. Steve thought that the barn would be safe if they could keep the fire out of the meadow grass.

" Let's clear the west side of the house first," Steve suggested. " Get the brush hook and go after that sumac. I'll tackle the berries with the scythe."

" Gosh, Steve! Those raspberries are Dad's pets! "

" Listen, kid! When that fire comes she'll come a-roarin'. It's no jump at all from those bushes to the house. They've got to go. Just can't be helped."

There was a grimness about Steve that made Dave obey. He got the brush hook out of the barn and went to work on the sumac. For a while there were no sounds except the chop-chop of the brush hook and the swish of Steve's scythe. It took them nearly half an hour to clear the patch of ground between the edge of the lawn and the woods.

"That ought to fix us," Dave said. "Flames can't jump fifty feet."

Steve leaned on the scythe and mopped his bare throat with a handkerchief. "I've seen 'em jump a hundred feet. It depends on the wind. Go look at Mom while I cut some grass near the barn."

Dave entered his mother's room on tiptoe. She was lying in bed with the sheet drawn up to her chin. Her dark hair was spread over the pillow and her face looked flushed. Her breathing was short and difficult. Occasionally she moaned. Dave lowered the shade to keep the glare out of her closed eyes. Last night she had merely been laid up with a cold — today she was like this. He wished that his father had not driven the truck to market.

"Want anything, Mom?"

Mrs. Martin made no reply. Dave tiptoed from the room. Steve was rolling a hogshead [1] out of the barn, and Dave helped him stand it upright under the house eaves.

"We'll fill that with water," Steve

[1] **hogshead:** a large cask or barrel.

said. "We'll fill everything we can find with water."

"It'll dry up the well."

"I know it. We'll have to carry buckets from the river."

It was three hundred yards to the river. They struggled back and forth, each carrying two buckets, until they'd filled the hogshead, a barrel, and all the pots and pans they could find. After that they got the ladder and sluiced dozens of bucketfuls over the shingled roof.

Dr. Buckley had been gone an hour and a half. The color of the smoke had turned to a sulfurous yellow. It was so thick now that Dave could not see the poultry houses.

Steve glanced worriedly up the road. "Where's that ambulance?"

"Maybe it was off on another call."

Dave picked up his buckets and made another trip to the river. It was easier to be doing something than to be standing still. When he climbed the ladder and sluiced water over the roof he noticed that the shingles dried almost immediately in the intense heat. There was not even enough water left on them to soak the ashes that kept falling on the shingles like a slow rain.

Steve yelled from the edge of the woods, "I hear a car."

Dave scrambled down the ladder. But it was not the ambulance — it was a roadster with Mary McCann at the wheel, and it was headed east. Mary saw them and pulled up.

"Hello, Mary," Steve said. "How's everything at your place?"

"We lost the house, Steve. The fire

hit us three hours ago and the house is still burning."

" You should have soaked the roof."

" We soaked the roof," Mary said. " And after that we covered it with wet blankets. It didn't do any good. A blowtorch couldn't have gone through those blankets any quicker."

" That's too bad, Mary."

" We saved our stuff, though," Mary went on. " Carried it all out into a plowed field. Fire won't burn dirt."

Steve nodded. " Maybe we ought to do the same."

Mary glanced critically at the house and barn and garden. " You haven't enough space, Steve. If the house goes the whole clearing'll be like a white-hot furnace."

" It can't be as bad as that."

Mary's jaw hardened. " I'm telling you, and I know. I think you ought to get out of here, Steve."

" We can't," Steve said. " Dad's away at market and Mom's sick."

" Pneumonia," Dave added.

" What! You'd better let me give all three of you a lift over to the beach. It's dangerous here! We could take your mother to the hospital."

Steve looked dubiously [1] at the roadster. " We're not supposed to move her. Doc Buckley said so. He promised to send the ambulance, and it ought to be along any minute."

Mary started to get out. " If you're staying, so am I."

Steve would not let her open the door. " No. You can't do anything here. I'd rather have you beat it to

¹ **dubiously** (dū′bĭ·ŭs·lĭ): with doubt.

the telephone and find out where that ambulance is."

" All right. I'd better get going."

" So long, Mary."

" So long, boys."

Dave watched her until she vanished in the smoke. He glanced inquiringly at Steve. All at once Steve's brown face looked years older.

" I hope she gets out all right," Steve said.

" Why wouldn't she get out all right? "

" If the fire hit the McCann place three hours ago it's gone past us to the south'ard. With the wind the way it is the road'll be a furnace almost any time now."

" Which means the ambulance can't get through."

" It can if it hurries. We're not surrounded yet." Steve's shoulders sagged under the weight of responsibility that he was carrying. " Perhaps we should have gone with Mary. But the ride might have been bad for Mom. And perhaps Mary exaggerated the danger. I hope we're doing right. I'm going to move a bed into the clearing. If the house actually burns we'll have to get Mom out quick. It's all we can do."

" I'll dump more water on the roof," Dave suggested.

" Forget it. You heard what Mary said about wet blankets? It's no use, kid. I'd rather have you take a walk off to the south'ard and look for that fire."

Dave crossed the road and entered the smoky woods. There was no sound except the moan of wind in the trees. Underfoot the brown pine needles were dry as tinder. Dave came out into a field a half mile from the house and saw that the woods beyond were in flames. Red sparks swirled up out of blackish smoke. He circled to the east to avoid being cut off. Behind and on one side of him the woods were a roaring furnace. The fire was a monster with a hundred mouths. It spread through the pines with express-train speed.

Dave jogged homeward. There was a treachery about the fire that scared him. It died down in one place only to break out unexpectedly in another. Hot ashes dropped on him and burned his flesh. He saw a young doe running in aimless terror. High up in a dead oak two fish hawks hovered over their nest; with one mighty pounce the fire swallowed birds and nest and tree. Dave shivered and jogged on. In the middle of a field a woodchuck was sitting outside his hole. The woodchuck did not look worried. He merely sat there looking on. Dave waved his arms and the woodchuck popped into the hole.

" Lucky stiff! " Dave thought. " His home's perfectly safe. Fire won't burn dirt. If we could just put our house underground for a few hours."

Dave stopped in his tracks. An idea had struck him. He started off again at a hard, fast run. Ignoring the threat of fire he cut across through the woods. Smoke blinded him. He bumped into trees and fell down. He scrambled up again and went on. Briers caught his clothes; his hands were bloody from tearing himself loose. It took five minutes to get home and it seemed like five hours. Steve was setting up a bed in the clearing near the barn.

Dave gasped, " Has the ambulance come? "

Steve shook his head. " Not yet. Where's the fire? "

" All over the map. The worst of it's about two miles up the river and coming straight down on us."

Steve shot a hopeless glance at the road. He said quietly: " From the looks of things the fire's got us cut off. I was a fool not to take Mary's offer."

" Listen, Steve! " Dave's breath was still coming in gasps. " I've got an idea. We'll sod the roof. It isn't very big and there's enough sod in Mom's lawn. A woodchuck gave me the idea — woodchucks don't have to worry about having their homes burn. There's time to do it if we work fast. Let's get a couple of spades."

Steve yelled, " Good kid! It's a chance! "

Dave was already running toward the barn. Steve was right on his heels. Each grabbed a spade and hurried to the west side of the house.

" I'll make a long cut," Steve said. " You make another parallel to it. Afterwards we'll chop 'em into foot lengths."

" The roof isn't steep. They won't slide off."

It was hard work. They labored like fiends in the smoke and broiling heat. There were no sounds except the wind in the pines and an occasional grunt from Steve. They chopped a row of sods and Steve climbed up on–

to the roof.

"Toss 'em," he said. "And keep 'em coming fast."

One row of sods made almost two rows along the roof. Steve jumped down and picked up his spade. The second row went much faster. They were halfway down the third row when Steve held up his hand.

"Listen!"

"I don't hear anything."

"That's the point." Steve grinned. "The wind's dropped. If it'll just stay calm we'll get this job done in time."

The calm lasted until the west side of the roof was completely sodded. Neither one of them knew how long it took. They now had come to the other side. Dave's back ached and the blood pounded in his temples. He felt that he had been toiling for many hours. He rested on his spade for a moment and pointed across the road.

"Fire," he said. "Look, Steve."

On the other side of the road fire crackled in the underbrush. It burned right up to the edge of the road.

"That won't hurt us," Steve said. "But when it comes down from the west along the river bank we'll know it."

"There's the wind," Dave replied.

Steve nodded. "It's getting hotter. Snap into it, kid."

For another eternity Dave chopped sods and tossed them up to Steve on the roof. The wind was like a steady blast from a furnace. Steve was laying the top row of sod along the peak when Dave heard the fire. It was a muffled roar that filled the whole west. Suddenly Steve jumped up.

"It's coming," he yelled. "I can see it."

"What about the porch roof?"

"We'll have to let it go. Hand me up buckets of water. We'll wet this stuff down just to make sure."

Dave could scarcely see in the yellowish murk. Water slopped over the edge of the bucket and fell on his wrists. Now he could hear the crackle of burning twigs above the roar of the flames. Steve jumped down from the roof.

"Inside with you! Quick!"

They dodged through the kitchen door and shut it behind them. Steve closed all the windows and then sat down with a broom across his knees. They stared at one another.

"If the house catches," Steve said, "we'll carry Mom outside. If it doesn't we'll sit tight. When the worst is over we'll go out and fight it the

best way we can."

Seconds later Dave knew that the
fire was on them. He knew it by the
terrific heat and the burning twigs
that fell past the window. Overhead
he heard a sound like a million silk
ribbons flapping in a gale. Things fell
on the roof. On all sides were spittings
and cracklings and loud reports. Then
abruptly it was over.

Steve jumped up. " Come on! Let's
go! "

Outside the smoke was suffocating.
The western woods were still a trac-
ery of flame. The fire had jumped
right over the house and caught the
meadow grass on the eastern side. In
passing it had covered the roof with
burning twigs, limbs, and debris. The
porch roof was blazing and tongues
of flame were licking up the sides of

the house. The bed that Steve had set up in the clearing was on fire. As Dave looked the barn caught and burned like kindling. Everywhere he looked small fires had started.

"Save the house," Steve yelled. "Forget everything else!"

They worked like beavers. The hardest job was putting out the fire on the porch roof. They fought it with water and brooms and dirt. The flames that had licked up the sides of the house were easier to control. Dave climbed up onto the sodded roof and kicked off the burning branches. From where he stood the house was an island in a sea of fire.

"Come on down," Steve called. "Let's put out all we can. No use working on the barn — it's a goner."

Dave climbed down just as a truck burst through the clouds of smoke. Mr. Martin sprang out and ran toward them. His eyebrows were singed and the sleeve of his coat was smoking.

"Where's your mother?"

"Inside, Dad," Steve said. "She's all right."

Mr. Martin's voice shook. "You — you saved the house!"

Steve pointed to the sods on the roof. "Dave thought of that stunt. It worked. If we hadn't sodded the roof I hate to think of what might have happened."

Dave lay flat on the porch with his head on his arm. Doc Buckley and his father and Steve were sitting on the steps. It was eight o'clock. Two hours ago the ambulance had come for Mrs.

Martin. The woods still smoked and the air smelled of burnt leaves. But there were no more flames.

"I gave 'em the right name," Dr. Buckley was saying. "But they made a mistake and went to Pete Martin's instead, way over beyond Pine Center. They wouldn't have been here yet except for the McCann girl. She checked up and found what was wrong."

"Will Mrs. Martin be all right, Doc?"

"Absolutely. She has a light case. And the experience didn't hurt her any because she never knew she was going through it."

Steve said grimly, "I did, though! I felt we were all goners until Dave thought of sodding the roof."

"That was a wonderful idea, Dave," Mr. Martin said. "I'm — I'm proud of you, son."

But Dave didn't reply. He lay motionless with his head on his arm. He was sound asleep.

A Hint in Time

1. How did Steve and Dave know the fire was getting close to their home?

2. Why didn't the boys and their mother leave with the doctor?

3. How did the news Mary brought make them realize that their situation was even more dangerous than they had supposed at first?

4. What gave Dave the idea of putting sod on the roof?

5. Describe what the boys saw and heard and felt as the fire went over them. What work did they have to do after the forest fire passed on?

Forest Fire

ELIZABETH COATSWORTH

The leaves were yellow, the leaves were red,
and bright and dry as the sun overhead,
the springs of the earth grew faint and slow,
and buckets came empty from wells below,
the wind went prying, now here, now there, 5
it tossed the dust and the leaves in the air,
it dried up the dew, the mists were driven
far away, and the clouds were riven
and scattered afar, the wind went whining,
it cleared the sky where the sun was shining. 10

Then the fire rose like an asp° from the dust
and the colored leaves, and it ran like rust
along the ground till it took on power
and it rose in the trees in tendril and flower,
and the wind gave a yell and the fire ran 15
with the wind behind it, and ruin began,
and the fire roared and the fire hissed,
and smoke whirled up instead of the mist,
and the sun went down and the moon arose
with its light as chill and pale as the snows, 20
and the fire glowed against that light,
a moving red against tranquil white,
and the wind went on and the fire strengthened,
and the stain of its blackened shadow lengthened,
and very low and weak and small 25
the farm crouched there in the path of it all.

11. asp: a small snake. (Notice the circle that is printed after the word to show you that it is explained in a footnote. This sign, instead of a number, will be used in all the poems in this book.)

A Close-up

1. How does the first part of the poem prepare the way for the fire? What part did the wind play in its growth?

2. What sights and sounds described in the poem make the fire seem vivid to you?

How do they compare with the ones described in the story " Red Peril "?

3. Could the poet and the short-story writer have seen the same fire? Judging from these two selections, what are a few ways in which poetry and prose differ?

Wolves in Flambeau Valley

J. PAUL LOOMIS

KEEP UP WITH THE CLUES.   In the lonely northern wilderness where men seek gold, airplane motors now hum over the dog-sled trails. But when there is a mystery to solve and a fight to win, a Husky and a horse may still be the best helpers the Canadian Mounted Police could wish for.

Like other mystery stories, this one offers you the double attraction of a good action story and a puzzle to solve. It is a game of wits between the writer and the reader, and the game has its own rules. The writer must include in his story all the clues necessary for an accurate solution, so that the reader has a fair chance to figure out what happened and who the criminal is. But, to keep the game interesting, the valuable clues are mixed in with other information, and the reader must first spot them and then put them together to find the right solution. This is the sport of reading mysteries. Keep your wits about you, weigh each bit of

information, and see how early you can untangle this mystery of the far North.

STEP over, old hay-burner — you're getting fat and lazy! " Corporal Park Langdon slapped the flank of Salteaux [1] to get room to go on with his morning currying of the big chestnut horse. He bent to run his brush down a hind leg of his four-footed pard and Salteaux gently but firmly nipped that part of the Mountie nearest him. Park straightened promptly.

" You fiddle-headed, goose-rumped cayuse! " Park rumbled. " You — " A bell on the wall rang whirringly.

" Wolverine   Lake."   Park   announced his detachment when he got to the telephone in his office. " Langdon speaking."

" Park, this is Barry." The voice of

[1] **Salteaux** (säl'tö').

the young constable who was stationed with Park here on the highway to Alaska came over the wire. Barry Quinton was on patrol. " I'm at Flambeau [1] River."

" Yeah."

" You know the man I have a telegram for — Lebec? [2] He's disappeared," Barry said. " And it could be he was murdered. He'd just come back from a prospecting trip an' brought gold — "

In a flash Park was thinking of the message. Lebec's son had arrived in Montreal, just discharged from a Canadian Army hospital in England. He was blind. Wanted his father to come. If it should prove true that Lebec was dead, what a painful answer it would be Park's duty to send the boy!

" — but the cabin's burned," the phone was transmitting. " No clues. I'm puzzled as a pup with his first polecat."

" Are you sure Lebec hasn't gone on another trip? " Park asked. " Trapping maybe. Cabin could have burned after he left."

" Well," Barry said, " a dog I think was his comes around the ash pile. He'd have taken a dog."

" Reasonable. Have you questioned everyone there? "

" There's hardly anyone to question," replied Barry. " Since the gold strike petered out, nearly everyone's drifted. A grouchy trader and a couple hard-shell miners are all I've found. They're clams. I thought you might run up."

The snow was not yet deep, for midwinter. A horse could still be used. A trail for cars was pretty well packed along the Highway. Park blanketed Salteaux and put him in the trailer. The light truck squeaked along in the cold, dry snow. After noon they reached the shacks — now mostly empty — at Flambeau River. Barry put Salteaux in a stable with his own horse.

Gurney, the hatchet-faced trader and keeper of the roadhouse, seemed to bristle at another questioning. Lebec's cabin was several miles away, he said, and he had seen the man but a few times. He didn't know anything about him except that he was a seasoned prospector and that he paid for his grubstake. [3] Which was more, he wedged in sourly, than he could say for the greenhorn miners who had stayed here in the north after war construction was done. He had never seen a dog with Lebec. " But he musta had one," Gurney added. " He bought a lot of dried fish for dog feed. This year there's no rabbits in the woods, y' know."

Park nodded. Reports had come to him of moose being killed by wolves, which seldom happened on rabbit years.

" But I c'd name y' a dozen deadbeats," Gurney rasped on, " who've slid outa this valley lately, any of 'em mean enough to've killed Lebec for a little poke of gold."

" Do you know he *had* gold? " Park asked pointedly.

" Had a little in his poke after

[1] Flambeau (flăm'bō').
[2] Lebec (lá·bĕk').
[3] grubstake: supply of food.

payin' me," Gurney admitted. " He c'd have had plenty at his — "

The squeak of footsteps outside stopped Gurney. There was the yelp and whine of tired dogs. The door was shouldered open. A huge man, now well into the room, stopped to blink at the two Mounted Policemen. Gurney was not taken aback.

" Thought you'd left, Trant," he said unpleasantly.

The man threw Gurney one scowl and brought his dark eyes under their frosty brown back to Park. His heavy features brightened. " I'm in luck to find you here," he said. " My pardner's been chewed by wolves. You can do more for him than Hard-pan Gurney."

Park and Barry quickly helped to bring in a man from the toboggan. " Burdick! " exclaimed Gurney, after a look at the man's face. The man sat up, uncertainly. He was younger than Trant and slender. His eyes showed pain and a sort of haunted look.

Park cut away the ripped clothing, clotted by blood and by flour that had been put on his wounds as a crude means to check bleeding. Barry took Trant's whimpering dogs to the stable. Trant only said, " Y' needn't have bothered," when Barry returned.

Burdick's left hand and arm were deeply slashed. One cheek bore gashes of fangs that had driven for his throat. He was weak, but the hemorrhage had stopped. With the nearest doctor three hundred miles away, Park got his first aid kit, boiled water, and cleaned and dressed the wounds as best he could. Burdick kept his teeth on his lip and made no sound.

Trant said, " Well, I reckon we'll be gettin' back."

" Wel' " exclaimed Park. " Surely you brought this man to the Highway in the hope of sending him down to Fort St. John. He can ride with one of us tomorrow to Wolverine Lake and we'll arrange somehow to send him on."

" Looks to me like you've done good as a doctor," Trant said. " An' I think the kid's scared as much as hurt."

Park spoke directly to Burdick. " Those wounds may be infected. Certainly they should be dressed every day. Do you want to go to a doctor? "

Burdick moistened his lips. " No," he said woodenly. " I'll be all right." Park gave him what he had left of antiseptic and bandages.

" Tell me how it happened. And when? " Park said.

" It was last night," Trant put in. " He was comin' in from our trapline, carryin' a beaver. Three wolves come at him. He shot one an' his rifle jammed an' he broke the gun over the head of one an' stood the other off with his knife. That's what they done to him though in half a minute an' it shuck him up some. But he'll snap outa that. C'm on, Slim."

" Do you live near Lebec's cabin? " Park asked Trant.

" No. He's up in the mountain, ain't he? "

" He has returned. And disappeared. We have an urgent message for him. If you can tell us anything —"

"Sorry," Trant said. "Maybe the wolves got him. Well, we're obliged to you." Barry had returned with their dogs and the two men started away through the snowy spruce.

Park and Barry saddled their horses and pushed through the snow to reach the site of Lebec's cabin while it was still light. Barry had combed out a few blackened cans but nothing to prove a man had been cremated there. "I brought a screen," said Park. "Little things like teeth are most durable. Was this snow on the ashes when you came here first?"

"A few inches," said Barry. "It's goin' to snow more," he added with a look at the gray sky.

"Where's the dog you spoke of?"

"I've never seen the dog," Park was surprised to hear Barry answer. "Just his tracks. See, over there. He comes every night."

Barry led the way through the now dark woods another three miles to the cabin of Larson and Berg. It was cramped and smelly, its occupants weathered miners, warped by a lifetime of following one golden dream after another to empty ends. They were staying in the valley, they said uneasily, to prospect the mountains around it in the spring for the rich source of the few nuggets found in the Flambeau's gravel bars.

No, they hadn't seen Lebec since autumn, before he'd hired some bush pilot [1] to fly him to a lake in the high mountains. The plane had brought

_____
[1] **bush pilot:** an odd-job commercial flyer who works in backwoods country.

him out recently. Where had it landed? On a lake twenty miles south. Yes, (sourly) maybe he'd found the lode they were seeking. Maybe he'd flown with his gold on out to Edmonton. They didn't know whether Lebec had a dog. They didn't know what had become of him.

"Why were you at Lebec's cabin three days ago?" Barry demanded. "Don't deny it. I tracked you here in spite of the last snow."

The men exchanged glances. "Ve youst vent to see if ve could find out vere Lebec had been and vat he found," Larson stated. "And ve found him gone and his shack burned."

"Then why didn't you report it?" Park asked.

"Vell, there vas no vun to report to but old Gurney, and how ve know he send vord on to you?" Berg said. "Maybe he done it. He cheat us every time he veigh gold. Maybe he shoot us for findin' out." They closed up then.

The two Mounties rode through darkness and falling snow back to the roadhouse. "Thin story," said Barry. "There's nothing to prove they didn't kill and rob Lebec and burn his shack."

"Nothing," agreed Park. "And nothing to prove Gurney didn't do it. He knew Lebec had gold, and he doesn't improve his case by being so eager to blame someone else."

"What chance that wolves got Lebec?"

"Wolves would have killed the dog too. And wolf stories, even Trant's, should be taken cautiously. A thousand hair-raising tales to the contrary, there are few if any proven instances of wolves attacking a man."

"Something sure chewed Burdick," Barry stated.

"Right. And there can always be a first case. If you noticed the width between those fang marks on Burdick's cheek you know it was something that could have torn out his throat or broken his neck. As a wolf could. But for good measure Trant threw in the beaver Burdick was carrying. I've never heard of beaver in these mountains. If there are they can't be caught in midwinter."

"What's that got to do with Lebec?"

"Nothing, maybe. And before we do anything else we've got to find something more solid than dog tracks to prove Lebec's dead! Well," Park finished, "one of us has to go back to the detachment. While I don't want to take the case away from you, it looks to me like so much plain old hard work that I'd be passing the buck to leave you alone with it."

"You're mighty welcome," Barry said. "I'll keep an ear to the phone and question everyone that comes down the Highway."

Next morning Park rode Salteaux to the site of Lebec's cabin before daylight, taking a light camp outfit with him. Gray dawn showed fresh dog tracks. With what snow had fallen in the night the fluff now lay more than knee deep to a horse. Heavy going for a dog. Neither did this last fall help with the job before Park, which

was sifting ashes. Cramped and smudged, when night stopped him and the gloom of the spot set him talking to the blanketed Salteaux, he could only report to himself, "Three bits of gold! Not much of a catch, huh? Not even a nail or a spoon or a metal button!"

Park pondered. "Salteaux, you know what I'll bet? That I'm not the first chap to sift those ashes! Someone wanted to get some charred bones maybe, to hide them better. Or he thought there was gold hidden in auger holes in the logs or chinks between the roof poles, which there seems to have been, and the surest way to find it was to burn the shack and sift the ashes. Maybe he had both reasons. But *who*, Salteaux, who?"

Still chewing on that, Park built a fire, melted snow in a pail, watered and fed Salteaux. Near the horse he laid spruce boughs for himself. When he had eaten he got into his sleeping bag without removing his clothes and let his fire die out. He meant to keep awake. But as the night wore on, pinching himself became less effective. How long he had been asleep he did not know when a questioning snuffle from Salteaux brought him alert. Looking in the direction the horse's ears pointed, Park made out the shape of a wolf against the snow.

Instinctively he drew and leveled his revolver. Then lowered the hammer. Salteaux was not really alarmed — not as he'd be at the scent of a wolf. Then the sniffing animal settled back on its haunches, pointed its nose straight up, and howled. It was the most dismal sound Park had ever heard. But it wasn't the long, throaty, fear-thrusting howl of a timber wolf.

The animal was a Husky, Park decided. A big sled-dog of the farther north, not so many generations descended from a wolf. But loyal now to man. To *a* man. Park whistled softly. The dog turned, its sharp ears keenly forward. Then in disappointment it skulked into the shadows. Park shucked himself out of his sleeping bag and stripped the blanket off Salteaux. He untied the halter and then his heels were nudging the horse into a gallop after the dog.

Diving through one clump of clawing spruce they saw the dog disappear into another. Emerging from that they saw nothing. They went back and chased him out, plowed on, gaining and losing distance. The deep snow was exhausting the dog but Salteaux too was blowing heavily.

The marvelous strength of the Husky, his advantage in getting through the brush, kept him ahead of them for nearly a mile. But suddenly, at a little meadow, he stopped, then broke at right angles to the straight course he had been keeping. Park and his horse cut across. Then they were over him as he wallowed in the soft snow. Park slid off and threw his weight on the dog, his mittened hands clutching the powerful muzzle. The dog was immense, nearly as big as a wolf, and a beautiful black and silver. As Park stroked the Husky with one hand and talked to him, the exhausted dog ceased his attempts to bite and the rumbling died in his throat. But he flinched often, and shaking off a mitten, Park found welts under his fur. One long cut might have been a bullet mark. Park called Salteaux within reach and while he untied the rope from his halter the horse and dog sniffed noses soberly and seemed to speak in some language of their own. Park knotted the rope around the dog's neck. Slowly they made their way back to the camp.

The dog ate ravenously, then howled at intervals, so Park didn't sleep much. With daylight he saddled up and let the dog lead him back along last night's trail. At the end of it Park could now glimpse a cabin. The dog seemed eager yet still afraid to go nearer. Park dismounted, touched the Husky reassuringly, and went on cautiously. The dog came at his heels, head low and hackles up.[1] But the cabin was empty. It was locked with a crude wooden latch it took Park but a few minutes to pick.

Those moments the dog whined and growled. He burst into the cabin with throaty snarls, but after one flashing look around he gave all his attention to sniffing and whining over some coarse spruce boughs spread in a corner. There was no doubt now in Park's mind that the man who had lain there was Lebec. But the men who had occupied two bunks on the wall opposite were not, by the savageness in the Husky's manner, his master's friends. Judging by his fear of the place, Park guessed the dog

[1] **hackles up:** hair standing up stiffly along the back of his neck, a sign of fear or anger.

had experienced their brutality. Blood on the spruce boughs, on the wall, on a club Park now saw under the lower bunk, proved how grim their handling had been.

The place had been empty but a few hours, for water in a pail had not frozen yet. A smell of scorched cotton caused Park to lift a lid of the stove. The fire had been nearly out when the cloth was thrown into the stove and it was not entirely burned. It was out of him.

Two tables in so small a shack were queer. Outside Park saw an answer. A four-strand radio aerial, high between two spruce. The kind that might be used with a sending set. That might be another answer to why Trant had hung onto Burdick. Maybe Trant couldn't work the thing. They had hidden the set, or taken it.

No trail could be seen leaving the cabin. But the dog's keen nose took

not a vast surprise to Park to recognize gauze and adhesive tape he had put on Burdick's arm two days before. With this fact a hunch that had been growing in Park burst into a full picture.

Burdick — Trant! They had held Lebec prisoner here. Why? To force him to show them where he'd found his gold? The wolf pack? It was here now — Lebec's Husky. He had made a powerful attempt to rescue his master. But no matter how badly Burdick had been injured, Trant wouldn't let his stooge be taken to a doctor by the police. They might get information

care of that. In a hundred yards Trant had ceased to brush over the trail. There had been a dog team, toboggan, and three men on snowshoes. Lebec could walk, then. Park pushed on, with a leash on the dog to hold him back. The shallow trail made by webs [1] did not help Salteaux very much. But the chestnut threw his splendid strength into the uneven race. The trail led south. Larson had said there was a lake that way where a plane could land. With a radio Trant and Burdick might have called a plane!

[1] **webs:** snowshoes.

Hours, then, of plodding. Park took his turns at breaking trail. But alone he wouldn't have had a chance. He believed they were gaining. Trant was having trouble too. His three dogs were overloaded. In one place he cached [1] a sack of flour, later some miner's tools. More than once there was the mark of where a man had fallen in the trail. Park wished for a storm. But it was noon of a fine flying day and — *and there was the drone of a plane!*

Now Park could see an opening ahead of him in the timber. He saw the plane circle and go down. Park broke trail till his chest heaved and the cold air he gulped tore his throat like a rasp. Then he turned the dog loose, mounted and called on Salteaux for all he had left. They broke out of the trees. On the small lake the plane taxied toward the men and dog team. It swung into position for the take-off. Park fired into the air and waved his arms in command to halt but the big man of the group used his club on dogs and men alike to get them to the plane. Salteaux was on a plunging gallop, his breath whistling like an exhaust.

One man wilted under a blow. One helped, clumsily, to drag him — and fell himself. Trant wheeled then and a gun in his hand began to cough. A bullet stung Park's left arm. He felt Salteaux flinch. Park set all his weight suddenly into his left stirrup and heaved Salteaux's head around to the right. The horse was thrown onto his

left side in the snow. Park, lying beside him, drew a long breath and steadied his revolver with both hands. He pressed the trigger and Trant dropped.

The pilot of the plane had nearly reached the group to help Trant but he now turned and ran for his plane. He'd leave them all here — wounded, spent! [2] Park aimed low. At his third shot the man went down.

The big Husky had reached the group now. Burdick had regained his feet. He yelled and threw himself into the snow, his arms covering his head. But the dog was only whining and licking the still face of his master. The exhausted Lebec had been rendered unconscious by Trant's blow.

Trant lay as though dead. Park turned him over. Cautiously. Yet Trant's gun roared almost in Park's face. For an instant it dazed and blinded him and though his hand convulsed on the trigger he missed. One of Trant's great arms swung

[1] **cached** (kăsht): hid where it could be found later.

[2] **spent**: exhausted.

round Park's knees and brought him down. The hammer of Park's gun clicked. Empty!

Wounded or not, the huge man had terrible strength. Even a blow from Park's gun, softened by Trant's fur cap, only made his grim face contort. And then Park's arm was gripped and twisted till he wondered if it broke. He was hanging to Trant's gun with his left hand like a steel trap. But he was going under. Trant was lurching up.

Then with a roar a black and silver fury struck Trant. Only the thick collar of his coat saved his throat. The dog leaped again. Trant let go of Park to shield his face. He bellowed as the ripping fangs sank through the sleeve of his mackinaw. This time Park's empty gun caught him at the base of his skull and knocked him out. Park dragged off the dog, and the Husky obeyed him. He handcuffed Trant.

Quickly reloading his gun Park searched the groaning pilot and then the plane. He bandaged the wound in the pilot's leg. " You'll fly us to a hospital," he ordered. " Get in. Will it carry five men? "

" She might," said the pilot through pain-stiffened lips.

Park loaded the others, lifting the gaunt Lebec easily, straining at the weight of Trant. He mercifully shot Trant's utterly spent dogs. He stared at the whining Husky and at his horse and shook his head.

" I'm running out on you, boys. But I can't help it — though you've done more than I have of this job. Salteaux

— " he said, taking the bridle off so there'd be no chance of its catching on brush, " you go *home!* Understand? Take this fellow with you. He just saved my life but he's nearly as heavy as a man and I can't risk the lives of the rest by putting him in the plane. Flambeau — that's what I'll call you," he said to the Husky — " you go with him." He cracked Trant's whip at both of them. Then he took his seat beside the pilot. From high in the air he could still see two dots on the white lake and couldn't tell whether they moved or not.

It was the day the first returning crow winged cawing over the detachment at Wolverine Lake in sign of spring that Park got a wire from Lebec in Montreal. He and Barry whistled Flambeau from the corral where he was romping with Park's horse. Salteaux and the Husky had been pals since their long trip out of the woods. Now the horse whinnied after the dog and Park opened the gate. The four walked together.

" It's going to hurt all of us," said Park, and Barry nodded. " But Flambeau, you'll be very glad when you get to the end of your long trip. You'll find your old master. And a new, younger one that needs you. They're going to send you to a school where they train smart dogs like you to help fellows who can't see as well as you can."

" Good name you gave him, then," remarked Barry.

" That's right," agreed Park. " Flambeau means ' torch.' "

Adding Up the Clues

1. Judging from his telephoned report to Park, why did Barry suspect foul play? Had he found any clues?

2. Who are the logical " suspects " that Park finds? Why does each invite suspicion?

3. What clues did Park discover in sifting the ashes of the cabin?

4. How did Lebec's dog put Park on the right trail? What did his behavior at the cabin tell Park?

5. What does " Flambeau " mean? Why is it a good name for this dog?

6. What did the title seem to mean as you read the first part of the story? What meaning did it have after you finished the story?

7. Barry and Park are Mounties — Royal Canadian Mounted Police. A committee should read books and articles about the Mounties and report to the class. Find some pictures to display with the report.

Lochinvar

SIR WALTER SCOTT

READ IT IN CHORUS. " There never was knight like the young Lochinvar," and there never was a more dashing poem of love and daring. Sir Walter Scott loved the tales of the Scottish border and retold many of them in his lilting verse.

Poetry is only half alive until it is read aloud. You must *hear* the rhythm of the lines and the echoing sounds of the words to enjoy a poem fully. Reading in groups, like singing in a chorus, is a fine way to get the musical effects of this poem. You'll need two solo readers, the deepest voice in the class for the bride's father (first solo), and a slightly lighter voice for Lochinvar (second solo). Divide the rest of the class into two groups, one made up of the lighter voices and the other of the lower ones. Notes in the margin tell you which lines are to be spoken by each group or solo reader.

Practice the parts until every one reads well together. Let Lochinvar practice some with the lighter voices so that his speeches in lines 30 and 41–42 fit smoothly into the group reading. Then put it all together in the final performance and feel the poem come to life!

Oh, young Lochinvar is come out of the west, | *All*
Through all the wide Border his steed was the best;
And save his good broadsword he weapons had none,
He rode all unarmed, and he rode all alone.
So faithful in love, and so dauntless in war,   5
There never was knight like the young Lochinvar.

He stayed not for brake,° and he stopped not for stone, | *Lower voices*
He swam the Eske River where ford there was none;
But ere he alighted at Netherby gate,
The bride had consented, the gallant came late: 10
For a laggard in love, and a dastard in war,
Was to wed the fair Ellen of brave Lochinvar.

So boldly he entered the Netherby Hall,
Among bridesmen, and kinsmen, and brothers and all.
Then spoke the bride's father, his hand on his sword   15
(For the poor craven bridegroom said never a word),
" Oh, come ye in peace here, or come ye in war, | *First solo*
Or to dance at our bridal, young Lord Lochinvar? "

" I long wooed your daughter, my suit you denied — | *Second solo*
Love swells like the Solway,° but ebbs like its tide —   20
And now I am come, with this lost love of mine
To lead but one measure, drink one cup of wine.
There are maidens in Scotland more lovely by far,
That would gladly be bride to the young Lochinvar."

The bride kissed the goblet: the knight took it up;   25 | *Lighter voices*
He quaffed off the wine, and he threw down the cup.
She looked down to blush, and she looked up to sigh,
With a smile on her lips, and a tear in her eye.
He took her soft hand, ere her mother could bar —
" Now tread we a measure! " said young Lochinvar.   30 | *Second solo*

So stately his form, and so lovely her face, | *Lighter voices*
That never a hall such a galliard° did grace;
While her mother did fret, and her father did fume,
And the bridegroom stood dangling his bonnet and plume; | *Softly, to get the*
And the bridesmaidens whispered, " 'Twere better by far, | *effect of whisper-*
To have matched our fair cousin with young Lochinvar." | *ing.*

One touch to her hand, and one word to her ear,   37 | *Faster*
When they reached the hall door, and the charger stood
    near;

---

7. **brake:** a dense growth of bushes. **20. Solway** (sŏl'wā) Firth is a narrow inlet between England and Scotland, where the tides get up great speed in their rise and fall. **32. galliard** (găl'yẽrd):
an old-fashioned dance.

So light to the croup the fair lady he swung,
So light to the saddle before her he sprung!   40
" She is won! we are gone, over bank, bush, and scaur;° | *Second solo*
They'll have fleet steeds that follow," quoth young Lochin-
    var.

There was mounting 'mid Graemes of the Netherby clan; | *Lower voices*
Forsters, Fenwicks, and Musgraves, they rode and they
    ran:
There was racing and chasing on Cannobie Lee,   45
But the lost bride of Netherby ne'er did they see.
So daring in love, and so dauntless in war, | *All*
Have ye e'er heard of gallant like young Lochinvar?

Enjoying Music in Poetry
1. If you read this poem aloud, you surely noticed the musical swing of the lines. Pick out several lines that have a break in the middle, like line 31. How does each half of the line balance with the other?

2. The poem has a galloping rhythm, with an accent on every third syllable: " For a lággard in lóve, and a dástard in wár." Read aloud a stanza in class to see if you can obtain the sounds of hoofbeats.

3. In what ways does Lochinvar fit your idea of a hero? How do you know that Ellen was glad to elope with Lochinvar? Why was the dance important in his plan?

41. **scaur** (skär): a steep, rocky embankment.

To Repel Boarders

JACK LONDON

This tame modern life is totally lacking in adventure, Paul lamented one night as he and his chum headed their sloop out into the bay. By the time they headed back for shore he had decided that strange and dangerous things can happen even in this day and age!

No; honest, now, Bob, I'm sure I was born too late. The twentieth century's no place for me. If I'd had my way — "

"You'd have been born in the sixteenth," I broke in, laughing, "with Drake and Hawkins and Raleigh [1] and the rest of the sea kings."

"You're right!" Paul affirmed. He rolled over upon his back on the little afterdeck, with a long sigh of dissatisfaction.

It was a little past midnight, and, with the wind nearly astern,[2] we were running down Lower San Francisco Bay to Bay Farm Island. Paul Fairfax and I went to the same school, lived next door to each other, and

"chummed it" together. By saving money, by earning more, and by each of us foregoing a bicycle on his birthday, we had collected the purchase price of the *Mist*, a twenty-eight-footer, sloop-rigged,[3] with baby topsail and centerboard. Paul's father was a yachtsman himself, and he had conducted the business for us, poking around, overhauling, sticking his penknife into the timbers, and testing the planks with the greatest care. In fact, it was on his schooner the *Whim* that Paul and I had picked up what we knew about boat sailing, and now that the *Mist* was ours, we were hard at work adding to our knowledge.

The *Mist*, being broad of beam, was comfortable and roomy. A man could stand upright in the cabin, and what with the stove, cooking utensils, and bunks, we were good for trips in her of a week at a time. And we were just starting out on the first of such trips, and it was because it was the first trip that we were sailing by night. Early in the evening we had beaten out from Oakland, and we

[1] **Drake, Hawkins, and Raleigh** were seagoing English adventurers in the days of Queen Elizabeth.

[2] **astern** (*à·stûrn'*): at the back of the boat.

[3] **sloop-rigged:** having sails placed like those of a sloop, a small vessel with one mast.

were now off the mouth of Alameda Creek, a large salt-water estuary [1] which fills and empties San Leandro Bay.

"Men lived in those days," Paul said, so suddenly as to startle me from my own thoughts. "In the days of the sea kings, I mean," he explained.

I said "Oh!" sympathetically, and began to whistle "Captain Kidd."

"Now, I've my ideas about things," Paul went on. "They talk about romance and adventure and all that, but I say romance and adventure are dead. We're too civilized. We don't have adventures in the twentieth century. We go to the circus —"

"But —" I strove to interrupt, though he would not listen to me.

"You look here, Bob," he said. "In all the time you and I've gone together what adventures have we had? True, we were out in the hills once, and didn't get back till late at night, and we were good and hungry, but we weren't even lost. We knew where we were all the time. It was only a case of walk. What I mean is, we've never had to fight for our lives. Understand? We've never had a pistol fired at us, or a cannon, or a sword waving over our heads, or — or anything.

"You'd better slack away [2] three or four feet of that mainsheet," he said in a hopeless sort of way, as though it did not matter much anyway. "The wind's still veering around.

"Why, in the old times the sea was one constant glorious adventure," he continued. "A boy left school and became a midshipman, and in a few weeks was cruising after Spanish galleons or locking yardarms with a French privateer,[3] or — doing lots of things."

"Well, there *are* adventures today," I objected.

But Paul went on as though I had not spoken:

"And today we go from school to high school, and from high school to college, and then we go into the office or become doctors and things, and the only adventures we know about are the ones we read in books. Why, just as sure as I'm sitting here on the stern of the sloop *Mist*, just so sure am I that we wouldn't know what to do if a real adventure came along. Now, would we?"

"Oh, I don't know," I answered noncommittally.

"Well, you wouldn't be a coward, would you?" he demanded.

I was sure I wouldn't, and said so.

"But you don't have to be a coward to lose your head, do you?"

I agreed that brave men might get excited.

"Well, then," Paul summed up, with a note of regret in his voice, "the chances are that we'd spoil the adventure. So it's a shame, and that's all I can say about it."

[1] **estuary** (ĕs'tu̇·ĕr'ĭ): the mouth of a river into which the tide flows.

[2] **slack away:** loosen, let out.

[3] **Spanish galleons** (găl'ē·ŭnz) were sailing vessels that often carried gold from the New World. A **privateer** was an armed ship commissioned to attack and capture or rob ships of another nation. The governmental license made the only difference between a privateer and a pirate.

"The adventure hasn't come yet," I answered, not caring to see him down in the mouth over nothing. You see, Paul was a peculiar fellow in some things, and I knew him pretty well. He read a good deal and had a quick imagination, and once in a while he'd get into moods like this one. So I said, "The adventure hasn't come yet, so there's no use worrying about its being spoiled. For all we know, it might turn out splendidly."

Paul didn't say anything for some time, and I was thinking he was out of the mood, when he spoke suddenly:

"Just imagine, Bob Kellogg, as we're sailing along now, just as we are, and never mind what for, that a boat should bear down upon us with armed men in it, what would you do to repel boarders? [1] Think you could rise to it?"

"What would *you* do?" I asked pointedly. "Remember, we haven't even a single shotgun aboard."

"You would surrender, then?" he demanded angrily. "But suppose they were going to kill you?"

"I'm not saying what I'd do," I answered stiffly, beginning to get a little angry myself. "I'm asking what you'd do, without weapons of any sort?"

"I'd find something," he replied — rather shortly, I thought.

I began to chuckle. "Then the adventure wouldn't be spoiled, would it? And you've been talking rubbish."

Paul struck a match, looked at his watch, and remarked that it was nearly one o'clock — a way he had when the argument went against him. Besides, this was the nearest we ever came to quarreling now, though our share of squabbles had fallen to us in the earlier days of our friendship. I had just seen a little white light ahead when Paul spoke again.

"Anchor light," he said. "Funny place for people to drop the hook. It may be a scow schooner with a dinky astern,[2] so you'd better go wide."

I eased the *Mist* several points, and, the wind puffing up, we went plowing along at a pretty fair speed, passing the light so wide that we could not make out what manner of craft it marked. Suddenly the *Mist* slacked up in a slow and easy way, as though running upon soft mud. We were both startled. The wind was blowing stronger than ever, and yet we were almost at a standstill.

"Mud flats out here! Never heard of such a thing!"

So Paul exclaimed with a snort of unbelief, and, seizing an oar, shoved it down over the side. And straight down it went till the water wet his hand. There was no bottom! Then we were dumbfounded. The wind was whistling by, and still the *Mist* was moving ahead at a snail's pace. There seemed something dead about her, and it was all I could do at the tiller to keep her from swinging up into the wind.

"Listen!" I laid my hand on Paul's

[1] **boarders:** people coming aboard a ship; in sea fights, an attacking party from the enemy ship.

[2] **a dinky astern:** a small boat tied behind the larger one.

arm. We could hear the sound of row-locks, and saw the little white light bobbing up and down and now very close to us. "There's your armed boat," I whispered in fun. "Beat the crew to quarters [1] and stand by to repel boarders! "

We both laughed, and were still laughing when a wild scream of rage came out of the darkness, and the approaching boat shot under our stern. By the light of the lantern it carried we could see the two men in it distinctly. They were foreign-looking fellows with sun-bronzed faces, and with knitted tam-o'-shanters perched seaman fashion on their heads. Bright-colored woolen sashes were around their waists, and long sea-boots covered their legs. I remember yet the cold chill which passed along my backbone as I noted the tiny gold earrings in the ears of one. For all the world they were like pirates stepped out of the pages of romance. And, to make the picture complete, their faces were distorted with anger, and each flourished a long knife. They were both shouting, in high-pitched voices, some foreign jargon we could not understand.

One of them, the smaller of the two, and if anything the more vicious-looking, put his hands on the rail of the Mist and started to come aboard. Quick as a flash Paul placed the end of the oar against the man's chest and shoved him back into his boat. He fell in a heap, but scrambled to his feet, waving the knife and shrieking:

[1] Beat the crew to quarters: beat a drum to call the crew to their battle positions.

"You break-a my net-a! You break-a my net-a! "

And he held forth in the jargon again, his companion joining him, and both preparing to make another dash to come aboard the Mist.

"They're Italian fishermen," I cried, the facts of the case breaking in upon me. "We've run over their smelt net, and it's slipped along the keel and fouled our rudder.[2] We're anchored to it."

"Yes, and they're murderous chaps, too," Paul said, sparring at them with the oar to make them keep their distance.

"Say, you fellows! " he called to them. "Give us a chance and we'll get it clear for you! We didn't know your net was there. We didn't mean to do it, you know! "

"You won't lose anything! " I added. "We'll pay the damages! "

But they could not understand what we were saying, or did not care to understand.

"You break-a my net-a! You break-a my net-a! " the smaller man, the one with the earrings, screamed back, making furious gestures. "I fix-a you! You-a see, I fix-a you! "

This time, when Paul thrust him back, he seized the oar in his hands, and his companion jumped aboard. I put my back against the tiller, and no sooner had he landed, and before he had caught his balance, than I met him with another oar, and he fell heavily backward into the boat. It

[2] slipped . . . rudder: the net went under the boat, moving lengthwise along the main timber (keel) and tangled up in the steering board (rudder).

was getting serious, and when he arose and caught my oar, and I realized his strength, I confess that I felt a goodly tinge of fear. But though he was stronger than I, instead of dragging me overboard when he wrenched on the oar, he merely pulled his boat in closer; and when I shoved, the boat was forced away. Besides, the knife, still in his right hand, made him awkward and somewhat counterbalanced the advantage his superior strength gave him. Paul and his enemy were in the same situation — a sort of deadlock, which continued for several seconds, but which could not last. Several times I shouted that we would pay for whatever damage their net had suf-

fered, but my words seemed to be without effect.

Then my man began to tuck the oar under his arm, and to come up along it, slowly, hand over hand. The small man did the same with Paul. Moment by moment they came closer, and closer, and we knew that the end was only a question of time.

"Hard up,[1] Bob!" Paul called softly to me.

I gave him a quick glance, and caught an instant's glimpse of what I took to be a very pale face and a very set jaw.

"Oh, Bob," he pleaded, "hard up your helm![2] Hard up your helm, Bob!"

And his meaning dawned upon me. Still holding to my end of the oar, I shoved the tiller over with my back, and even bent my body to keep it

[1] **Hard up:** swing the tiller (which guides the rudder) hard to head the boat away from the wind.
[2] **helm:** the entire steering mechanism, tiller and rudder.

over. As it was the *Mist* was nearly dead before the wind, and this maneuver was bound to force her to jibe her mainsail [1] from one side to the other. I could tell by the " feel " when the wind spilled out of the canvas and the boom tilted up. Paul's man had now gained a footing on the little deck, and my man was just scrambling up.

" Look out! " I shouted to Paul. " Here she comes! "

Both he and I let go the oars and tumbled into the cockpit. The next instant the big boom and the heavy blocks swept over our heads, the mainsheet whipping past like a great coiling snake and the *Mist* heeling over with a violent jar. Both men had jumped for it, but in some way the little man either got his knife hand jammed or fell upon it, for the first sight we caught of him, he was standing in his boat, his bleeding fingers clasped close between his knees and his face all twisted with pain and helpless rage.

" Now's our chance! " Paul whispered. " Over with you! "

And on either side of the rudder we lowered ourselves into the water, pressing the net down with our feet, till, with a jerk, it went clear. Then it was up and in, Paul at the mainsheet and I at the tiller, the *Mist* plunging ahead with freedom in her motion, and the little white light astern growing small and smaller.

" Now that you've had your ad-

[1] jibe her mainsail: shift the boat so that the wind would fill the sail from the opposite side and swing around its heavy pole at the bottom, called the *boom*.

venture, do you feel any better? " I remember asking when we had changed our clothes and were sitting dry and comfortable again in the cockpit.

" Well, if I don't have the nightmare for a week to come " — Paul paused and puckered his brows in judicial fashion — " it will be because I can't sleep, that's one thing sure! "

Adventure, Modern Style

1. What was Paul's complaint about modern life? Why did the sixteenth century appeal to him?

2. How did the boys' adventure begin? What really caused the attack on the *Mist*?

3. Explain the maneuvers by which the boys repelled the boarders. How did the boys show they could think and act fast when danger threatened?

4. What was the last thing the boys had to do before they could make their escape? How did they do it?

5. How did their adventure resemble the ones Paul had been dreaming about? Discuss with your classmates the idea that the days of adventure are past. First make sure everyone agrees on what is meant by " adventure."

Sailor Talk

America's coasts, lakes, and rivers have always attracted hosts of sporting sailors. Even if you live out on the wide, dry prairies, the chances are that you will some day find it handy to understand boating terms. See if you can recall the meaning of each of these words or phrases used in the story you have just read.

astern	tiller
sloop-rigged	hard up the helm
slack away	boom
keel	dinky

If you do not remember what one means,

skim back through the footnotes and find it. Get the meaning clearly in mind and then read the sentence where it occurs. Then you will have some equipment for reading sea stories or carrying on a conversation with a sailing fan.

Old-Timer

MARION GARTHWAITE

MARCIA was trying various ways of draping back the canvas flaps at the rear of the covered wagon she was making for the Old-Timers' parade. Her brother Bob was hammering busily inside, when the rest of her family came trooping out to the barn to see how she was coming along.

"Now, that's not bad," Mr. Allison said heartily. "Not bad at all."

Marcia squinted anxiously at the canvas stretched taut over the hoops. "Faint praise isn't enough, Dad. I need encouragement. Is it good enough for a prize?"

"It looks very real," approved her mother. "The old, patched canvas is just right. The water bucket underneath and the wooden tub on the side are fine."

Bob poked his head out from under the canvas. "Don't forget there'll be lots of competition."

"I know," groaned Marcia. "Ev-erybody in town is entering a float."

"Well, there are lots of prizes," consoled twelve-year-old Jimmie. "Our band hopes we'll get one."

"There's a prize for horsemanship, too," Bob told his father. "You'd better try for that, Dad, riding with the cattlemen."

"I'm worried about the horses," said Mrs. Allison. "The wagon is old, and the brake is worn. Zeke seems like a nice steady chap, but he hasn't been around horses very much. Do you think that the mare can be trusted to behave herself on an asphalt street?"

"They always sand the streets," Mr. Allison said. "As long as she's on the sand, she won't slip."

"But she isn't used to crowds," Mrs. Allison went on, "or bands or shouting. I wish you'd drive, Robert. I'd feel much better about the whole thing. Or that Marcia would use an

"Old-Timer" by Marion Garthwaite from *The American Girl Magazine*, July 1949. Reprinted by permission of the author.

automobile truck like the Rotary and some of the others."

The family hooted at the idea. A covered-wagon truck!

" I've warned Zeke to give the mare her head," [1] said Mr. Allison.

Bob went back to his hammering. " It's a good thing the judges can't see the inside of the wagon," he called. " It looks like a porcupine. But this way it will be a lot easier to pull the nails out when we're through."

" You ought to have some things inside," Mrs. Allison suggested, forgetting about the horses. " And some people. Those old wagons were piled high with things. Bedding and household treasures and food. Whole families lived in them for months. There's Great-aunt Jinny's dresser, Marcia, if you want it. It's solid and could be wired to the bed of the wagon. With some quilts, the little trunk in the attic, and perhaps the walnut rocker, it would really be complete. We'll talk about it some more later." And she and Mr. Allison went back through the arbor to the kitchen.

" Why don't you try to borrow Aunt Caroline's old pioneer dress, Marsh? " asked Bob. " You could sit in the back looking out."

" She's never lent it to anyone yet," Marcia said. " Can't you just hear her? ' I should say not! That dress came across the plains a hundred years ago. Every stitch of it's handmade. It should be in a museum. The very idea! ' That's what she said last

---

¹ **give the mare her head:** hold the reins lightly so that there will be little pressure on the bit in the horse's mouth.

---

year when Miss Jackson wanted to borrow it for the high school play."

" I dare you to ask her for it," Bob urged.

" Ask whom for what? " came a sharp voice from the direction of the arbor. Bob ducked into the wagon.

" Good evening, Aunt Caroline," said Marcia. " How do you like our covered wagon for the parade tomorrow? "

Aunt Caroline eyed the wagon critically, walking all around it, her old eyes missing nothing. " Very good as far as it goes," she finally commented. " But nobody ever drove an empty wagon across those deserts and mountains."

" That's what Mom said. She's going to give me some quilts and Great-aunt Jinny's dresser. And the walnut rocker. I'd sit in it if I could borrow your brown pioneer dress," Marcia finished hopefully.

" Certainly not! " snapped Aunt Caroline. " That dress is an heirloom. Every stitch of it handmade over a hundred years ago. It ought to be in a museum."

" I know." Marcia sighed. " That's what we were saying."

" The only thing that's ever happened to that dress in a whole century is the mousehole just below the pocket. The cloth in that dress was woven by hand from flax raised on your great-great-grandfather's farm. It was dyed and cut and stitched by your great-grandmother. It's an heirloom. It ought to be in a museum."

" I know," Marcia agreed. " I didn't expect to wear it, really. But it would have been just right, wouldn't it? "

Aunt Caroline marched around the wagon again. She thumped the wooden washtub, hanging on the side.

"Yes, it would," she snapped. "Come over in the morning and try it on. But if you let anything happen to that dress . . ." Her voice trailed off as she made her way through the dusk of the arbor.

The next morning, as they drove through the back streets to where the parade was forming, Marcia was very proud of her covered wagon. Zeke, the young boy who helped Mr. Allison on the ranch, was up on the front seat. With his sideburns, broad-brimmed hat, jeans, and boots, he looked like a gangling Abe Lincoln. Marcia sat in the back of the wagon, looking out. The brown dress with its tiny lace collar, her hair wound in a smooth bun at the nape of her neck, made her look older. Peering over the backboard of the wagon sat Aunt Caroline's little goddaughter, Cynthia, her curls bobbing under a quilted bonnet.

Miss Jackson, dean of girls at the high school, leaned out of the antiquated surrey she was driving and called, "Marcia Allison, you're perfect! You look like an old painting."

The mare nickered and pranced sideways into the wagon tongue, her eyes rolling. Zeke raised the reins to let her know someone was keeping an eye on her.

"I'd hate to travel for months like this," Marcia said.

"They had lots of courage, those pioneer women," agreed Miss Jackson.

The parade was slow in starting. The mare fretted and stamped until her sides under the heavy harness were white with lather.

At long last, they began to move. First the marshal. Then the cattlemen. Following them came the grammar school band, with Jimmy tootling away for dear life. There were horse-drawn floats or automobile trucks for every organization in town. The old Yosemite Valley stagecoaches had been repaired and repainted and filled with old-timers. There were Indians from North Fork, dancing tribal dances. Between the county-library float, representing "Little Women," and the Circle Dot riders, Marcia jolted and rumbled along in her covered wagon.

The parade turned at Flume and started down Yosemite Avenue. The curbs were lined four deep with people. The streets had been cleared of cars. Already the people along the way were cheering and clapping for the covered wagon. Marcia was very proud.

They would cross the railroad tracks, pass the chamber of commerce and the library, and then Courthouse Park. The judges' stand was a flat truck parked under the sycamores in front of the grammar school. Marcia did hope her entry would win a prize.

The covered wagon started to bump over the railroad tracks. Suddenly a lone engine, standing on the siding near the Valley Feed and Fuel, let off a blast of steam and started backing down the track. The mare reared and flung herself against the roan horse. The roan's feet slipped on the steel rails, and before Zeke could hold him, the horse was down. Plunging and backing, the mare smashed into the wagon tongue. By the time the roan was on his feet, both horses were out of control. Zeke pulled on the reins, but the team plunged out of the line of march. The wagon sideswiped the library float as they passed, careening down Yosemite Avenue at a dead run.

Marcia was on her feet as the roan went down. She pushed Cynthia down on the pile of bedding.

" Grab the dresser," she told the frightened child, " and hang on! "

She clawed and shoved her way over the bundles in the bed of the wagon to the front seat. The people on both sides of the street were screaming and running from the curb, as the covered wagon lurched and swayed, threatening first the people on the sidewalk and then the floats in the parade.

As Marcia pulled herself up to the wagon seat, she thought of the grammar school band on foot down the street. The mousehole in the brown dress caught on a nail. She tugged at it. There was a ripping sound, and the brown dress was torn to the hem.

Highway Ninety-nine was just ahead. Zeke was pulling with all his might on the reins. Marcia climbed into the driver's seat.

" Give me the reins," she shouted. " I know how to drive them."

Zeke wouldn't listen. He was standing, his face white and set beneath his false whiskers, his feet braced against the wagon.

" Give the mare her head! " shouted Marcia.

Zeke only sawed harder on the reins.

People were snatching children back from the curbs, shouting. The parade floats were having trouble with their own horses.

Marcia grabbed the reins. " I know them," she yelled at Zeke, " I can hold them. You take the brake."

Bracing herself upright, she held the reins in strong, steady fingers. She let the mare have her head. Zeke clung to the brake, one leg thrust out to keep Marcia from being thrown off.

Past the judges' stand and the grammar school, past Courthouse Park, Marcia held the horses. She knew she must get the mare under control before they reached the band. Children had no sense. They might scatter. Now the horses steadied to a hard gallop. The wagon stopped its crazy lurching. Marcia could hear little Cynthia crying. She sounded frightened, but not hurt.

Past the huddled Indians, past the Rotary float with its huge wheel, past the old-time locomotive, Marcia concentrated on holding the horses to the lane between the line of march and the curb. Ahead she could see the band, and then the cattlemen. Beyond them was the turning point of the parade. Yosemite Avenue was not sanded beyond J Street. She would have to stop the runaway horses before they left the sand, or they might go down.

" Push harder on the brake, Zeke! " she shouted.

There was a frightful screeching as Zeke threw his whole weight on the brake. The horses started afresh. But the long race was telling on them. Responding to the drag of the brakes on the old wheels and the steady pull on the reins, they slowed down.

One of the cattlemen rode back until he was in front of the children. Several others followed. Marcia knew the first rider was her father. Her arms ached with the pull of the reins. She tried not to think of the brown dress. Cynthia was safe, the covered wagon was still upright and slowing up, and Daddy was between the crazy horses and the children in the band. At the edge of the sand, Marcia pulled with all her might on the roan, but held the tender-mouthed mare easily. The roan broke into a walk. The mare tried the unequal pull and faltered. By the time the wagon rolled upon the unsanded asphalt, the horses were trotting. Zeke jumped down and ran to their heads. The wild ride was over.

Mr. Allison rode down to join them.

" Thank goodness you're all right, and no one got hurt," he said, as he helped Marcia down. " You did a marvelous job, dear. That mare should never have been in the parade."

He and Zeke led the team down the street to a shady stretch. He came back for Cynthia, lifted her in front of him on his horse, and rode off in search of her mother. Marcia, weak

in the knees now that the ride was over, sank down on someone's lawn. She could hardly see the parade for tears. Her covered wagon was out of the running, and Aunt Caroline's beautiful old linen dress, which Marcia had promised to guard, was torn from hip to hem.

A rider drew up to the curb.

" Miss Allison? " he asked. " Please report to the judges' stand."

Marcia nodded, too sick at heart to care. Maybe there was a fine or something for breaking up the parade. Maybe someone was hurt that she hadn't seen. She walked along, holding the torn skirt together, hoping to find her mother or someone she knew. At the library she saw Aunt Caroline on the steps.

" I can't face her before all these people," she told herself.

But to her surprise she found herself walking right past the flagpole and up the library steps.

" Marcia! " cried Aunt Caroline, and put her arms about her.

" Look, Aunt Caroline." Marcia's eyes brimmed with tears. " Look what I've done to your lovely dress! "

" It doesn't matter," said Aunt Caroline. " It doesn't matter at all. Nothing matters but that you are safe, and Cynthia is safe, and all those children. I don't know whatever possessed me to hang on to a mousehole all these years. We can take out a little strip of material below the pocket. It will never be missed. All those yards of material, and me hanging on to a mousehole! You can tell your granddaughter some day, when you hand the dress over to her, how that seam happened to get there."

"Marcia Allison," blared the loud-speaker. "Miss Marcia Allison wanted at the judges' stand."

"Come on, my dear," said Aunt Caroline. "We'll have to see what they want."

Marcia walked up the rough wooden steps to the truck, clutching the torn edges of the brown dress.

"Miss Allison," said the head of the Old-Timers' parade, "we want to commend you for the way you handled your team. We feel that your prompt action averted a possible tragedy that would have marred the day for everyone. We can't give your float a prize, because we can't truthfully say we saw any of the details. But we feel that you have more than earned another prize. It gives the judges great pleasure to award you the prize for the best horsemanship we have seen today. Call at the hardware store any time after Monday, and Mr. Spence will make out the check."

A burst of applause up and down the street made Marcia realize his little speech had gone out over the loud-speaker. She went down the steps in a daze. Aunt Caroline was beaming.

Miss Jackson passed by in her old surrey and slowed down. She leaned out, the jet beads on the ancient bonnet she was wearing winking in the sun.

"Looks like the Allison women didn't use up all the family courage crossing the plains," she called. "Oh, dear! Isn't that your old pioneer dress she's wearing, Caroline?"

"Not any longer," answered Aunt Caroline. "As soon as Marcia and I have mended it, I'm going to give it to her."

A Run for Her Money
1. Why was Aunt Caroline's speech about her pioneer dress funny? In what way did she change her attitude toward the dress by the end of the story?
2. What started the runaway? What special dangers frightened Marcia most?
3. Why couldn't Zeke stop the horses? How did Marcia finally get them under control?
4. What did Miss Jackson mean when she told Marcia "Looks like the Allison women didn't use up all the family courage crossing the plains"?
5. Marcia hoped to win a prize for a good idea and hard work. For what qualities did the judges award her a prize? What other prize did she win?

People's Names Become Words
When something new turns up, a word must be coined to name it. During the War Between the States, General A. E. Burnside, a Union Army commander, let his whiskers grow down the sides of his cheeks and started a new style in beards. The handiest name for the new style was his own, especially when it was turned around to make *sideburns*. That word seemed to describe the whiskers as well as identify their origin. Who wore *sideburns* in the Old-Timers' parade?

Many other words have been made the same way. *Silhouette*, a name for a shadow picture that represents a figure in solid color against a light background, was originally the name of a French finance minister who was pictured in political cartoons as a mere shadow of a man. By looking in a large dictionary find the story behind these words: *davenport, derby, lynch, volt, macadam.*

Emergency — Stand By!

TOM POWERS

PRINT HELPS TELL THE STORY. The airline pilot flying through the clear night sky high above the earth must depend on the control-tower operator at the airport to tell him when the weather below is too bad for a landing. Imagine that you're aboard the plane as you listen to this pilot and operator talk through the stormy air.

When you find any part of a story printed in a different style of type, the change means something. You remember that in plays the speeches of the characters are printed in regular type, but the stage directions (or in a radio play, sound effects) are printed in a slanting type called *italics*. In the play that follows there are no stage directions or sound effects, yet both regular type and italics are used. Be sure to figure out from these " print signals " who is speaking.

B ARTON, *a modern transport pilot, talking to Los Lunas Field by radio. Johnny, his copilot, sits beside him. The passengers are in the cabin behind them, as the plane goes tearing through the night, over New Mexico.*

Barton, in 241, calling Los Lunas . . . Barton, in 241, calling Los Lunas.

(*Los Lunas to* BARTON. *O.K. Go ahead.*)

Hello, Bugs. Barton, in 241, Guyinas [1] to Los Lunas, over Guyinas River, 2500 feet, heavy stuff. Take this . . . there's a lot of it. Approaching Harville, I was directed by Bolivar Airport to make a landing at Harville Emergency Field. Landed just after dark, 9:32 — 9–3–2 — and boy, does that field need some work done on it! Picked up emergency case, appendicitis, Ethel Bevins. . . . B–E–V–I–N–S. Nobody with her; husband, Samuel Bevins, is in Los Lunas, already. Bolivar operator promised to get hold of him, and have him at your airport when we get in. Take this: Doctor, at Harville, says, advise Los Lunas Hospital prepare operate, immediately. Miss Harris, our stewardess, reports patient O.K.

(*O.K.*)

Bolivar reports snow back there, and it don't look like May Day at

¹ Guyinas (gĭ·ē′nås).

Vassar, up here.

(*Yes, heavy snowstorm from north-northeast. . . . Ceiling dropping.*[1])

I got that. . . . Heavy snowstorm from north-northeast . . . Well, hold it off ten minutes, Bugs, and I'll bring the patient in, before the first flake flutters.

(*What's that?*)

Never mind, skip it. It was poetry. So long . . .

Well, Johnny, nice, neat little blizzard trying to sneak in between us and Los Lunas. Go back and tell the poor kid to keep her nerve up. Her husband's on his way out to the field, now. Tell Harris to be sure to put a pillow between her and her landing belt. Say, did you see what she had in her hand when we carried her in? Her baby's shoe. For good luck, she said.

Barton, in 241, calling Los Lunas. Barton, calling Los Lunas.

(*O.K. . . . go ahead, Barton.*)

Say, were you right! . . . Here comes the snow, and here we go into it. Good-by ceiling. Climbing up to get above it . . . 3500 feet.

(*I tell you, Barton, you'd better turn back.*)

Listen, baby, we can't go back.

(*Don't think you ought to come in.*)

I know, but . . .

(*It's a blizzard.*)

O.K., but . . .

(*And it's heavy.*)

Listen, Toots, we've got to get this gal to the hospital soon.

(*What about the regulations?*)

Yeah? The guy that wrote those

regulations meant them for transport ships. This one's just been converted into an ambulance.

(*It says on page 122 . . .*)

Yeah . . . and you know what it says on page 304: " In an emergency, the pilot makes all decisions."

(*There ain't no page 304.*)

Well, it would say it, if there was a page 304.

(*You can't come in, Barton.*)

No? . . . Well, come up here and stop me. Still climbing 4100 . . . no top yet.

(*Hey, Barton, Mr. Bevins is here.*)

Who did you say?

(*Bevins.*)

Her husband? . . . swell! I guess he's worried sick. Say, get him in your radio tower, and let me talk to him. It might cheer the poor guy up.

(*He's in here now.*)

Oh, is he? Can he hear me?

(*Sure, go ahead.*)

Hello . . . Mr. Bevins . . . Listen, this is Barton, the pilot, that's bringing your wife from Harville. We're up here, in the dark, coming along about 300 miles an hour. She was awful sick, Mr. Bevins, but she's doing all right. Dr. Schultz took your baby over to his house. Try not to worry, Mr. Bevins. Our stewardess is a trained nurse, and she's doing everything she can. I'll tell her you're waiting for her. And say, she brought along the baby's shoe, for luck, she said. Don't you worry — she's fine. Hey, Bugs, he'd better stay in the waiting room while we land, and you cut out your little side chats, and concentrate on your Uncle Dudley, for

[1] *Ceiling dropping:* clouds getting lower.

here I come.

(*O.K.*)

Oh, it's you, Miss Harris . . . how is she? As bad as that, huh? Is Johnny with her? Well, we'll try to put the bus down without a jolt.

Oh, here's Johnny. You'd better go back, Miss Harris, and tell her her husband is at the airport, with an ambulance, waiting.

We must be just over Amsterdam, Johnny . . . What's that? She sent me what? Well, I'll be durned! Yeah, I'll keep it here in my pocket until we land, and if I don't land easy on this snow, I hope this baby's shoe kicks me all over the town of Los Lunas. They've got good landing lights on that field. We can go in blind, on the radio beam, but I'll get a word of advice from Bugs, to help us in through this stuff.

Barton, calling Los Lunas. Barton, calling Los Lunas. Barton, calling Los Lunas. Barton, in 241, calling Los Lunas . . . Calling Los Lunas. Better try somebody else. Barton, in 241, calling Bolivar Airport . . . Calling Bolivar Airport . . . Calling Los Lunas. Johnny, go in and tell the passengers to buckle on their safety belts while I keep trying.

Barton, in 241, calling Los Lunas . . . Barton, in 241, calling Los Lunas . . . Barton, in 241, calling Bolivar . . . Barton, in 241, calling — practically anybody . . . Danny Kaye . . . Joe Stalin . . . Li'l Abner . . . Barton, in 241, calling General Eisenhower. Hey, Los Lunas, how do you think I'm going to land on your cockeyed stubblefield if you don't help me a little?

(*Go ahead, go ahead.*)

Oh, is that you, Bugs? Hey, Bugs, Los Lunas . . . if you can hear me, set out some lights on the field. We'll be in before they can flicker a flick.

How is she, Johnny? Hot dog! No, I can't hear a thing, but I think he's getting me, all right. If you can hear me, Bugs, I ought to be just passing over Beacon 366. Going to switch on-to the beam [1] and fly in blind. Keep pinching your left ear for luck, and so long. Keep your eye on the altimeter,[2] Johnny. Here we go, onto the beam. There's the beam's pretty little voice – gosh, Johnny, what did pilots do before they had these things? – listen to it – " Tit – tah – tit – tah." [3]

We're left, off our course, Johnny . . . Still left.

There, " Tah – ah," she says; if we can keep on that steady note, we can get her in. Read me the altitude as I drop down. I'll try to pick up those landing lights, but we couldn't hardly see the Goddess of Liberty tonight . . . not till she prodded us with her torch in the fuselage.[4] 1450 feet . . .

Oh, oh! we're off it, to the right.

O.K. She's singing steady again . . . 1300 . . . God pity the poor postman on a night like this. Yep . . . 1200 . . . We ought to be over the Reservoir by now, but I couldn't see Times Square. . . . Better try Bugs again.

Barton, calling Los Lunas . . . Barton, calling Los Lunas . . . 1100

. . . Listen, Bugs, in case you can hear me . . . About over the Reservoir, on the beam . . . 1100 . . . going to drop down, to land . . . patient fine . . . keep the home lights burning. Here I come. . . .

We're off to the right, Johnny.

There we are, on it again. Here, Johnny – a thousand feet . . . open the little side glass and see if you can see those blinking lights. 900 – ugh . . . ugh! – It sure is a blizzard. How deep do you think the snow will be on the field? 800 – Did you tell the passengers that it's all just a lot of fun, and that we love diving through this stuff? 700 – Can't you see anything, Johnny? Put your belt on. Do what I tell you. . . .

Do what I tell you. 600 – No use bumping your nose off if I don't make it. Put it on – that's right. 500 – Can't you see the ground at all? I can't, either. We ought to be nearly over the beam . . . let's wait for it. She ought to cut out in a minute.

Yep! There she goes. We're right over the beam, at 500. That's swell!

Tah! And there it is singing again. That makes it about perfect, and here we go down. Watch the altimeter, Johnny. There mustn't be any little hitch in this. Hey, pat that baby's shoe, in my pocket, for luck, will you? 400 – Here we go. This is one of those tricks that you never know if you'll get a medal for, or have your license taken away. 300 –

We're left again. Here. Good Lord! This is no time to . . .

Gosh, there's the beam singing again! Attaboy! 220 – Stick your

---

[1] **switch onto the beam:** steer by a continuous series of short notes radioed out from the field.
[2] **altimeter** (ăl·tĭm′e·tẽr): an instrument that shows the height above sea level.
[3] **Tit . . . tah:** He imitates the sound the beam makes. The sound changes to show when the plane gets off course, with different sounds for right and left.
[4] **fuselage** (fū′se·lĭj): the main body of the plane, to which the wings and tail are attached.

head out, Johnny, and see if . . . 150 . . . see if I've gone blind, or if his lights are not on. 100 . . . For the Lord's sake, Johnny, can't you see anything? This is getting pretty . . . durned . . . Uh huh! . . . Never mind. There they are . . . I see 'em. Good old Bugs, he did hear me. He can cuss me all he wants to . . . 50 . . . feet . . . here we go, right over the hangars, and down onto the . . . wait . . . easy now . . . Down we . . . go! . . . There you are, Johnny, taxi us in, will you, across the field? The snow's not too deep yet.

Well, Miss Harris, did she stand the landing all right? Swell; go back and tell her the baby's shoe brought us luck.

Well, Johnny, I'll switch onto Bugs and let him tell me what he thinks of me while you taxi us through the snow.

(*So, you made it, you crazy nut.*)

Yep, we made it. On the ground once more. Patient doing fine.

(*Main office wants you on the phone.*)

What? Main office wants me? Well, tell 'em to hold the phone, till Johnny gets us across the field. But before I find out whether I get a medal for this stunt or get fired, I've got a date with myself, to drink a little health — yeah, out of a lady's shoe.

Keeping Track of the Speakers

1. What part of the play was printed in italics inside parentheses? Did you find that the different styles of print keep the speakers straight in your mind?

2. The author of this play has said that the speeches in parentheses need not be spoken. "These speeches are effective," he says, "but it goes just as well without them." Explain or demonstrate in class how this is true.

3. Was Barton responsible for having the sick woman on his plane?

4. Did the baby's shoe really bring luck to either the mother or the pilot?

5. How does the radio beam help a pilot? What do we mean when we say that a person is " on the beam " or " off the beam "?

The Grave Grass Quivers

MacKINLAY KANTOR

An unsolved mystery may be almost forgotten after many years, but it is still a mystery. In this tense story a young doctor, who is taking over the practice of old Dr. Martindale, finds himself acting the part of an assistant detective.

MYSTERY AND ADVENTURE

WE WERE alone, out there in the soft spring sunshine. We dug silently, carefully. We had been digging for ten minutes, when my shovel struck against something, and something cracked.

After that, it wasn't long before we began to uncover things. "Murdered," Doc said once, and then he didn't talk any more.

It began in Doc Martindale's office, which, as soon as he retired, was to be my office, on a cool spring afternoon in 1921.

"How's it going?" asked Doc.

"I guess it'll be pretty slow here, to live," I said, childishly.

"Not much excitement," agreed Doc. He went to the door and picked up a copy of the Cottonwood *Herald*. "Yes, local news is slow, pretty slow. There's a sample of a Cottonwood thriller."

It told of the plans for Arbor Day. The children of the public schools were going to set out some trees as a memorial to the local boys who had died in the World War.

. . . and selected as their choice, American elms. The trees will be planted on the Louis Wilson farm, above the Coon River. Mr. Wilson has agreed to donate a small plot of ground for this purpose. It is thought that these trees, standing on a high hill above the river and overlooking a majestic view of our city, will be a fitting memorial.

Ceremonies are to begin at 2 P.M. Rev. J. Medley Williams of the Baptist Church will deliver a —

Doc pulled his gray beard and laughed. "A few meetings, a church social, once in a while a fire or an auto accident! Life comes — and goes — without much hullabaloo."

Then I had to laugh also, and a bit sheepishly. "I guess I'm rather silly. Of course those are the important things in most people's lives. But I would like to get called in on a nice, exciting murder once in a while!"

Doc was silent for a moment. He appeared to be thinking heavily, as if he had taken me seriously. "Murders," he said, after a moment. "Once before the war, a section worker stabbed his wife. Then back in '96, an insane farmer shot his neighbor. But, come to think about it, those are the only murders we've ever had here in all my years of practice." He seemed much impressed. "Think of that, think of that! Only two murders since 1861."

"And who," I inquired idly, "was murdered in 1861?"

He tugged at his beard again, and cleared his throat. "Well," he said slowly, "it was my father and my brother."

"Oh." And I scarcely knew what to say. "I'm sorry, Doctor, I —"

"No matter." He shrugged. "It's a long time. I was just a boy then."

My curiosity was aroused. "What are the details, Doctor? That is, if you don't —"

"Oh, I don't mind. . . . Sit down and take it easy." He fumbled around for his matches, and his fat, brown cigar had been fogging the room for several minutes before he began.

" My brother Titus — he was a lot older — had run away from home when he was small, and gone West with some folks. He didn't come back until the spring of '61. And when he came, what a time! "

He laughed his short, dry laugh.

" Titus had struck it rich. He had about seven thousand dollars in gold with him.

" Pa and Titus decided to take the gold to Hamilton. There was a sort of bank opened up there, and the folks were afraid to risk keeping so much money around home.

" They were pretty careful, too, and didn't tell around town much about what they planned. They started out at night, figuring to get clear away from Cottonwood and the settlers who knew them, before daylight. Pa and Titus were big, strapping men. They looked very strong, sitting up on the board laid across the plank wagon-box, and Titus carried a navy revolver on his hip and a Sharps rifle across his knees."

Doc Martindale shifted his fat, bumpy body in his old swivel chair. " And that," he said, " was the last we ever saw them.

" On the evening of the second day after my folks left," Dr. Martindale continued, " a farmer rode up in front of our house, and said that he had seen our team down in a clump of willows by Little Hell Slough, hitched to a wagon, and that the menfolks were not with the wagon. The team had been dragging around, and tried to go home, but they got hung up in the willows."

Old Doc was silent for several minutes.

" That was a terrible night," he said simply. " Before we all got down to Little Hell Slough — most of the neighbors were with us — we found the team in those willows, pretty muddy and hungry, and tangled up in the harness, too.

" None of the stuff in the wagon had been taken except — sure: the gold was gone. The blankets were still there, and Titus's rifle, but his navy revolver wasn't anywhere around. And there was no other sign of Pa and Titus.

" I drove Ma and the girls home, in that wagon. Ma sat there beside me on the board, stiff and solemn. Once she said, ' Georgie, if they're gone and gone for good, you'll get the man who did it. Won't you? ' I began to cry, of course. I says, ' Yes, Ma. I'll take care of you always, Ma. . . . But if they're dead, it wasn't a man who killed 'em. It was men. One man wouldn't be a match for Titus alone.' "

Doc was buried in the thickening shadows of the office. I couldn't see his face any more.

" Then I went back with the men. We searched the river, up and down the hills around Cottonwood, too, clear down to the East Fork. And never found a thing.

" In that wagon there was just one clue — just one thing which made it certain in our minds that they were dead. That was a little spot of dried blood on the floor of the wagon, right behind the seat. About half as big as your hand. Seemed like, if they'd been shot off the wagon, there'd have been more blood. Then, too, the horses were a fairly young team and they might have cut loose and run away if any shooting had started.

"It was always the general opinion that the murderers had disposed of the bodies in the river. But personally, I always hung to the idea that Titus and Pa were killed in some mysterious way, and their bodies buried. . . . No other clue was ever discovered, and no further information of any kind was ever unearthed.

"I didn't quit searching for months. Eli Goble helped me, too; he worked like grim death. But we couldn't find a thing."

I asked, "Who was Eli Goble?"

There was the dull scraping of Doc's shoes on the floor. "Seems to me that you cashed a check this noon, boy. Where did you cash it?"

Somewhat perplexed, I told him. "At the bank across the street."

"Well, that's Eli Goble. And where are you living temporarily — until you can find rooms or an apartment to your liking?"

"At the — Oh, of course, Doctor. The Goble Hotel."

He chuckled. "Everything in this town's Goble, boy. He came here in '59 with a man named Goble, but that wasn't Eli's real name. He had heard that his folks came from Ohio, but didn't know anything about it. You see, his family was killed in the Mint Valley massacre, about 1840, and he had been kidnaped by the Indians. Lived with the Sioux until he was sixteen — could talk the language like a native, too. In fact, lots of folks used to think he was part Indian. But he wasn't. And during the search, he thought all the trailing experience which he had had when among the Indians might be of some account. But even that didn't help. We couldn't find a thing."

I said, slowly, "He's rich, now?"

Doc sighed, and began to hunt around for the light switch. "Suspecting Eli Goble, are you?" He chuckled. "I don't believe anybody ever did, before. He never had a cent to his name for years after that. A few months later he enlisted in the army, served all through the war, and didn't come back here till 1867. In the meantime, through someone he met in the army, he had been trying to get track of his family. And eventually he succeeded. Found the original family back in Ohio. He got what money was coming to him, brought it out here to Cottonwood, invested it carefully, and made good. He retained the name of Goble for convenience's sake. Now he's almost ninety, but he's one of the richest men in the state, and one of the tightest. He never lets go of a nickel until the Goddess of Liberty yells for mercy."

The big yellow light hissed into being. It glared down on the white-enameled table, the glistening cabinets and instruments, the old desk and rows of books. Doc Martindale stood there in the middle of the office and nodded his head. "That's the story, boy. Real live mystery, just sixty years old this spring."

We were just putting on our hats, and Doc was struggling into his old brown slicker, when the telephone rang. Martindale took up the receiver. "Doctor Martindale speaking."

"Oh," he said, after a moment. "Well." And then he winked quickly at me above the telephone. "Did you use any of that stimulant I left last time? . . . Yes. I'm leaving the office now, to go home, and I'll stop in. Yes."

He replaced the receiver on its hook. "Speak of the devil," he said. "Eli Goble's just had another heart attack. Nothing to get excited about. He has them frequently. We'll stop in to see him for a minute."

The Goble house was only a few minutes' drive from the main business streets. . . . Lights glowed from most of the windows as we came up the sidewalk. "You can tell that Eli's flat on his back," said Doc. "If he was around, he wouldn't let them burn all that electricity."

The old man watched us from his pillow, with black, red-rimmed eyes, deeply sunk beneath the moldy fuzz of his eyebrows. He was breathing heavily.

"Well, Eli. How do you feel? This is Dr. Patterson, Eli."

The old man seemed to glare broodingly at me.

"Don't feel — so — good," Goble managed with difficulty.

Martindale began to open his bag. "Oh, nothing to worry about, Eli." He made a perfunctory examination.

"You'll feel better soon."

The old man mumbled and coughed; and we went down the shadowy stairway, and out to the front door.

It was four o'clock the next afternoon when Doc Martindale and I arrived at the office, following a round of calls on widely separated cases.

When we returned in Doc's old touring car, it was to find the Cottonwood *Herald* spread on the table with plenty of black ink decorating the front page.

Eli Goble Gives Park to City
Local Businessman and Pioneer
Settler Decides on Memorial
Plans Changed for Tomorrow's
Dedication

At a special meeting of the city council this afternoon, it was unanimously agreed to accept the gift tendered by Eli Goble, revered Civil War veteran and early settler in Cottonwood, who today offered to give the town of Cottonwood some thirty acres of beautiful woodland, to be known as "Goble Memorial Park."

It is understood that Mr. Goble has been ill, and that is the reason for a delay in his plans.

"The grand old man of Crockett County" stipulated in the terms of his gift that the proposed Memorial Grove of trees should be set out somewhere in the new park area. This necessitated a hasty change in plans. Instead of being planted on the north hill, on the Louis Wilson farm above the Coon River, the trees will be set out on the brow of the east hill, which is included in the thirty acres donated by Mr. Goble.

A big parade, forming in the city hall square, will officially open the Arbor Day ceremonies at two o'clock tomorrow afternoon. . . .

We leaned there, side by side, with our hands upon the desk, and read that newspaper story.

Doc tapped the paper with his forefinger. " I'll go on record as saying," he declared, " that this is the first thing Eli Goble ever gave away in his life — at least the first thing in which there wasn't some chance of his getting value received out of it. And I don't see what he can get out of this, except glory. . . . Eli doesn't care a rap for glory."

Two patients drifted in for examination. When I left an hour later, I looked back to see Doctor Martindale sitting there in his swivel chair, a tired hulk, still reading the Cottonwood *Herald*.

At five-thirty in the morning, old Doc was beating on my door. I arose, startled, wondering what could have made him summon me so insistently.

He came into the hotel room and waited while I threw on my clothes. " What is it? " I asked, between splashes of cold water.

" We're going out and do a little digging," he said.

I nodded. " Appendectomy? Or what? "

" Nothing so unimportant," Doc replied. And his eyes looked as if he had been awake all night — red-rimmed and circled. " Real digging. No one will know where we are." . . . I was still too sleepy to press

him for more details, or to wonder what it was all about.

But when we got out to the curbing in front of the hotel, and I glanced into the rear seat of Doc's car, there lay two spades, a scoop shovel and a pickax.

I turned with an exclamation of astonishment.

" Get in," said Doc. And I did, without any more words. We seemed to be heading north of town. Two minutes later our car was making the Coon River bridge rattle and bang in every loose joint.

" This is the Louis Wilson farm," said Doc. At the farthest corner of the cornfield we climbed out, taking the shovels and ax with us. Doc was breathing hoarsely, but the strange pallor had left his face. His eyes were bright and intent; there was something almost furious in their gleam.

He led me through a fringe of oak timberland, coming out on a sloping knoll where one solitary oak tree stood, stunted and twisted by many winds. The grass beneath our feet was coarse, tangled, flat-bladed. Native prairie sod, without a doubt. Far away, a band of crows was circling over the river, cawing with faint and raucous cries.

" This is the north hill," said Doc. " There's the town."

It was a very high hill, this bald mound on which we stood. The thin, brittle grass was tufted with hundreds of pale, lilac-pastel flowers. The blossoms grew on short, fuzzy stems; the petals shaded from white to purple, with a heart of yellow in each flower.

"They're beautiful," I said. "I never saw anything like them before. What are they?"

"Windflowers. Easter flowers. Or I guess the more modern name is pasqueflower. Pretty things, aren't they? One of the earliest we have around here. . . . Well, I'm going to get busy."

Doc dropped the shovel he was carrying, and I was just as willing to relinquish the heavy load in my own arms. I went over and sat down against the gnarled oak tree, which was the only tree on all that bald, brownish hill. A million facts and statements and conjectures seemed boiling in my brain; I could make nothing out of them.

Before my eyes, Doc Martindale was behaving in a very strange manner. He was walking slowly in vague, indefinite circles, his eyes staring at the ground in front of him. I had the strange notion that Dr. George Martindale, after unloading the sad story of his youth, had taken two days in going deliberately and completely insane.

He thrust a small piece of stick into the ground, moved away, surveyed the spot carefully, and then came back to set up another stick, several feet from the first. He repeated this process two more times. He now had an uneven rectangle, eight or ten feet long, marked at its corners by the bits of stick. "We'll try it here," he said.

Without another word, he removed his coat, lifted the pickax, and sent its point into the ground.

As I have said before, we were alone — out there in the thin sunshine of early morning. We dug silently. After Doc had penetrated some two feet in depth, at one side of the rectangle, he moved out toward the middle of the space he had marked. I followed, with my shovel.

We had been digging for about ten minutes, when we began to find things.

"Murdered," said Doc.

We were finding them, picking out the disordered relics from the rich earth where they had lain so long, tibiae, ribs . . . phalanges [1] . . . the rusty remains of an ancient revolver.

Doc straightened up, and spoke to me gently. His face was set and strained; it might have been cast in iron. "There's a sheet and a grain sack or two in the car," he said. "Will you go over and bring them?"

I was glad of the opportunity to get away for a few minutes. When I came back, Doc had most of the bones covered with his coat. The knees of his trousers were dark and earthy; he had been kneeling in the loose mold of the grave, picking out the smaller fragments.

"I want a witness," he said, shortly. "Take a look at this." From beneath the coat he withdrew a human skull and turned it slowly for me to see. There was a complete and noticeable fracture, such as might have been caused by the blow of a sharp

[1] **tibiae** (tĭb′ĭ-ē): The tibia is the large bone between knee and ankle; **phalanges** (fă-lăn′jĕz): small bones of the hand or foot.

ax. "The other is the same way," he added, and replaced the skull tenderly.

Then I spoke for the first time. "Can you identify them?"

"Easily," he said. "There's a Masonic pocket piece, the revolver, the knives and things. . . . The pocket piece is the best bet. It's engraved with Pa's name. Not corroded at all. I rubbed it up and could read the engraving."

Wisely, he made no attempt to identify or isolate the separate skeletons. The bones made awkward bundles, in the grain racks. We worked slowly, carrying them and the shovels back to the car. I was too stunned by the grim reality to ask any questions. We went away and left that uneven black hole in the middle of the blooming windflowers.

Back in town, we went to Doc Martindale's garage, behind his little house on Omaha Street, and left the bundles there. Then we hurried to the office; fortunately there had been no phone calls at either house or office. It was after seven o'clock, and yet I had no desire for breakfast.

Doc sat at his desk and thumbed through a stack of old letters and notebooks. "Clell Howard's living in Long Beach," he muttered. "Got his address somewhere. . . . And Eph Spokesman is with his niece out in Portland. I've got to send telegrams right away." Then, strangely enough, he seemed to discover me standing there. "You go around and look at Mrs. Gustafson and the little Walker boy; tell them I'm busy on an emer-

gency case. Don't say a word to anybody."

"I won't," I promised.

He said, "And be sure you don't forget the parade. It forms at 2 P.M. at the city hall square. You'll want to see that." And then he turned back to his rummaging.

I had all of the bedfast patients bandaged and dosed and sprayed and examined before 1:30 P.M. At two o'clock I was standing, with a group of citizens, on the steps of the Cottonwood city hall. . . .

At twenty minutes after two, the crowd was somewhat impatient. There had been a large turnout; the Boy Scouts were there, and the members of the American Legion, chafing and shifting in line. There was even a huge truck, splashed with vivid bunting, on which were the grove of memorial elms all ready to be set out, their dirt-encrusted roots sticking from beneath the scarlet shimmer of flags, like so many witches' claws.

This crowd was waiting for Eli Goble, albeit waiting impatiently. If a man was so kind as to give away thirty acres of land, one could at least expect him to show up for the dedication. It was almost two-thirty before a big Cadillac touring car slid around the corner by the oil station. Yes, it was Eli Goble. I could see that bearded, skeleton shape sitting hunched in the rear seat, a Navaho blanket across his knees. His narrow-eyed son, vice-president of the bank, was driving.

I had a clear view of Doc Martindale, accompanied by a fat, pink-faced man who seemed very nervous, emerging from a dark stairway across the street.

I shouldered through the knotted humanity. Once or twice I had a quick glance at Doc and the pink-faced man, over the heads of the crowd. They were walking rapidly toward the corner where the Goble car was parked; the pink-faced man was drawing a folded paper from his pocket, and he seemed more nervous than ever.

We reached the corner simultaneously. A benign citizen, who wore a white silk badge, "Chairman," fluttering from his coat, was leaning at the side of the car, conversing with Eli Goble and his son.

"Daniel," said Doc Martindale.

The chairman turned.

"Get up on the city hall steps," Doc directed him, "and announce to the crowd that Mr. Goble's physician refuses to allow him to participate in the exercises. Then get them started with their parade."

Daniel began to stammer and sputter.

"Go 'long with you," ordered Doc, firmly. He opened the door of the back seat, and he and the pink-faced man slid in beside Eli Goble. And then Doc saw me standing there. "Get in the front seat, Dr. Patterson," he called, and before I knew it, I was sitting beside Vincent Goble, who was too excited to even bow.

"I don't understand this," he said importantly. "You're carrying things off with a very high hand, Dr. Martindale. It is my father's wish that — "

Doc's lips were thin and firm beneath his scraggly beard. "You keep your mouth shut, Vincent," he said. Vincent Goble gasped. "Drive around the corner on Queen Street out of this crowd, and pull up at the curb."

The younger man's face was flaming with rage, but he obeyed the command. The Cadillac purred ahead, past the corner, past the alley, past the crowd. A block away it drew up beside the curb.

Vincent Goble and I swung around to face the trio in back. Eli Goble sat in the middle, clutching and contracting his hands against the red triangles of the Navaho blanket.

"Go ahead, Ed," said Dr. Martindale.

The little pink-faced man gasped apologetically, and fluttered the folds of the paper in his hand. He began a whispered jumble of phrases: "As sheriff of Crockett County, it is my duty to place you, Eli Goble, under arrest. You are charged with the murder of Titus Martindale, and William Martindale, on or about the twenty-fourth of April, in the year 1861 — "

Vincent Goble snarled. The old man still sat there, motionless except for the parchment hands which twisted in his lap. "Ain't true," he managed to whisper. "It — ain't true."

"You cowards!" cried his son. The banker's face was livid. "You'd devil the very life out of an old man with some crazy superstition like that! You'd — "

Doc Martindale said, "Drive up to the sheriff's office, Vincent. We want to talk things over."

"Like the devil I will! Like — "

Ed Maxon, the sheriff, gulped fear-
fully. "Yes, Mr. Goble. That's right.
Have to ask you to bring your father
up to my office."

And so, we went. Vincent, cursing
beneath his breath, Doc Martindale
silent as the tomb, Ed Maxon twisting and rubbing a damp hand around
his collar. And Eli Goble sitting
there under the blanket, his eyes like
black caverns, and saying: "I —
never done it. You'll see. I never done
— that."

"You saw the gold at the house.
And made up your mind — "

"No."

"You followed them out there on
the east prairie. Or maybe you were
lying there, waiting for them."

"I never — done it."

"Say, Dr. Martindale. If my father
should have another heart attack and
die while you're questioning him — "

"I'm a physician, Vincent. And
Eli's my patient. I'll look out for him
if he starts to faint. . . . Eli, you
killed them from ambush."

"I never. Never did."

"Then you left the bodies in the
wagon, took the team, and drove out
to the north hill. It was a long drive
— must have taken hours to get out
there. But you figured that nobody
ever went up there, and it was away
from the beaten track, and it would
be a good place to hide the bodies."

"I — I — George, I'm an old man.
I — "

"Blast you, Martindale! You — "

"Sit down, Vincent, and shut up.

I'm not going to fool with anybody
today. . . . Let's take your pulse,
Eli. . . . Hm. Guess you can stand
it. All right. You buried them out on
the north hill. Maybe you drove the
wagon back and forth over the grave
— an Indian trick. Trick you learned
from the Sioux. And probably you
scattered lots of grass and brush
around."

"No. *No.*"

"Titus had his gun strapped on;
you left them in the ground, just as
they were. You didn't take anything
out of the wagon except those buckskin bags. Then you drove clear
around town again, and drove over
by Little Hell Slough. You left the
team there, and skinned out. Took
the gold somewhere and hid it, probably."

"Ain't so. Lie. . . ."

"Then you laid low, and waited
to join in the search. You were clever,
Eli. Clever as an Indian. . . . You
helped me search, too. Oh, how we
searched! We even went right across
that north hill. But we never saw
anything that looked like a grave.
. . . You kept it covered up, Eli.
You were smart."

"Don't. . . . Don't talk so — I
can't — "

"You let my father alone! — "

"Now, Mr. Goble. Please. Control
yourself. Please — "

"You concluded that seven thousand dollars was a big fortune. Well,
it was. Worth waiting for. So you
enlisted in the army, took your
chances — I'll give you credit for
nerve there, Eli — and turned up

after the war with that story about finding your relatives and your family property back in Ohio. Yes, you were smart."

" I never — never done it."

" Why did you give this park to the city? "

" Mmmmm. I — "

" The *Herald* carried that Arbor Day announcement, night before last. And right away you had a heart attack. And the next morning you came out with that gift to the city. *Provided* — "

" Vincent. Vincent. Make 'em let me — "

" I'll — "

" Here, hold him! "

" I've got him. Now, Mr. Goble, you'll have to sit down."

" Don't be a fool, Vincent. This is true — all true. It's taken me sixty years to find out, but I've found out. You gave that park to the city of Cottonwood, Eli Goble, *provided* that they set out the memorial grove over there, on the east hill, instead of on the north hill. You didn't want anybody digging on the north hill, did you? It had never occurred to you to buy Louis Wilson's farm, so there wouldn't be a chance of people digging that ground up."

" No. Don't talk so, George. Old. I'm an old an' — "

" Well, it was the first thing you ever gave away in your life. And it set me to thinking. I thought, ' Why didn't Eli want that memorial grove planted up there? ' And then I began to understand things. I went up there this morning. Dr. Patterson was with

me — I have a witness to what I am now about to relate. He saw me dig; he saw me find things. I found *them,* Eli."

Vincent Goble was slumped forward, his head buried in his hands. Eli sat there in the sheriff's big chair, staring across the table. He seemed to be looking squarely through the opposite wall.

" They were murdered, Eli. Their skulls had been broken. A heavy sharp blow at the back of each skull. I found them."

The old man's lips were gray and rubbery. He whispered, " No, I never done it. Can't prove it was me."

" A hatchet, Eli. Someone had thrown a hatchet — or maybe two hatchets, in quick succession. They were sitting on that wagon board, in the bright moonlight. It would have been easy for anyone who could throw a tomahawk."

Doc fumbled in the breast pocket of his coat, and brought out three squares of yellow paper. " I'll read to you all," he said calmly. " Three telegrams. The first one I sent myself, early this morning, to Clell Howard, in Long Beach, California, and to Ephraim Spokesman in Portland, Oregon. Remember those names, Eli? Clell was mayor here, once. And Eph Spokesman — everybody knew him. Here's my telegram: ' Please reply by wire completely and at my expense. During the old days at Cottonwood, what man was skillful at throwing a knife or hatchet. Search your recollection and reply at once.'

" Here's the first reply I got. It

came from Ephraim Spokesman's niece. Came about eleven o'clock. You can read it yourself, gentlemen. It says: 'Uncle Eph very sick but says man named Goble thought to be a half-breed was only one who could throw hatchet. Wants to hear full details why you ask.'

"Along about eleven-forty-five, I got a telegram from Clell Howard. Here it is: 'Hello old neighbor regards to you. Am almost ninety but recall perfectly how I lost five dollars betting Eli Goble couldn't stick hatchet ten times in succession in big tree by Halsey blacksmith shop.'"

The room was perfectly still, except for the hoarse sputtering in Eli Goble's throat. "No," he whispered tremulously. "No."

Doc Martindale pointed to the further corner of the dusty old room. There was a table, which none of us had noticed before, and on that table was a white sheet, rumpled and bulky. "Eli," said Doc, quietly. "They're over there. In the corner."

The aged man stiffened in his chair. His back arched up, the shoulders quaking; his claw hands seemed wrenching a chunk of wood from the table in front of him.

"Father!" his son cried.

Eli Goble shook his head, and dropped back in his chair, his deepset eyes dull with a flat, blue light. "The dead," he whispered. "They found me. They're here in this room. I done it. I killed them. Titus and Bill. Yes. Yes."

Vincent Goble dropped down, his head buried in his arms, and began to sob — big, gulping sobs. The sheriff twisted nervously in his seat.

"George. You — you gonna send me to — prison? You gonna have them — hang me? I'm old. . . . I done it. Yes."

Doc Martindale cleared his throat. "Yes, you are old, Eli. Lot older than I am. It's too late, now, to do anything about it. I told my mother I'd get the man, and — But I can't see what good it would do, now, to send you to jail or even try you for murder."

Sheriff Maxon wiped his forehead. "The law," he said shrilly, "the law must take its course! Eli Goble, you must — "

"No," said old Doc, decisively. "I'm running this show, Ed. Without me, without my testimony and the case I've built up, there isn't any show against Eli. I won't prosecute him, or furnish evidence."

"But he confessed to his murder!" shrilled Maxon. "He — "

Doc nodded. "Orally. Yes, but what if Vincent and Dr. Patterson and myself all swear that he never confessed? What if I destroy — the evidence!"

Maxon shook his head and bit his lips.

"How much is your father worth?" asked Doc of Vincent Goble.

The banker lifted his face, on which the weary, baffled tears were still wet. "Couple of million, I guess."

"All yours," whispered Eli. "All yours . . ."

"Maybe," Doc nodded. "Seven thousand dollars! Quite a nest egg, in those days. Like fifty thousand, now. Or even more. No, gentlemen. Money won't do me any good. It can't bring back Titus and my father. But it can still do good. Yes."

Eli Goble's eyes had closed, like dark windows on which ragged curtains had been drawn. "I've seen 'em — I've seen 'em. Always. Since I got old — they come back. I had to give in. Yes."

"You'll go home," said Doc. "I'll give you something to put you to sleep. Then, after you have a little rest and get your strength back, you'll have a lawyer up at your house. You will give, to this county in which you live, one million dollars for the purpose of founding and endowing a modern hospital, where every inhabitant can secure the best medical and surgical attention, free of charge. How does that sound?"

Head still buried in his arms, Vincent Goble nodded drunkenly. His father had opened his eyes and was shivering, still staring through the blank wall ahead of him. "Yes. Anything. I give — anything. But take me away. I want to go — home. I'm old. I don't want to stay in this room. I don't want to stay with — *them.*"

After Eli Goble was in bed, and asleep, Doc and I came out into the damp warmth of the spring afternoon. Martindale looked ten years older than he did the day before. "After this," he said, "after everything is taken care of, I'll let things go. . . . You look after the practice beginning next Monday."

Our feet sounded flat and talka-

tive, echoing on the long sidewalk. "One thing," I said. "I can't understand how you found the place. I can see how you reasoned out the rest — about that grove and about Eli Goble's not wanting the trees planted up there. But how did you know where to dig? We could have been up there for days, turning the soil."

Doc felt in his pocket for a cigar which wasn't there. "Windflowers," he said quietly. "They were scattered all over that hill. Beautiful, like you said. But I knew enough to dig where there were no windflowers. The grass on that hill looked pretty much alike, all over, but there weren't any flowers growing in that place I marked off. Those little purple flowers are funny. They only grow on native soil. You can't get them to grow where the sod has ever been turned."

An Almost Forgotten Mystery

1. How do the two newspaper stories connect with the murder mystery? Why did the second story arouse Doctor Martindale's suspicions? If Goble had been a generous person, do you think his crime would ever have been discovered?

2. Why didn't Doctor Martindale and others suspect Goble at the time of the murder?

3. Did you try to guess what was in the telegrams the doctor sent? Do you think the answers would have convicted Goble without a confession?

4. While you were reading, did you wonder how the doctor knew just where to dig? What connection is there between the title of the story and the last conversation between the two doctors?

5. Does the punishment given to Goble seem right to you? Why or why not?

Roundup

Perils and Escapes

1. Which people in these stories had to rely on strength and endurance to win out? Which ones won because of quick thinking? Were any merely lucky?

2. Are forest fires or snow storms ever a threat to your own home? Does your section of the country sometimes suffer from floods, earthquakes, tornadoes, or hurricanes? Can you write or tell of close escapes that people have had from these perils?

3. Do any men in your community work at jobs that bring them into daily contact with danger? Have several members of the class interview them and make reports to the group.

Action in Your Own Life

1. Is it natural to crave some excitement in your life? Discuss in class whether it is more fun to get your excitement through your own activities or through watching or listening to someone else's activities.

2. Tell some kinds of exciting action for young people that are worth while or wholesome. Name others that are dangerous or destructive. Is your home community doing a good job of providing its youngsters with wholesome activities? If so, write a letter to the city authorities thanking them for their work in your behalf. If not, have a class committee draw up suggestions for improvement and send a report to the authorities.

3. Write a narrative about the most exciting event in your own life. Put in enough description to make it seem real to your reader. Tell how you felt at critical moments, so that the reader will share your excitement.

Ab Carmody's Treasure, by Cyrus T. Fisher (Holt, 1948)

Ab goes to Guatemala in search of a family and strikes the trail of a mysterious treasure.

Arctic Venture, by Kenneth Gilbert (Holt, 1948)

Chuck finds action and excitement when he goes along with his father to trade with Eskimos.

Around the World in Eighty Days, by Jules Verne, new ed. (Didier, 1950)

This story thrilled the world in 1872 and is still hard to beat. You'll find more thrills in Verne's *Mysterious Island* (Scribner, 1918).

Black Falcon, by Armstrong Sperry (Winston, 1949)

The son of a Louisiana planter sails with Jean Lafitte to raid the English in 1814.

Bob Clifton, Jungle Traveler, by Dock Hogue (Holt, 1951)

Realistic and thrilling account of a lion hunt in Africa.

Boy with a Pack, by Stephen W. Meader (Harcourt, Brace, 1939)

He headed west in 1837, when travel called for courage and hardihood.

The Count of Monte Cristo, by Alexander Dumas, adapted by Mabel Dodge Holmes (Globe, 1945)

A great old thriller shortened for fast, easy reading.

The Dark Frigate, by Charles Hawes (Little, Brown, 1934)

An action-packed seafaring tale.

David Livingstone: Foe of Darkness, by Jeanette Eaton (Morrow, 1947)

The life of the great explorer held more adventure than most novels.

The Edge of Danger, compiled by Margaret C. Scoggin (Knopf, 1951)

An exciting collection of true stories of adventure, like the author's earlier book, *The Lure of Danger* (1947).

Flying Ebony, by Iris Vinton (Dodd, Mead, 1947)

Whaling, pirates, shipwreck, lifesaving, and a magnificent horse fill Jonathan's life at sea and ashore.

Great Moments in Exploration, by Marion Lansing (Doubleday, 1928)

True happenings as thrilling as any imaginary ones.

Madeline Takes Command, by Ethel C. Brill (Whittlesey, 1946)

For a week the French girl and her young brothers defend their home in Canada against Indian attacks.

Marooned in Du-Bu Cove, by Evelyn Cheesman (Bell, 1950)

Young castaways on a rocky shore in New Guinea imitate Robinson Crusoe.

A Nose for Trouble, by Jim Kjelgaard (Holiday, 1950)

Game wardens in the north woods battle poachers to prevent slaughter for gain.

Quest in the Desert, by Roy Chapman Andrews (Viking, 1950)

A fictional account of the writer's exciting experiences exploring the Gobi desert.

The Secret of the Lighthouse, by Dorothy Smith (Crowell, 1950)

Twin girls and their brother find a mystery as well as a home in an abandoned lighthouse.

Smoke Jumpers, by Marjorie H. Atlee (Houghton Mifflin, 1945)

Men of the Forest Service use parachutes to speed their fight against forest fires.

Visibility Unlimited, by Dick Grace (Longmans, 1950)

Excitement and daring mark this true story of a pilot's adventures in war and in commercial flying.

Wronghand, by Geraldine Wyatt (Longmans, 1949)

A young trail-driver gets his herd of longhorn steers through, in spite of Comanches and other obstacles.

Parks from Standard Oil Co. (N.J.)

Outdoors

Under the Greenwood Tree

WILLIAM SHAKESPEARE

For many years this poem, of all our literature, has been one of the best known and best loved invitations to enjoy the outdoor life. Read the poem aloud to see how smoothly it rolls off your tongue. Note, too, how the poet's " Come hither, come hither . . ." imitates the bird call that he mentions.

Under the greenwood tree
Who loves to lie with me,
And turn his merry note
Unto the sweet bird's throat° —

3-4. **And turn . . . bird's throat:** sing it right back at the bird.

Come hither, come hither,
    come hither!   5
  Here shall he see
  No enemy
But winter and rough weather.

  Who doth ambition shun
And loves to live i' the sun, 10
  Seeking the food he eats
  And pleased with what he gets —
Come hither, come hither,
    come hither!
  Here shall he see
  No enemy 15
But winter and rough weather.

When I Was a Boy on the Ranch

J. FRANK DOBIE

RAMBLING ON A RANCH. You are about to hear Frank Dobie chat about the good times he had growing up on a ranch in Texas. This is a "true" story that concerns real people and real happenings. Such writing is called *nonfiction,* a name which keeps it separate from fiction, or stories that are imagined by the writer. Both kinds of writing can be interesting and exciting, though in each a different way is used to tell the story. In a fiction story, the writer usually makes the events stick close to the main plot. If the story is about a boat race, for example, the plot is not suddenly interrupted by a description of mountain climbing. But in a true story the writer will ramble very often, just as our own lives have a way of rambling.

When Frank Dobie tells about his boyhood, he moves from one thing to another — from " playing ranch " to riding horses to exploring the brush country. Don't expect everything in his story to fit into a neat pattern. You will find a variety of happenings and discussions and descriptions. As the author rambles about the ranch, pointing out this and that, read along leisurely but expect to cover a lot of ground. There is a lot to see in this Western place. It offers some unusual games and sports, and it teems with animals, wild and tame.

THERE were six of us children and our ranch was down in the brush country [1] of Texas between the Nueces [2] River and the Rio Grande. The automobiles have outrun the horses since then; radios have drowned out many a cricket's voice and many a coyote's wailing cry; in many a ranch yard the lights of Delco plants have dimmed the glowing points of the fireflies — " lightning bugs," we called them. But the ranch of our childhood is still a ranch. And south of it clear to the Mexican border, and northwest of it into the Rocky Mountains and on up beyond the line where Montana joins Canada, there are millions and millions of acres of other ranches on which boys and girls live.

Despite automobiles these boys and girls still ride horses. Despite radios they still listen in the evening to crickets and frogs, and sometimes in the night to the wailing cries of coyotes. As for electric lights on the ranches, they light such small spaces that the fireflies in the grass and the stars in the sky never notice them.

[1] **brush country:** land covered with low, scrubby growth.
[2] **Nueces** (nū·ā′sĕs).

"When I Was a Boy on the Ranch" by J. Frank Dobie from *Second Saint Nicholas Anthology.* Reprinted by permission of the author.

The country is still country. For all the changes brought by invention, ranches are still ranches.

So if I tell how we children lived on our ranch, I'll also be telling how children still live on other ranches scattered all over the western half of the United States.

We liked ranching so much that our best game used to be "playing ranch." There were fine live oak trees between the yard fence and the pens about the stables and barns, and it was in the shade of these trees, especially during the summer, that we built our "ranches."

To build a pasture we drove little stakes close together in the ground until a plot about as big as a kitchenette was inclosed; sometimes the pasture was made by setting up "posts" of stakes in the ground and then stretching cords, in imitation of barbed wire, from one corner of the "pasture" to the other. Each ranch had several pastures, and of course each ranch had headquarters, where houses and corrals were built. The houses were generally of boards; the corrals were of pickets laid between pairs of upright posts.

Fencing in the pastures was never so much fun as getting them stocked. It took work to fence in land and improve it with dirt tanks,[1] which never would hold water very long. It took patience to construct corral gates that would open and shut and to make a house that would not fall down when a turkey stepped on it or a pup ran

[1] **tanks:** pools with sides built up with packed dirt.

against it. But stocking this land with cattle and horses and goats was nothing but fun.

We had two kinds of cattle — high-grade cattle and common "stuff." The horn tips of real cattle — which were clipped off at branding time — became our purebred animals. Sometimes we had hundreds of them. Our "common Mexican cattle" were represented by oak balls.

But we prized our horses far more than our cattle. Horses consisted of sewing-thread spools; most of our clothes were made on the ranch, and those clothes took an astonishing amount of thread. Moreover, when we went visiting we had our eyes open for discarded spools, but visits of any kind were rare and those that brought spools were rarer. A spool has a long "side" that can be branded and it has a long "back" that can be saddled. I can't think of any better kind of play-horse than a spool.

The ranches in our part of the country had herds of white Mexican goats. White-shelled snails were abundant in our neighborhood, and these shells became our goats. A live snail would not stay in a pasture, for he can climb straight up and carry his shell with him, so our goats were always empty shells. There were no sheep in the country; we had never heard anything particularly good connected with sheepmen; and so we had no sheep — just cattle, horses, and goats.

Each of us had a brand. Mine was **NEv**, which an uncle of mine named Neville used. Fannie's was ⚥, Elrich's was an E; Lee's brand was L. The two younger children were too small to build ranches and brand herds by themselves; consequently if Henry and Martha got into the game, they got in as "hired help." Our branding irons were short pieces of bailing wire, with a crook at one end. This kind of branding iron is called a "running iron." When we had occasion to brand, we built a fire close to ranch headquarters, heated the "running irons," and burned our brands on the spool-horses, the common oak-ball cattle, and the fine horn cattle.

Like real ranchmen, we bought and sold stock. When a trade was made, the cattle or horses — we seldom traded goats — had to be gathered up, driven to the shipping pens, loaded on the railroad cars, transported, and delivered. Then after they were delivered they had to be branded with the brand of the new owner. (A great many of the "common cattle" were decayed on the inside and when they

were branded collapsed into nothing!) We had to sell cheap for the very simple reason that dollars were scarce and cattle were plentiful.

The dollars we had, however, were extraordinarily good dollars of sound coinage and pure metal. The ranch kitchen used a considerable amount of canned goods, particularly canned tomatoes, salmon, and sardines, along with some peaches and corn. We held the empty can in a fire with tongs until the solder started to run, and then caught the solder in an old spoon, pouring it into a round wooden box that had once held bluing. The diameter of this round bluing box was — and still is — about that of a silver dollar. The dollars we coined were sometimes thicker than a silver dollar and they were always heavier, but in buying cattle they were worth just as much.

We had another source of metal for our dollars. In the fall of the year hunters would be on the ranch, either camped out or staying with us at the house. They usually shot up a good many boxes of shells practicing on trees. After the shooting was over, we children gouged out the lead bullets lodged in the trees and melted them into dollars.

I spoke of shipping cattle. The train was a string of empty sardine cans coupled to each other with wire hooks. Motive power was the chief problem. We tried hitching horned frogs and green lizards to it, but neither pulled with any strength. A horned frog would sometimes pull an empty wagon made of a cardboard matchbox. Old Joe, the best dog we ever had, would pull the train pretty well if he went in a straight line, but when he didn't, he caused several bad wrecks that overturned cars and spilled cattle out. If a delivery of cattle had to be made promptly, the simplest and surest way to make the engine pull the train was to tie a string to it and pull it yourself.

Of course there were *real* horses and *real* cattle to interest us. Children brought up on a ranch usually learn to ride only a little later than they learn to walk. Old Stray, Dandy, and Baldy were the horses on our ranch that could be trusted with the youngest children. Old Stray was a common Mexican pony that some Mexican had ridden down and turned loose on our ranch. When we first saw him he was as thin as a stick-horse. Nobody claimed him, so after a while we used him. He seemed to appreciate having plenty of grass to eat but he had no intention of ever exerting himself again. In short, he was not only gentle but "pokey." If a child fell off him, he would stop and graze until the child got up again. Baldy was an enormous horse, and by the time a boy was big enough to scramble upon his back without help from a man or a friendly fence, that boy was nearly ready for "long pants."

Dandy was a black horse of thoroughbred trotting stock. He alone of all the horses was entitled to corn the year around. The other horses lived mostly on grass. We rode Dandy sometimes as well as drove him, but he had too much life in him for mere beginners. He was as kind and intelligent as he was lively. One time when my brother Elrich was very small he toddled into Dandy's stall while Dandy was eating. The flies

were bothering Dandy and he was switching his tail and stamping his feet. He knew that the little boy was in danger. He put a hind foot against the child and shoved him out of the stall. He did not kick him — just shoved him.

By the time I was eight years old I had several horses to ride. There was Maudie, a little Spanish mare, that would kick up when I punched her in the shoulder with my finger or pointed my hand down toward her flank or tail. Later there was Buck, a horse raised on the ranch. He was a bay with a white face and stocking feet. I kept him as long as he lived and he died on the ranch where he was born. He could be turned loose in camp and would not stray off. Once when I was running to head some wild steers and Buck gave a quick dodge, the saddle, which was loosely girted, turned, throwing me to the ground and nearly breaking my hip. Buck could "turn on a dime," and stop as quickly as one can snap a finger. On this occasion he stopped so suddenly that he did not drag me a foot, though I was still in the saddle when my hip struck the ground. He was the best cow-horse I ever rode. Often when we were alone I talked to him. By the time I was twelve years old and a regular ranch hand, I was sometimes on him from daylight until long after dark. More than once I went to sleep riding him. I loved him and he loved me. I think of Buck oftener now than I think of many people who have been my friends.

As range cows do not give as much milk as dairy cows, we usually had a pen full of them to milk, especially in the summertime. Each cow had her calf, and the calves were allowed part of the milk. A Mexican man usually did the milking, but it was the privilege of us boys to bring in the calves from the calf pasture each evening and then to ride them.

Now, riding calves is about as much fun as a ranch boy can possibly have. The calf is roped around the neck, and a half hitch, called a " bosal," is put around its nose. Then, using the rope as a bridle, the boy mounts. Until the calf is gentled, it will " pitch like a bay steer." One calf that I remember particularly was a black heifer with a white face. She became very gentle and we named her Pet. I trained Pet so well that I could mount her and guide her all over the calf pasture. Usually, no matter how well " broke " to riding, a calf won't go where you want it to go. It won't go anywhere. Saddles don't fit calves or grown cattle and, although it was sometimes fun to saddle yearlings, what actual riding we did was bareback. As we grew older

we caught range cattle coming into the big pen to water and rode the calves and yearlings.

Each of us children had a few head of cattle to call our own. They were for the most part dogies or of dogie origin. A " dogie " is a motherless calf. When one was found on the range, it would be brought in and some cow with a calf of like age would be tied at night and morning and forced to let the motherless calf share her milk. We had one old muley cow that was so kind to dogies that the dogie always fared better than her own offspring. She would moo to it and lick its hair and otherwise mother it.

Pet was originally a dogie. When she grew up and had calves of her own, we milked her. If she was a good " saddle horse," a red-roan calf that she had was a better one. Pet had so many calves and those calves grew up and had so many calves of their own that the little stock of cattle coming from her helped materially to put me through college one year.

We went to a country school, which was on our own ranch, where the children of five or six other ranch families attended. Most of them rode to school horseback. One of our games was " cats and dogs." This we boys — for girls did not join in it — played at noon recess. The " cats " would set out in the brush afoot. About three minutes later the " dogs," mounted on horses and yelling like Apache Indians, would take after them. The brush had thorns and the idea of the " cat " was to get into brush so thick that the " dog " could

not follow him, or to crawl into a thicket where he could not be seen. Sometimes the chase would last until long after the bell had sounded. I remember one great chase that kept us out until three o'clock. An hour later eight or nine boys were alone with the teacher and a pile of huajilla [1] switches.

Another game on horseback that the older boys played was " tournament." Three posts are erected in a line a hundred yards apart. Each post has an arm of wood about a yard long. Hanging from this arm is a metal ring about two inches in diameter. It is held by a spring clasp so that it can be easily disengaged. The runner takes a sharpened pole — the " tournament pole " — in his right hand and, holding it level, with the point out in front of him, runs lickety-split down the line of rings trying to spear them. The game requires skill. Buck was a wonderfully smooth-running horse, and he and I together hooked plenty of rings.

My sisters and girl cousins joined us in playing Indian and in making houses. Our ranch was built on a dry

arroyo,[2] or creek, named Log Hollow. Just below the house this creek had bluffs about forty feet high. For years we children worked periodically at digging caves back into the bluffs. Here we played Indian. If the soil had not been so gravelly and consequently inclined to cave in, we might have made dwelling places as ample as some of the ancient cliff dwellings. As it was, we got the caves

[1] **huajilla** (wä·hēl′yȧ): a shrub that grows in Texas and Mexico.

[2] **arroyo** (ȧ·roi′ō).

big enough for us to hide in. When Long Hollow ran water after a rain, we made water wheels of sticks and cornstalks and watched them turn.

The house of our own construction that we enjoyed most was in a tree. It was a live oak called "the Coon Tree," from the fact that a coon hungry for chickens had once been found in it. Climbing up into this tree was an enormous mustang [1] grapevine. This grapevine afforded us a kind of ladder to the limbs of the Coon Tree. We took planks up to these limbs and nailed them so that we had a solid floor.

In our country we did not have many fruits, but around the ranch house were prolific pomegranate bushes. No matter how dry the season, these pomegranates always bore fruit. In the summertime we would pick pomegranates, borrow some sugar, spoons, and glasses from the kitchen, and, with a jug of water, gather on the platform in the Coon Tree for a picnic. We had a rope with which to pull up the jug and a bucket containing the other articles. The point of the picnic was to make " pomegranateade " out of sugar, the fruit seeds, and water.

Sometimes we took books and read in the Coon Tree. *Beautiful Joe* and *Black Beauty* were favorites. Our real house had matting on the floor, and when this matting was discarded and we covered the platform in the Coon Tree with it, we felt that we had reached the height of luxury. I don't understand why none of us ever fell out of the Coon Tree.

I have spoken of our life with horses and calves. There were other animals to interest us, as there always are in the country. The trees about the ranch were inhabited each spring and summer by hundreds of jackdaws, a kind of blackbird. They built their nests in the trees so flimsily that disaster to the newly hatched birds was inevitable. Before they could fly or even walk, young birds would fall out of the trees and sprawl helpless on the ground, a ready prey for cats, turkeys, and other enemies. The distressed cries of the parent jackdaws were at times almost deafening, but these parents could do nothing toward getting their young back into the nests. We used to pick up the young birds and put them in straw-filled wooden nail-kegs, which we placed on the roofs of a shed and smokehouse [2] under the Coon Tree. I have seen three or four parent jackdaws feeding their young at the same time in one of these kegs. Sometimes each keg held as many as eight young birds.

Scissortails built their hanging nests in the very tops of the higher trees, but their young never fell out. We never tired of watching the scissortails fly, especially if they were chasing a hawk, darting at his head and driving him away. The wrens nested in tool boxes in the stable, in coils of rope, even in the leather toefenders — called tapaderos [3] — cover-

---

[1] The wild grapes native to this area were called **mustang** grapes. Can you guess why?

[2] **smokehouse:** a house for smoking meat.
[3] **tapaderos** (tăp·à·dā′rŏs).

ing the stirrups of saddles. When we found these nests, we made it our duty to warn our father and the Mexican laborers not to disturb them. One time a saddle had to go unused for weeks until a wren that had built in the tapadero of one stirrup had brought off her brood.

Under Mother's direction we raised chickens, turkeys, and guineas. The guineas were good "watchdogs," alarming, with their wild cries, everything and everybody within hearing distance when a hawk was approaching. Hawks, chicken snakes, and coyotes were constant enemies of the barnyard. We boys sometimes set traps for the coyotes. I remember seeing my mother, before I was old enough to handle a gun, shoot one with a rifle very near the house.

The evening call of the bobwhite [1] brought — as it yet brings — a wonderful peace. In the early morning of certain times of the year we could hear wild turkeys "yelping" out in the brush back of the field. Once a large flock of them grazed up to the schoolhouse, but the teacher would not let us out to chase them. Although deer were plentiful, and some other children in the country had a pet fawn, we never had one. Once while riding in the pasture I halted a long time to watch a doe kill a rattlesnake.

I can honestly say that we did not enjoy "tormenting" animals and that we did not rob birds' nests. But when we snared lizards with a horse-

hair looped on the end of a pole; when we poured buckets of water down the holes of ground squirrels to make them come out; and when we hitched horned toads to matchboxes, we no doubt did torment those animals, though we seldom injured them. I have since killed noble buck deer, mountain lions, wild boars, and other game, but no memory of hunting is so pleasant as that of rescuing little jackdaws, of restoring a tiny dove fallen from its nest, and of watching, without molesting them, baby jack rabbits in their cotton-lined nest against the cowpen fence — memories all of a ranch boy.

Ranch girls and boys always find so many ways to play and so many creatures of nature to interest them that the days are never long enough. And no life can be long enough for a ranch-bred boy or girl to forget the full times of childhood.

Reading Nonfiction

1. How much ground did you cover in this nonfiction story of ranch life? List as many different activities and interests of the ranch children as you can remember without looking back at the story. Can you tell how one memory led the writer to recall another? See how many such "bridges" from one topic to another you can find.

2. What modern inventions are now common on ranches? Does Mr. Dobie think they have made much change in ranch life?

3. How was each part of a real ranch represented in the play ranches? How were the "silver dollars" made?

4. Which game seemed to you more fun, "cat and dog," or "tournament"? Why? Can you guess where the game "tournament" came from? How can you find out?

5. Name some of the favorites among

[1] The quail is called **bobwhite** because that is what his call seems to say.

the cows and horses the ranch boys had. Tell what impressed you most about one of them.

6. Were the young ranchers kind to wild animals or cruel to them? Discuss.

7. How do your own games and outdoor activities compare with Frank Dobie's? Discuss with your classmates whether the city or the country offers more fun to youngsters.

Be a Word Detective

A good detective looks for clues when he is trying to solve a case. In the same way a good reader looks for clues to the meaning of unfamiliar words he runs across. The best place to look is in the words and phrases that surround the difficult word — the context. For example, Frank Dobie writes: " Motive power was the chief problem. We tried hitching horned frogs and green lizards to [the train], but neither pulled with any strength." You can guess from the second sentence that *motive* means " moving," and *motive power* is any force that causes something to move.

See if you can track down the clues that hold the meaning of *disengaged* on page 61, *prolific* on page 62, *matting* on page 62, *torment* on page 63.

On a Wisconsin Farm

JOHN MUIR

When John Muir's Scottish father decided to make a new home for his family in America, he opened the path John later traveled to become one of our great naturalists. Not even the hard work on a pioneer farm could dim the boy's delight in outdoor life in the new world.

BEFORE leaving Scotland, Father promised us a pony ride when we got to America, and we saw to it that this promise was not forgotten. Only a week or two after our arrival in the woods he bought us a little Indian pony for thirteen dollars from a storekeeper in Kingston who had ob-tained him from a Winnebago [1] or Menominee [2] Indian in trade for goods.

He was a stout handsome bay with long black mane and tail, and, though he was only two years old, the Indians had already taught him to carry all sorts of burdens, to stand without being tied, to go anywhere over all sorts of ground fast or slow, and to jump and swim and fear nothing — a truly wonderful creature, strangely different from shy, skittish, nervous, superstitious civilized beasts. We

[1] **Winnebago** (wĭn'ē·bā'gō).
[2] **Menominee** (mē·nŏm'ĭ·nē).

"On a Wisconsin Farm" from *Story of My Boyhood and Youth* by John Muir. Reprinted by permission of and arrangement with Houghton Mifflin Company, the authorized publishers.

turned him loose, and, strange to say, he never ran away from us or refused to be caught, but behaved as if he had known Scotch boys all his life; probably because we were about as wild as young Indians.

One day when Father happened to have a little leisure, he said, " Noo, bairns,[1] rin doon the meadow and get your powny and learn to ride him." So we led him out to a smooth place near an Indian mound back of the shanty, where Father directed us to begin. I mounted for the first memorable lesson, crossed the mound, and set out at a slow walk along the wagon track made in hauling lumber; then Father shouted, "Whup him up, John, whup him up! Make him gallop; gallopin' is easier and better than walkin' or trottin'." Jack was willing, and away he sped at a good fast gallop. I managed to keep my balance fairly well by holding fast to the mane, but could not keep from bumping up and down, for I was plump and elastic and so was Jack; therefore about half of the time I was in the air.

After a quarter of a mile or so of this curious transportation, I cried, " Whoa, Jack! " The wonderful creature seemed to understand Scotch, for he stopped so suddenly I flew over his head, but he stood perfectly still as if that flying method of dismounting were the regular way. Jumping on again, I bumped and bobbed back along the grassy, flow-

---

[1] **bairns** (bârnz): Scottish for "children." You can figure out the other words that are spelled to suggest the Scottish accent.

ery track, over the Indian mound, cried, " Whoa, Jack! " flew over his head, and alighted in Father's arms as gracefully as if it were all intended for circus work.

After going over the course five or six times in the same free, picturesque style, I gave place to brother David, whose performances were much like my own. In a few weeks, however, or a month, we were taking adventurous rides more than a mile long out to a big meadow frequented by sand-hill cranes, and returning safely with wonderful stories of the great long-legged birds we had seen, and how on the whole journey away and back we had fallen off only five or six times. Gradually we learned to gallop through the woods without roads of any sort, bareback and without rope or bridle, guiding only by leaning from side to side or by slight knee pressure.

Great was the delight of brothers David and Daniel and myself when Father gave us a few pine boards for a boat, and it was a memorable day when we got that boat built and launched into the lake. Never shall I forget our first sail over the gradually deepening water, the sunbeams pouring through it revealing the strange plants covering the bottom, and the fishes coming about us, staring and wondering as if the boat were a monstrous strange fish.

The water was so clear that it was almost invisible, and when we floated slowly out over the plants and fishes, we seemed to be miraculously sustained in the air while silently exploring a veritable fairyland.

We always had to work hard, but if we worked still harder we were occasionally allowed a little spell in the long summer evenings about sundown to fish, and on Sundays an hour or two to sail quietly without fishing rod or gun when the lake was calm. Therefore we gradually learned something about its inhabitants — pickerel, sunfish, black bass, perch, shiners, pumpkinseeds,[1] ducks, loons, turtles, muskrats, etc.

We saw the sunfishes making their nests in little openings in the rushes where the water was only a few feet deep, plowing up and shoving away the soft gray mud with their noses, like pigs, forming round bowls five or six inches in depth and about two feet in diameter, in which their eggs were deposited. And with what beautiful, unweariable devotion they watched and hovered over them and chased away prowling spawn-eating[2] enemies that ventured within a rod or two of the precious nest!

Our beautiful lake, named Fountain Lake by Father, but Muir's Lake by the neighbors, is one of the many small glacier lakes[3] that adorn the Wisconsin landscapes. It is fed by twenty or thirty meadow springs, is about half a mile long, half as wide, and surrounded by low finely modeled hills dotted with oak and hickory, and meadows full of grasses and sedges and many beautiful orchids and ferns.

One hot summer day Father told us that we ought to learn to swim. This was one of the most interesting suggestions he had ever offered, but precious little time was allowed for trips to the lake, and he seldom tried to show us how. " Go to the frogs," he said, " and they will give you all the lessons you need. Watch their arms and legs and see how smoothly they kick themselves along and dive and come up. When you want to dive, keep your arms by your side or over your head, and kick, and when you want to come up, let your legs drag and paddle with your hands."

We found a little basin among the rushes at the south end of the lake, about waist-deep and a rod or two wide, shaped like a sunfish's nest. Here we kicked and plashed for many a lesson, faithfully trying to imitate frogs; but the smooth, comfortable sliding gait of our amphibious[4] teachers seemed hopelessly hard to learn. When we tried to kick frog-fashion, down went our heads as if weighted with lead the moment our feet left the ground.

One day it occurred to me to hold my breath as long as I could and let my head sink as far as it liked without paying any attention to it, and try to swim under the water instead of on the surface. This method was a

---

[1] **pumpkinseeds:** a kind of sunfish.

[2] **spawn-eating:** " spawn" is a term for the eggs of fish, frogs, and other animals that live in water.

[3] **Glacier lakes** formed in the hollows scooped out in earlier ages by the great caps of ice which once covered the northern part of the North American continent.

[4] **amphibious** (ăm·fĭb′ĭ·ŭs): able to live both on land and in water.

great success, for at the very first trial I managed to cross the basin without touching bottom, and soon learned the use of my limbs. Then, of course, swimming with my head above water soon became so easy that it seemed perfectly natural. David tried the plan with the same success. Then we began to count the number of times that we could swim around the basin without stopping to rest, and after twenty or thirty rounds failed to tire us, we proudly thought that a little more practice would make us about as amphibious as frogs.

On the fourth of July of this swimming year, one of the Lawson boys came to visit us, and we went down

After a few turns in the pool, it occurred to me that it was now about time to try deep water. Swimming through the thick growth of rushes and lilies was somewhat dangerous, especially for a beginner, because one's arms and legs might be entangled among the long, limber stems; nevertheless I ventured and struck out boldly enough for the boat, where the water was twenty or thirty feet deep. When I reached the end of the little skiff I raised my right hand to take hold of it to surprise Lawson, whose back was toward me and who was not aware of my approach; but I failed to reach high enough, and, of course, the weight of my arm and the stroke against the over-leaning stern of the boat shoved me down and I sank, struggling, frightened and confused.

As soon as my feet touched the bottom, I slowly rose to the surface, but before I could get breath enough to call for help, sank back again and

to the lake to spend the great warm day with the fishes and ducks and turtles. After gliding about on the smooth mirror water, telling stories and enjoying the company of the happy creatures about us, we rowed to our bathing pool, and David and I went in for a swim, while our companion fished from the boat a little way out beyond the rushes.

lost all control of myself. After sinking and rising I don't know how many times, some water got into my lungs and I began to drown. Then suddenly my mind seemed to clear. I remembered that I could swim under water, and, making a desperate struggle toward the shore, I reached a point where, with my toes on the bottom, I got my mouth above the surface, gasped for help, and was pulled into the boat.

This humiliating accident spoiled the day, and we all agreed to keep it a profound secret. My sister Sarah had heard my cry for help, and on our arrival at the house inquired what had happened. "Were you drowning, John? I heard you cry you couldna get oot." Lawson made haste to reply, "Oh, no! He was juist haverin (making fun)."

I was very much ashamed of myself, and at night, after calmly reviewing the affair, concluded that there had been no reasonable cause for the accident, and that I ought to punish myself for so nearly losing my life from unmanly fear. Accordingly at the very first opportunity, I stole away to the lake by myself, got into my boat, and instead of going back to the old swimming bowl for further practice, or to try to do sanely and well what I had so ignominiously failed to do in my first adventure, that is, to swim out through the rushes and lilies, I rowed directly out to the middle of the lake, stripped, stood up on the seat in the stern, and with grim deliberation took a header and dove straight down thirty or for-

ty feet, turned easily, and, letting my feet drag, paddled straight to the surface with my hands as Father had at first directed me to do.

I then swam round the boat, glorying in my suddenly acquired confidence and victory over myself, climbed into it, and dived again, with the same triumphant success. I think I went down four or five times, and each time as I made the dive-spring shouted aloud, " Take that! " feeling that I was getting most gloriously even with myself.

Never again from that day to this have I lost control of myself in water. If suddenly thrown overboard at sea in the dark, or even while asleep, I think I would immediately right myself in a way some would call " instinct," rise among the waves, catch my breath, and try to plan what would better be done. Never was victory over self more complete.

New Thrills and Skills

1. How did their father teach the boys to ride the pony? What advice did he give them on learning to swim? Did he seem to worry about their getting hurt? Do you approve of his attitude?

2. After the boys built their boat, what new interests did they find in the lake? How does the writer convince you that it was a beautiful lake?

3. What discovery of John's helped him to learn to swim? How did he save himself when he nearly drowned? How did he conquer the fear caused by this experience?

4. Why do you suppose Muir's boyhood interests gave him a good background for his career as a naturalist? A committee should be chosen to report to the class on his later life.

Outdoors

More Context Clues

In Frank Dobie's account of boyhood you had a chance to be a word detective and search for clues to the meaning of unfamiliar words. The *context* of a word usually helps you to know its meaning, but to make sure, you will often want to look up its definition in a dictionary. Check the following words first in their context and then compare *your* guess about meaning with the definition in a dictionary. Be sure you get the right pronunciation, too.

Knowing the Flowers

ROBERT BENCHLEY

When a chap who considers himself an expert on wildflowers sets out for a hike with a chap like Robert Benchley, who manages to find something funny wherever he goes, the expert may have a hard time of it. But Benchley will have fun — and so will you.

A LITTLE learning may be a dangerous thing, but a lot of learning may turn out to be even worse. I have tried to know absolutely nothing about a great many things, and, if I do say so myself, have succeeded fairly well. And to my avoidance of the responsibilities which go with knowledge I lay my good digestion today. I am never upset when I find that I know nothing about some given subject, because I am never surprised.

The names of birds and flowers, for example, give me practically no worry whatever, for I never set out to learn them in the first place. I am familiar with several kinds of birds and flowers by sight, and could, if cornered, designate a carnation or a robin as such. But beyond that I just let the whole thing slide and never torture myself with trying to remember what the name of that bird with the yellow ear is or how many varieties of gentians there are. (By the way, what ever became of gentians? Are they used only for models in elementary school drawing classes?)

People who specialize in knowing the names of birds and flowers are always in a ferment, because they are always running up against some variety which stumps them. Show an ornithologist [1] a bird that he can't name and he is miserable for a week. He goes home and looks up reference books, writes letters to the papers asking if someone can help him, and tosses and turns at night, hoping that his subconscious will solve the problem for him. He develops an inferiority and, unless closely watched, may actually do away with himself out of sheer frustration. It isn't worth it.

I once had a heartbreaking experience with a flower-namer. He was one of those men who began when they were boys spotting the different types of wildflower, and, at a hundred yards, could detect a purple wolf's cup [2] (or " Lehman's dropsy ") and could tell you, simply by feeling

a flower in the dark, which variety of " bishop's ulster " it was. There was practically no wildflower of North America that he didn't know to speak to, and he took a little more pride in his knowledge than was really justified. At least, so it seemed to me.

I found myself on a walking trip through Cornwall with this man one summer, for, when he wasn't spying on wildflowers, he was very good company. On account of the weather, we spent the first five days of our walking trip in the taproom of an inn at a place appropriately named Fowey (pronounced Pfui), and on the first sunny day set out with our knapsacks on our backs and a good song ringing clear. Looking back on it now, I don't see what ever got into me to be doing so much walking.

Along about noon we came to a large field which was completely covered with multicolored wildflowers. There must have been a thousand different varieties, or, at any rate, a hundred. I saw what was coming and winced. I was going to be a party to a botany exam. Little did I realize

---

[1] **ornithologist** (ôr′nĭ·thŏl′ô·jĭst): a student of bird life.
[2] You may be sure Benchley is only making up fancy flower names of his own.

that I was also to be a party to a tragedy.

My companion went over to the edge of the field and examined a red flower by the roadside. His face took on a worried look. He didn't recognize the species! He looked at a blue flower next to it. He didn't recognize that, either! He gave a hurried survey of the five square feet surrounding him and blanched.[1] He said nothing, but I could tell from his staring eyes and damp brow that there was not one variety of flower that he could name.

He ran into the field, stooping over and straightening up like a madman, turning round and round in circles and looking wildly about him, as a dog looks when ten people start whistling at him at once. Here was not only one flower that he had never heard of before, but a whole field full — hundreds and hundreds of unknown blossoms, all different and all staring up at him waiting to be named.

A chameleon[2] is supposed to go insane when placed on a plaid. This man was in danger of going raving crazy from pure chagrin.[3]

I tried to get him to leave the field and continue our little march, but he hardly heard what I was saying. He would pick a flower, examine it, shake his head, mop his brow, pick another, wipe the perspiration from his eyes, and then throw them both to the ground. Once he found some-

thing that he thought was a poppy and his joy was pitiful to see. But the stamen or something was wrong, and he burst into tears.

There was nothing that I could do or say, so I just sat by the roadside with my back turned and let him fight it out with himself. He finally agreed to leave his Waterloo,[4] but the trip was ruined for him. He didn't speak all that day, and that night, after we had gone to bed, I heard him throwing himself about the bed in an agony of despair. He has never mentioned wildflowers since.

I cite this little instance to show that being an expert in any one line is a tremendous responsibility. For, if an expert suddenly finds out that he isn't entirely expert, he just isn't anything at all. And that sort of thing gets a man down.

Downfall of an Expert

1. Why was a lot of learning really worse for the expert than a little learning would be for most people?

2. Describe the way the expert behaved when he came to the field of strange flowers. Do you think there actually was such a field? Why, or why not?

3. Does the writer seem to think that it is a bad idea to be interested in the names of birds or flowers? What does he think is dangerous?

4. There's no better way to amuse other people than by making fun of yourself. What are some of the things Benchley tells on himself in order to amuse the reader? Perhaps you can think of a joke on *yourself* that would amuse the class.

---

[1] **blanched:** turned white.

[2] **chameleon** (ká·mē′lḗ·ŭn): a lizard that changes its color to match its surroundings.

[3] **chagrin** (shá·grĭn′): distress caused by failure.

[4] **Waterloo:** the battle in which Napoleon was decisively defeated; therefore, any scene of disastrous defeat.

Climb to Victory

WILLIAM O. DOUGLAS

It was not mere pleasure in outdoor exercise that first led young Bill Douglas into mountain climbing. It was, rather, weakness and misery. Over the years he found such happiness in the mountains that he still takes to the high trails whenever he gets a vacation from his duties as Associate Justice of the Supreme Court.

THERE was a driving force that took me first to the foothills and then to the mountains, though I myself did not recognize it for what it was until years later. From the time I was about twelve years old I took every occasion to slip out of town for hikes into the foothills. The occasions were not frequent, for each day after school I delivered newspapers and on Saturdays I worked in stores, creameries, and cold storage plants. In the summer months I worked in the packing houses and orchards at all the jobs that were available — thinning of fruit, spraying, irrigating, picking, making boxes, packing fruit, icing and loading refrigerator cars. There was a regular sequence of fruit during the summer — cherries, apricots, peaches, pears, and apples. But there were gaps between the crops. And in the fall, winter, and spring, there were Sunday afternoons, holidays, and occasional evenings when a few hours would be free. On these occasions I explored the foothills.

I would leave the town and head toward the Selah Gap, the point of the foothills nearest my home on North Fifth Avenue. There I would test my legs and lungs against the hillside. It was hard work: two miles at the fast pace of perhaps five or six miles an hour; the climb of a hillside 500 feet or more in elevation; then a return to home and bed, dead tired, every muscle of my legs aching. Time and again I followed this routine, turning my back on more pleasant diversions that Yakima [1] offered.

A friend who preferred the shade of the locust trees in the city, the movies, and the reading room of the Y.M.C.A. would taunt me about these trips. He conceded that it took something special to climb the monotonous foothills over and again. But he

[1] Yakima (yăk′ĭ·mô), Washington, his home town.

added, " Being a fool don't hurt any either."

It was, however, infantile paralysis that drove me to the outdoors.

I had had it when I was a small child. I ran a high fever for several weeks. All but the country doctor despaired of my life, and he had only a slightly more optimistic view. He finally confided in Mother and gave her his candid opinion: There was a good chance that I would lose the use of my legs; even if I did not, I would not live long — probably not beyond forty. He had no remedy for the short life. He did, however, have a prescription for the legs — a prescription that the medical profession forty years later had hardly improved upon. His prescription was frequent massage in salt water, a fifteen-minute massage every two hours every day for weeks.

Mother kept a vigil.[1] She soaked my legs in warm salt water and rubbed it into my pores, massaging each leg muscle every two hours, day after day, night after night. She did not go to bed for six weeks. The fever passed; but the massages continued for weeks thereafter.

I vaguely recall the ordeal. I lay in bed too weak to move. My legs felt like pipestems; they seemed almost detached, the property of someone else. They were so small and thin that Mother's hands could go clear around them. She would knead them like bread; she would push her hands up them and then down, up and down,

up and down, until my skin was red and raw. But she would not stop because of that. She said she wanted me to be strong, to be able to run. She told me that when she was a girl she could run like the wind; no one could catch her. She wondered if I would ever be able to do so. And then she'd laugh and rub my legs — rub and rub and rub — and two hours later, rub some more.

One day the doctor came and I sat on the edge of the bed. I could not stand alone. I reached for Mother's hand, pulled myself up, and stood there weak and unsteady. I tried to walk but could not. I saw tears in Mother's eyes, and she and the doctor went away to have a whispered conversation.

The massages were continued. I lay in bed most of the time. Each day I tried to walk a bit. The weakness in my legs gradually disappeared. My feet would flop a bit; the muscles of my knees would twitch; curious numb sensations would come and go. But before many months I relearned to walk, and the frailty which the disease had caused seemed to pass. Someone said that the salt water and massages had effected wonders. Mother was silent awhile and then said, " So did my prayers."

But the ordeal had left its scars. Mother believed the doctor implicitly, and was convinced that the sand would fast run out of my glass.[2] So she set about to guard my health, to protect me against physical strains, to do all sorts of favors designed to

[1] **vigil** (vĭj′ĭl): keeping awake to keep watch or perform a duty at regular intervals.

[2] That is, that he would not live long.

save my energy. I was waited on, hand and foot. Worse than that, I began to hear what Mother was saying to others: " He's not as strong as other boys; he has to be careful what he does — you know, his legs were almost paralyzed."

This solicitousness [1] set up a severe reaction. It seemed to me I was being publicly recognized as a puny person — a weakling. Thus there began to grow in me a great rebellion. I protested against Mother's descriptions of me. But I believe my rebellion was not so much against her as it was against the kind of person I thought I was coming to be.

The crisis in my attitude was reached when I was around thirteen years old. I wore knee breeches, knickerbocker style. Black cotton stockings covered my legs. I was spindly. Concentrated exercise, like sprinting or wrestling, made me feel faint; and sometimes I'd be sick at my stomach or get a severe headache. I was deeply sensitive about my condition and used many a stratagem [2] to conceal my physical weakness.

One day I was walking to school, carrying a pile of books under one arm. I heard a group of boys coming behind. They were older boys in the same public school, but strangers to me. As they caught up, one said, " Look at that kid's skinny legs. Aren't they something? Did you ever see anything as funny? "

The others laughed; then another

one said, " Sure would cover them up if they were mine."

The words were a lash across my face. The laughter burned like an iron on my neck. I was humiliated and ashamed. I wanted to retort. But I trembled and my throat became dry so I could not answer. Then, as quickly as a flash flood, came tears.

I could not face up to the boys because of the tears. I had to turn away. It seemed that by crying I had not only confirmed but had proved the charge twice over. I stood condemned in the public eye — a weakling.

A great depression swept over me and lingered for months. I didn't want to go to school. I wanted to hide. I wanted long trousers — an idea that Mother pooh-poohed. I wanted to stay indoors. I felt ashamed of my appearance. I became self-conscious and shy. I was irritable and sensitive to criticism.

I imagined I saw in the appraising eyes of everyone who looked at me the thought, " Yes, he's a weakling." The idea festered. As I look back on those early years, I think I became a rebel with a cause. My cause was the disproof of the charge of inferiority that had been leveled by the jury of my contemporaries. [3] There was no one in whom I could confide; no one to whom I could express my inner turmoil and tension. So the revolt grew and grew in my heart.

One day I met another boy, whom I had known at Sunday school, com-

[1] **solicitousness** (sŏ·lĭs′ĭ·tŭs·nĕs): anxious concern.

[2] **stratagem** (străt′à·jĕm): a trick used to deceive others.

[3] **contemporaries** (kŏn·tĕm′pŏ·rĕr′ĭz): people his own age.

ing in on a fast walk from the country. He was a husky, long-legged chap, to me a perfect physical specimen. I asked him where he'd been, and he replied that he had been climbing the foothills north of town. I asked him why he did it. He told me that his doctor had advised it; that he was trying to correct certain difficulties following an illness. He was climbing the foothills every day to develop his lungs and legs.

An overwhelming light swept me. My resolution was instantaneous. I would do the same. I would make my legs strong on the foothills. Thus I started my treks, and used the foothills as one uses weights or bars in a gymnasium. First I tried to go up the hills without stopping. When I conquered that, I tried to go up without change of pace. When that was achieved, I practiced going up not only without a change of pace but whistling as I went.

That fall and winter the foothills began to work a transformation in me. By the time the next spring arrived, I had found new confidence in myself. My legs were filling out. They were getting stronger. I could go the two miles to Selah Gap at a fast pace and often reach the top of the ridge without losing a step or reducing my speed. Following these hikes the muscles of my knees would twitch and make it difficult for me to sleep at night. But I felt an increasing flow of health in my legs, and a growing sense of contentment in my heart.

These early hikes put me on intimate terms with the hills. I learned

something of their geology and botany.[1] I came to know the Indian legends associated with them. I discovered many of their secrets. I learned that they were always clothed in garments of delicate hues, though they seemed to be barren. I discovered that though they looked dead and monotonous, they teemed with life and had many moods.

During the summer months of the following ten years I made many trips into the Washington Cascades. These treks into the mountains usually were no mere overnight or weekend jaunts; often they would last a week or two or even longer. On these trips I almost always had companions: Bradley Emery, Elon Gilbert, Douglas Corpron, or my brother Arthur. We usually went by foot, carrying our supplies on our backs.

In this fashion I hiked through much of the wild country between Mount Adams and Mount Rainier on the eastern slopes of the Cascades. I walked most of the trails in that region, climbed most of the peaks, explored many of the ridges, fished or looked down into practically all of the numerous lakes, camped in dozens of the meadows, and sampled the trout in almost every stream in that vast watershed. But for infantile paralysis I might not have done so.

Though I usually went by foot with a pack on my back, one of the earliest trips — and my first one into

[1] **Geology** is the science dealing with the history of the earth, especially as recorded in rocks. **Botany** is the study of plants.

the beautiful Klickitat Meadows — was at the same time both more luxurious and more painful.

One June, Elon and Horace Gilbert and their cousin Gilbert Peck were leaving early in the week by horseback for the Klickitat Meadows. I had a job picking cherries and could not afford to leave until Saturday. So we arranged that they would take the camp outfit, including my bedroll, in by pack train and meet me by midafternoon on Saturday near the top of Darling Mountain. . . .

On the appointed day I arrived at the rendezvous on Darling Mountain, and it was not long before my three friends appeared in a rush, with whoops and hollers, on horseback and leading a horse for me. There were shouts of greetings, a short account of my trip, a description of plans that had been arranged, and then we were off.

I had driven horses in the orchards, and I had ridden work horses bareback from field to barn; but I had never been in the saddle. I hardly had my feet in the stirrups and the reins in my hand before my young friends were headed for camp four miles distant on the Klickitat Meadows.

They rode like uncivilized Indians — on the dead run. There was no more holding my horse than turning the tide. He was not to be denied the companionship of the other horses or the prospect of early grazing in the lush Klickitat Meadows. The first half-mile led through willow and aspen and low-hanging fir. I lost my hat and almost my neck from overhanging branches.

On a swerve in the trail on a downhill pitch, I lost my stirrups. I regained them only to lose them again and again. But I never let go the reins or the horn. I " pulled leather " [1] all the way. I had no control whatever of the horse.

It was a gentle downhill slope, which my horse took on a dead run. As he raced on and on in his mad way, I bounced to the rhythm of his pounding hoofs. He raced like a demon through a stand of giant tamarack and into a sizable grove of aspen. The leaves of the aspen trembled and shook as if they were cymbals [2] in the hands of some weird dancer. Those who had preceded us in earlier years had carved their initials and dates of their journeys into the white bark of these trees. Those cuts had healed leaving dark scars. Those scars combined with the natural dark splotches on the trunks of the aspens took fantastic forms. They formed faces — grotesque and distorted. "They are leering at me," I thought. "They are laughing — laughing at my bouncing." And as I raced by, bouncing in the saddle, the quivering of the leaves of the aspen, the laughter of their scarred trunks made it seem as if the trees themselves were twisting and weaving in some strange dance of a dervish. [3]

[1] "pulled leather": held on to the saddle, as no good rider would have to do.

[2] cymbals (sĭm'bălz): brass plates which are clashed together to make a ringing sound.

[3] dervish (dûr'vĭsh): a member of a Moslem religious order, famed for violent dancing.

I beat the saddle incessantly as I bounced up and down. I bounced so hard I jarred my teeth. I bounced so hard I was constantly winded. I could not have yelled a command to the fleeing Indians had I been in earshot and had my life depended on it.

And then there was the pain in my legs. The legs that I had thought were getting strong and hardy had collapsed on me. Sick and puny? Legs like pipestems? Not as strong as other boys? Those were questions that pounded in my head. This was prophecy come true. The shooting pain in my legs was not imagination. No one was shouting at me derisively about them. Now my weakness appeared in a tangible form. In only a few minutes my legs had crumbled.

Through history books I had read of tyrants putting men on the rack [1] for torture. Maybe this was it, the rack with all its promise of anguish fulfilled. I later learned that the hips, the knees, and the ankles are all springs which when rightly used

make the saddle as comfortable as an armchair. But there was no co-ordination among the springs that day. Indeed, the springs were not functioning; they were out of order.

The hips were the first to go; they froze in excruciating [2] pain. Each lunge of the horse made it seem as if the muscles in the hips were being torn asunder. I felt like a man who was being quartered. [3] The pain shot down the leg to the knee. The knees and the ankles ached under the hammering from the saddle. Each movement of the horse was like a knife thrust in the thigh. There was no relief. On and on we went, through patches of willow where the branches raced across the cheek, cutting hard into the skin.

On and on my horse raced, like a demon through a wilderness. Shortly we came to Cuitan Creek, a yard or so wide with a dark lava bottom. He vaulted this as if he were winged,

[1] **rack:** an apparatus used to torture people by stretching their bodies.

[2] **excruciating** (ĕks·krōō′shĭ·āt′ĭng): agonizing.
[3] **quartered:** In medieval times, criminals were sometimes condemned to be "quartered," literally cut into four pieces.

landed on the other side, and kept on going at his terrible pace without missing a beat. He galloped recklessly through rock fields. Then he started to scrape the trees as if to be rid of his helpless, frightened rider.

The "whoas" had long ceased. I was silent and grim. For me the problem was one of survival. Leaving the horse in safety by my own volition was out of the question. My legs were paralyzed. I could not have dismounted by myself had the horse been standing still. To fall under these pounding hoofs was a frightful thought, but even more frightful was the thought of losing face before my pals. "You couldn't take it, eh?" Or darker thoughts never uttered, "Maybe the guy should have stayed home. Let's not have him the next time."

We soon came to Coyote Creek, where later I caught eight- and ten-inch cutthroat and rainbow. This creek, with its dark lava bottom, is eight or ten feet wide. My horse would not be denied. He jumped that too, hurling me against the can-

tle [1] as he left the ground and then pitching me against the horn as he landed. I hung on, though I did not recover from the shock. Then the demon ran uphill the remaining 200 yards to the meadows, almost tossing me over his rear as he lurched frantically up the side of the ravine.

How I hung on I never knew, but hang on I did. It was not over twenty minutes, I suppose (though it seemed an eternity), from the time we started until we reached the meadows. Then we shot through a grove of fir and were at the edge of a beautiful expanse of green grass, a half-mile wide and a mile and a half long. "It's all over," I thought. "I finally made it."

Not so. We were at the meadows; but off to the left I saw the disappearing tail of Elon's horse. The gang was heading for another camping place. So on we went, at a dead run, for another half-mile, my anguish increased by the respite [2] that had come so close but yet been denied.

At last I saw the camp. It was at the junction of Coyote Creek and the

---

[1] **cantle:** the part of the saddle that sticks up at the back.

[2] **respite** (rĕs′pĭt): temporary relief from pain.

Little Klickitat near the lower end of the Meadows. As my horse slowed to a trot and then to a walk, I became as nonchalant [1] as I knew how. Easing him over to a high rock, I stepped gingerly out of the saddle. I stood there regaining my poise as we bantered back and forth. I was so lame I could hardly walk; and that lameness I could not conceal. But even cowboys limp, and my limping did not cause me to fall from grace.

My legs, however, ached and trembled. They seemed paralyzed, and I wondered if the old trouble had returned. The answer was not long coming. For I wiggled my toes and knew at once that I was all right. But could I walk? Would anyone laugh?

Yet those worries were overshadowed by one that was even more serious. My posterior was in a most painful condition. I could not conceal it much longer. The four-mile gallop had worn raw spots on my buttocks — raw, burning spots that clung to my trousers. I needed medical attention badly. I announced the fact. While my announcement produced great merriment, there was no ridicule. I was a casualty and some casualties were expected.

Off came my trousers for an inspection. The decision was that I was to lie on my stomach and receive medication. A large rock, as big as a grand piano, stands near the junction of the two creeks. On that rock I lay while my three youthful pals gleefully attended to my wounds and in due

[1] **nonchalant** (nŏn′shả·lảnt): coolly unconcerned.

course patched me up in commendable style.

I remember that we had a wonderful supper that night. We also had a big campfire in the open grassy flat that lies in between the mouths of the Little Klickitat and Coyote Creek. There were delicacies from home, cookies and cake. The food came horseback, too, so there was no stinting.

The sixteen-mile hike and the four-mile gallop had made me very hungry. I ate my fill and excused myself from kitchen duty that night, promising to do double duty the next day. I was sore and weary and tired beyond compare. My legs were so lame they ached.

I put my bedroll down on the grass by the Little Klickitat. As I slipped between the blankets, Elon came over to me. He was of slight build and not more than five feet six. His hair was brown, his eyes hazel. He always had a cheerful word for everyone. He took pains to see that his companions were comfortable. He seemed to find joy in doing little things for his friends. Then his eyes would dance and a note of tenderness would come into his voice. This night he leaned down close to me and quietly said, " Say, fella, you're O.K. You sure can go it the hard way."

I swallowed a lump in my throat and murmured thanks. Pride swelled in my heart as I lay for a moment looking at the myriad stars that hung so close to earth it seemed they could be touched. The Little Klickitat sang softly to me. I went to sleep triumphant. Those whose opinion I valued more highly than any on earth had rendered their verdict.[1]

Weakling Wins Approval

1. What did the doctor think of young Bill Douglas's chance to live an active, healthy life? How did his mother save him from paralysis?

2. Explain whether you think the boys on the street would have made fun of his

[1] **rendered their verdict:** announced their decision about a person on trial.

legs if they had known about his illness.

3. Why did he begin taking hikes into the mountains? Tell some of the goals he set for himself.

4. Why was the wild mountain ride a test for Bill? How did it make him think of earlier days when he was first stricken with polio?

5. Why did Elon's few words to Bill that night mean so much to him?

6. Why would you expect a boy like Bill to win success in later life? Have several class members report on Justice Douglas's later experiences as a mountain climber.

Poems of Outdoors

GETTING outdoors makes most people feel so good that they have to express their feelings some way. Most folks turn their high spirits into physical activity. Others who have a knack with words may write a poem, as Richard Le Gallienne did in "I Meant to Do My Work Today."

> I meant to do my work today
> But a brown bird sang in the apple tree,
> And a butterfly flitted across the field,
> And all the leaves were calling me.
>
> And the wind went sighing over the land,
> Tossing the grasses to and fro,
> And a rainbow held out its shining hand —
> So what could I do but laugh and go?

"I Meant to Do My Work Today" from *The Lonely Dancer* by Richard Le Gallienne. Copyright, 1913, 1941, by Richard Le Gallienne. Reprinted by permission of Dodd, Mead and Company.

Poetry seems to be especially suited to express that good-to-be-alive feeling. That is why, all through the ages, nature has been a favorite subject of poets. No matter what part of outdoor life you like best — pathways, seaways, or skyways — you can find a poem that tells just how it looks or how it makes you feel. The samples collected here give you some idea of the variety of scenes and moods the poets have recorded.

PATHWAYS

EYES AND EARS TO LEND. For a short ramble along any sort of path, you can have no better companion than a poet. It is not easy to tell all the ways a poet is different from other people, but you can put your finger on a few. For one thing, he notices more than you and I usually do. He sees and hears and smells and feels with unusual keenness. Another talent of the poet is his ability to put his impressions into words that create images — pictures and sights and sounds — for the reader.

"God uses us to help each other so," one poet said, "lending our minds out." As you read these outdoor poems, take advantage of the loan. Enjoy the imagery that lets you share all the many impressions and feelings the poet finds along his path.

Tewksbury Road   JOHN MASEFIELD

It is good to be out on the road, and going one knows not where,
  Going through meadow and village, one knows not whither nor why;
Through the gray light drift of the dust, in the keen cool rush of the air,
  Under the flying white clouds, and the broad blue lift of the sky.

And to halt at the chattering brook, in the tall green fern at the brink   5
  Where the harebell grows, and the gorse, and the foxgloves purple and
    white;
Where the shy-eyed delicate deer troop down to the brook to drink
  When the stars are mellow and large at the coming on of the night.

Oh, to feel the beat of the rain, and the homely smell of the earth,
Is a tune for the blood to jig to, a joy past power of words;   10
And the blessed green comely meadows are all a-ripple with mirth
At the noise of the lambs at play and the dear wild cry of the birds.

The Daffodils

WILLIAM WORDSWORTH

I wandered lonely as a cloud
That floats on high o'er vales and
   hills,
When all at once I saw a crowd,
A host, of golden daffodils;
Beside the lake, beneath the trees,   5
Fluttering and dancing in the breeze.

Continuous as the stars that shine
And twinkle on the milky way,
They stretched in never-ending line
Along the margin of a bay: 10
Ten thousand saw I at a glance,
Tossing their heads in sprightly
   dance.

The waves beside them danced: but
   they
Outdid the sparkling waves in glee:
A poet could not but be gay,   15
In such a jocund° company:
I   gazed — and   gazed — but   little
   thought
What wealth the show to me had
   brought.

For oft, when on my couch I lie
In vacant or in pensive° mood,   20

16. jocund (jŏk'ŭnd): merry. 20. pensive:
thoughtful and a little sad.

They flash upon that inward eye
Which is the bliss of solitude;
And then my heart with pleasure fills,
And dances with the daffodils.

Stopping by Woods
on a Snowy Evening

ROBERT FROST

Whose woods these are I think I
   know.
His house is in the village though;
He will not see me stopping here
To watch his woods fill up with snow.

The little horse must think it queer   5
To stop without a farmhouse near
Between the woods and frozen lake
The darkest evening of the year.

He gives his harness bells a shake
To ask if there is some mistake.   10
The only other sound's the sweep
Of easy wind and downy flake.

The woods are lovely, dark and deep.
But I have promises to keep,
And miles to go before I sleep,   15
And miles to go before I sleep.

Enjoying Imagery in Poetry

1. After you finish reading the poems, what pictures remain clearest in your mind? When you think of one you especially like, skim back over the lines and find the poet's exact description. Use some of his words in telling about your impression of the image.

2. Were any sounds or smells or physical feelings described as clearly as the sights? Find the lines that express them and read them aloud to the class.

3. Which poem gave you the most complete feeling that you were at the poet's side, sharing his experience? Repeat some of the imaginative phrases to show why you chose that poem.

4. Why did Wordsworth like to remember the daffodils? Have you any memories of beautiful sights that have the same effect on you? Think of times that you have been on a country road or a city street. Select one scene and try putting it into words that will make others see it, too.

SEAWAYS

MUSIC IN POETRY. There's music in the sea, in the swing of the waves and the tides, in the murmur of soft surf and the thunder of heavy breakers. These sounds repeat themselves, over and over. In the following poems about the sea, you will find that poets use repetition to make their own kind of music.

Rhyme, the repetition of sounds at the ends of lines, is an old friend to you by now. But you may not have noticed the repetition of sounds at the beginning of words within a single line, as in " one road *l*eads to *L*ondon." This kind of word music is called alliteration (ă·lĭt'-ẽr.ā'shŭn). Usually it is found within a line, but often the sounds at the beginning of words keep echoing all through a stanza. You'll find that this sort of mel-

ody adds to the music of rhyme in all kinds of poetry. But somehow it seems to fit especially well into poems about the sea, which has so much repetition in its own music.

Roadways   JOHN MASEFIELD

One road leads to London,
    One road runs to Wales,
My road leads me seawards
    To the white dipping sails.

One road leads to the river,   5
    As it goes singing slow;
My road leads to shipping,
    Where the bronzed sailors go.

Leads me, lures me, calls me
   To salt green tossing sea;   10
A road without earth's road-dust
   Is the right road for me.

A wet road heaving, shining,
   And wild with sea gulls' cries,
A mad salt sea-wind blowing   15
   The salt spray in my eyes.

My road calls me, lures me
   West, east, south, and north;
Most roads lead men homewards,
   My road leads me forth   20

To add more miles to the tally
   Of gray miles left behind,
In quest of that one beauty
   God put me here to find.

Exiled   EDNA ST. VINCENT MILLAY

Searching my heart for its true sorrow,
   This is the thing that I find to be:
That I am weary of words and people,
   Sick of the city, wanting the sea;

Wanting the sticky, salty sweetness   5
   Of the strong wind and shattered spray;
Wanting the loud sound and the soft sound
   Of the big surf that breaks all day.

Always before about my dooryard,
   Marking the reach of the winter sea,   10
Rooted in sand and dragging driftwood,
   Straggled the purple wild sweet pea;

Always I climbed the wave at morning,
   Shook the sand from my shoes at night,
That now am caught beneath great buildings,   15
   Stricken with noise, confused with light.

If I could hear the green piles groaning
   Under the windy wooden piers,
See once again the bobbing barrels,
   And the black sticks that fence the weirs,°   20

20. **weirs** (wērz): enclosed areas in the water, for catching fish.

If I could see the weedy mussels
    Crusting the wrecked and rotting hulls,
Hear once again the hungry crying
    Overhead, of the wheeling gulls,

Feel once again the shanty straining   25
    Under the turning of the tide,
Fear once again the rising freshet,°
    Dread the bell in the fog outside —

I should be happy — that was happy
    All day long on the coast of Maine!   30
I have a need to hold and handle
    Shells and anchors and ships again!

I should be happy, that am happy
    Never at all since I came here.
I am too long away from water.   35
    I have a need of water near.

27. freshet: an overflow of water.

A Wet Sheet and a Flowing Sea   ALLAN CUNNINGHAM

A wet sheet° and a flowing sea, | *Light voices*
    A wind that follows fast
And fills the white and rustling sail | *Deep voices*
    And bends the gallant mast;
And bends the gallant mast, my boys,   5 | *Mixed chorus;*
    While, like the eagle free, | *faster*
Away the good ship flies, and leaves
    Old England on the lee.°

O for a soft and gentle wind! | *Light voices*
    I hear a fair one cry;   10
But give to me the snoring breeze | *Deep voices*
    And white waves heaving high;
And white waves heaving high, my lads, | *Mixed chorus;*
    The good ship tight and free — | *swing it!*
The world of waters is our home,   15
    And merry men are we.

1. sheet: a rope or chain used to control the angle of a sail to the wind. 8. lee: the direction away from the wind.

There's tempest in yon hornèd moon, | *Deep voices*
   And lightning in yon cloud;
But hark the music, mariners! | *Light voices*
   The wind is piping loud;   20
The wind is piping loud, my boys, | *Mixed chorus;*
   The lightning flashes free — | *strong and clear*
While the hollow oak° our palace is,
   Our heritage the sea.

    23. The "hollow oak" is the ship, fashioned of stout oak timbers.

Finding Music in the Sound of Poetry

1. Find some lines that repeat the first sounds of words (alliteration) within a single line. Find stanzas that repeat one or more initial sounds all the way through. Read some of the stanzas aloud, first giving a strong emphasis to the repeated sounds, and then reading naturally. You will find that by this method you can make the music sound the way the poet intended it to.

2. These poems give you three different views of the sea. Which one tells of:

   a. homesickness for life at the seashore?

   b. the call of the sea to a sailor ashore?

   c. a sailor happy to be back at sea once again?

3. Did you find that the poets lend you their eyes and ears in these poems, just as they did in the "Pathways" poems? Read aloud lines that make clear pictures of the sea. Read others that make sea sounds seem real for you.

4. Have you ever been homesick as the writer of "Exiled" was homesick for her life beside the sea? Perhaps you can recall a time when you traveled away from home. Put down in short phrases some of the things you remembered with longing. Make the thought clear in your own mind first, and the words will come to you. Work in some alliteration to make a little poem.

SKYWAYS

Land and sea and sky — these make up our outdoor world. For centuries men have explored the land and sailed the sea, but until recently they could only look up at the sky. Here are two views of the sky by earthbound poets — one in awe of the violence that sometimes comes from the sky, one in simple admiration of its beauty. The third writer is not only a poet but also an aviator, and he loves the wide freedom of the sky as a sailor loves the open sea.

The Hurricane   WILLIAM CULLEN BRYANT

Lord of the winds! I feel thee nigh,
I know thy breath in the burning sky!
And I wait, with a thrill in every vein,
For the coming of the hurricane!

And lo! on the wings of the heavy gales,   5
Through the boundless arch of heaven he sails;
Silent and slow, and terribly strong,
The mighty shadow is borne along,
Like the dark eternity to come;
While the world below, dismayed and dumb,   10
Through the calm of the thick hot atmosphere,
Looks up at its gloomy folds with fear.

They darken fast; and the golden haze
Of the sun is quenched in the lurid haze,
And he sends through the shade a funeral ray —   15
A glare that is neither night nor day,
A beam that touches with hues of death
The clouds above and the earth beneath.
To its covert° glides the silent bird,
While the hurricane's distant voice is heard   20
Uplifted among the mountains round,
And the forests hear and answer the sound.

Darker — still darker! the whirlwinds bear
The dust of the plains to the middle air;
And hark to the crashing, long and loud,   25
Of the chariot of God in the thundercloud,
As the fire bolts leap to the world below,
And flood the skies with a lurid glow.

What roar is that? — 'tis the rain that breaks
In torrents away from the airy lakes,   30
A whirling ocean that fills the wall
Of the crystal heaven, and buries all.
And I, cut off from the world remain
Alone with the terrible hurricane.

19. **covert** (kŭv′ẽrt): shelter.

When You Walk

JAMES STEPHENS

When you walk in a field,
Look down
Lest you tramp
On a daisy's crown!

But in a city
Look always high,
And watch
The beautiful clouds go by!

High Flight   JOHN GILLESPIE MAGEE, JR.

Oh! I have slipped the surly bonds of earth
And danced the skies on laughter-silvered wings;
Sunward I've climbed, and joined the tumbling mirth
Of sun-split clouds — and done a hundred things
You have not dreamed of — wheeled and soared and swung   5
High in the sunlit silence. Hov'ring there
I've chased the shouting wind along, and flung
My eager craft through footless halls of air.

Up, up the long, delirious, burning blue
I've topped the wind-swept heights with easy grace,   10
Where never lark, or even eagle flew —
And, while with silent, lifting mind I've trod
The high untrespassed sanctity° of space,
Put out my hand and touched the face of God.

13. **sanctity:** holiness.

High Above Us

1. Does Bryant seem to be more excited or fearful as he watches the approach of the hurricane? Read aloud the parts of the poem that support your answer. Explain what is meant by lines 20–22.

2. Do you think the writer of " When You Walk " is happier out in the country or in the city? Why?

3. What does the aviator like best about the sky? Guess whether he flies transport planes, or a small solo plane, or a military plane. What clues does the poem give you?

4. Can you remember without looking back at the poem what picture of the sky was recalled in " The Daffodils "? If not, look back and find it.

5. Tell other views of the sky that poets might write about. Describe the kind of sky you like best.

Roundup

What Do You Enjoy Outdoors?

1. If you could spend a vacation on a ranch, on a farm like the Muirs', or in the mountains, which would you choose? What would you like especially about that sort of vacation?

2. What are the chief kinds of outings available to you and your friends? Are these outings as popular as other kinds of entertainment? Discuss the reasons why they are, or are not.

3. Can you describe the behavior of the birds and animals that live near you? Which ones are most interesting? Why?

4. Do your moods affect your liking for different kinds of weather? When do you like a rainy day? a stormy day? a mild, springlike day? a brisk, nippy fall day?

Make a Book of Outdoor Poems

The outdoor poems in this book are only a sample of many that have been written. Look for others in the poetry collections in your library and in the literature books used by other classes. Let each member of the class pick a favorite and copy it neatly on unruled paper. Then put them all into one binder to make a class anthology.

Write Your Own Outdoor Poem

If you like outdoors and notice outdoor scenes and creatures, you can write a good free-verse poem. Do it this way. First, concentrate on the thing you want to picture to your reader. Then write your impressions, using words that will tell exactly what you see and how you feel. Then you will have an original outdoor poem to go in the class anthology.

Your Bookshelf

Adventure North, by R. G. Emery (Macrae Smith, 1947)
In search of uranium in Alaska.

Avalanche Patrol, by Montgomery M. Atwater (Random House, 1951)
Fine outdoor sport, a mystery, and fast action in a story of forest rangers. By the same author, *Hank Winton, Smokechaser* (1947), about a young forest-fire fighter.

Bridled with Rainbows: Poems About Many Things of Earth and Sky, selected by Sara and John E. Brewton (Macmillan, 1949)

Dude Girl, by Doreen Foote (Dodd, Mead, 1951)
About a pack trip to drive horses from Wyoming to California.

Forest Ranger, by Jack Hambleton (Longmans, 1949)
Dogsleds and airplanes carry the young ranger on his rounds in the far North. Continued in *Abiti Adventure* (1951)

Green Seas and White Ice, Far North with Captain Mac, by Miriam MacMillan (Dodd, Mead, 1948)
Braving icebergs, ice floes, and stormy weather to explore the land of the Eskimos. You will enjoy, too, Mrs. MacMillan's *Etuk, the Eskimo Hunter* (1950).

High Harvest, by Elizabeth Low (Harcourt, Brace, 1948)
A girl helps Vermont farmers to adopt modern methods and save their homes.

Hoofbeats on the Trail, by Vivian Breck (Doubleday, 1950)
A girl tries mountain-climbing and camping in the Sierras. More of the same life in *High Trail,* by the same author (1948).

In Woods and Fields, by Margaret Waring Buck (Abingdon, 1950)
A guide to the birds, insects, and flowers you will find on your outdoor jaunts.

Jeff White: Young Trapper, by Lew Dietz (Little, Brown, 1951)
A winter of wilderness trapping brings Jeff up against a mysterious murder.

Let's Go Camping: a Guide to Outdoor Living, by Harry Zarchy (Knopf, 1951)
Everything you need to know for successful camping out.

The Life of Audubon, by Clyde Fisher (Harper, 1950)
The great naturalist followed an outdoor trail most of his life.

Paul Tiber — Forester, by Maria Gleit (Scribner, 1950)
A boy who loves trees brings them to cover the ash dumps of his mining town.

Sea and Shore, by Clarence J. Hylander (Macmillan, 1950)
Exploring plant and animal life at the water's edge.

Sea Room, by Fran Martin (Harper, 1947)
Joe's one love is sailing boats.

The Secret Camp, by Irena Balinska (Morrow, 1947)
Modern boys prove to be efficient woodsmen.

Showdown, by T. Morris Longstreth (Macmillan, 1950)
After a plane crash in the Canadian wilderness, learning to live outdoors was urgent.

Summer Green, by Elizabeth Coatsworth (Macmillan, 1948)
Poems full of outdoor sounds and sights and feelings.

Tophill Road, by Helen Garrett (Viking, 1950)
Moving to the country sounded like hard luck until they tried it.

Traplines North, by Stephen W. Meader (Dodd, Mead, 1936)
The true story of a real woodsman.

Wild Trek, by Jim Kjelgaard (Holiday, 1950)
Adventure and thrills outdoors in northern Canada.

Family and Friends

The Lonesome Bear

HARRISON KINNEY

Where there are children there are likely to be pets. And where there are pets — well, in this story you will find out what *that* may lead to. Most families are willing to put up with some trouble for the sake of the children's pets, but what should a father do when a bear moves into his bedroom in the middle of the night?

UNTIL he was twelve my brother George was the unofficial leader of a gang of boys about his own age in Fairfield. Being four years younger than George, I was never included in the activities of this group, but one day I was sitting on a lower limb of an apple tree in our back yard when my brother George came up to the tree with his hands in his pockets.

" Let's start a store," he said. You put up the counter and I'll try to get the stuff."

" All right," I said, climbing down from the tree.

After George had gone I erected a counter with two boxes and a board, facing our driveway. When he got back, he pulled out a two-pound box of chocolates, a half dozen all-day suckers, a box of marshmallows, and eight chocolate bars. He arranged these on the counter.

" I'll go tell the gang to come and buy this candy from us," my brother George said.

" All right," I said.

George went away again and I was sitting on the ground, eating one of the chocolate bars, when a brown bear lumbered down through the apple orchard and came up to the candy counter, sniffing at the articles on the board.

"You'd better go away," I told the bear. "My brother George will get mad if you eat his candy."

The bear sat down and stared at the candy. After a while George and his gang came up the driveway. They stopped quite a distance from the counter when they saw the bear.

"You get away from that bear," one of the boys yelled to me. "He'll kill you with one swing of his paw."

"No, he won't," I said, patting the bear on the head.

"Give him some candy to eat and maybe he'll go away," another boy shouted.

So I took the wrappers off two candy bars, opened the box of marshmallows, and placed them on the ground in front of the bear. The animal just sniffed at the candy, but when he found the marshmallows he slid into a crouch and began chewing them, looking at me occasionally, his head bobbing, as he ate.

"I guess he just likes marshmallows," said my brother George. "We'll get him some more for you to feed him and maybe he'll go away."

"The state will pay you a twenty-five-dollar bounty for a bear," another boy said to my brother George. "They kill sheep. Why don't you keep him and get the money?"

"I guess we could keep him in the icehouse," said George.

"How are you going to get him in the icehouse?" somebody asked.

"I think he'll follow my brother in," George replied. "You lead him in the icehouse," George said to me.

"All right," I answered.

So after the bear finished eating the marshmallows he followed me into the icehouse. My brother George locked the door after us and I climbed out the small trap door in the wall.

George told me not to tell anybody about the bear, for fear he would not get the money for himself. I promised I wouldn't.

My brother George promised to keep me in candy if I fed the bear. The diet was a rather irregular one, consisting largely of raw potatoes from a sack in our cellar, and meat bones I got from the butcher's store. The sawdust in the icehouse had dried into a comfortable bed for the bear. My family had had no use for the building after my father bought an electric refrigerator for our house.

After a few days the bear refused to eat anything. He would sit and make hoarse, whimpering noises in his throat.

"I think he wants some marshmallows," I told my brother George, who was standing outside the icehouse at the time.

"I'll get some," George said.

He went away and came back with a box of marshmallows, which he passed to me through the trap door. I opened the box and the bear rooted into them, getting marshmallow on his nose and whiskers and chomping them noisily, looking at me as he ate them. When he had finished them he ate the raw potatoes and meat bones. I told George the bear was eating everything.

"We'll just give him some marshmallows once in a while," George said. "I guess he'll be all right."

The night the bear got out of the icehouse, one of my mother's aunts was visiting us. She was given my room, while a couch was set up in my parents' room for me as a temporary arrangement. During the warmer nights of midsummer we always left the doors open, inside the house, for purposes of circulation; all except my brother George's room in the attic. George walked in his sleep occasionally, so my father always locked him in at night and let him out in the morning. The trap door of the icehouse could only be secured from the inside, so George and I had propped a piece of two-by-four against it from the outside. It was always a matter of speculation as to how the bear was able to dislodge it. Everybody was asleep the night that the bear came into my father's room and tried to crowd under my couch to go to sleep. The couch had two folding sides, and the grunting animal lifted the couch at one end in his attempt to get his bulky body under it. In this manner the couch was pushed across the floor until it banged against the opposite wall. The bear snorted loudly in the darkness and lay down.

My father was a light sleeper. "Where are you, George?" he asked, sitting up in bed and thinking it was my brother George walking in his sleep.

"George isn't here," I said.

"Good Lord, son!" said my father. "Are you making all that noise?"

"No, sir," I said. "I think it's the bear."

"All right," said my father, lying down again. "Just don't wake your mother."

"No, sir," I replied.

After a few minutes my father sat up in bed again. "What did you say that noise was, son?" he asked quietly.

"I think the bear is sleeping under my bed," I said.

My father sat in the darkness for a time, thinking this over. Finally he turned on the table lamp beside his bed. This awakened my mother.

"What is it?" my mother asked with alarm. "Is it George again?"

My father got out of bed in his nightshirt without saying anything. He came over to the couch, got down on his hands and knees and looked at the bear under the couch.

"He eats marshmallows," I said.

Father got up and solemnly walked over to my mother's side of the bed. "We must all remain calm," he said. "Your aunt musn't be upset. I don't think anybody is in immediate danger. There's a bear in our room."

My mother began weeping softly. "We'll all be torn limb from limb," she said.

"He won't hurt you," I told her.

My father asked me where the bear came from and I told him. My mother went into the next room to sleep with her aunt, and my father and I pulled the couch off the bear. The bear sat up and yawned.

"I never saw a bear like this that liked to be around people," said my father, crossing his bare feet in contemplation, and leaning against the bedpost in his nightshirt.

"I think he follows me because I feed him marshmallows," I said.

"We must always be kind to animals, son — wild or domestic," my father told me.

"Yes, sir," I said.

"His coat isn't shaggy like a wild bear's at all," said my father, looking at the bear. "I think he's tame."

"Can we keep him?" I asked.

My father didn't answer me. He wandered slowly downstairs and came back with his ukulele. He sat down in a rocking chair in his nightshirt and absently strummed some basic cords. The bear sat and listened to the music, staring at my father.

"This is a very friendly bear, son," said my father after a while. "Maybe we can keep him until his owner shows up."

"Yes, sir," I said.

The next day my father and I went across the street to the courthouse, with the bear plodding behind us.

"We'd like to get a license for a bear," my father told Miss Barnes, the clerk in the outer office.

Miss Barnes took off her glasses and looked at my father for a moment. Then she stood up quickly and looked at the bear, sitting on the floor beside me.

"What kind of a license do you want?" Miss Barnes asked slowly, still looking at the bear.

"We want him for a household pet," my father said.

"He eats marshmallows," I told Miss Barnes, patting the bear on the head.

"He does?" said Miss Barnes stupidly. "Just a moment." She got up and went into the inside office, looking cautiously at the bear over her shoulder. After a while the door of the inner office opened a crack and Mr. Gordon, the town clerk, peeked out. He finally pushed the door wide open. Three or four other people stood behind him and stared at the bear, which was sitting beside me, looking out the courthouse window.

"Do you really mean to keep this animal in your home as a pet for a seven-year-old child?" Mr. Gordon asked my father.

"He's a civilized bear," said my father, a little annoyed. "He's lots more trustworthy than some dogs in town that I know of. You can get a dog licensed. Why can't you license a bear?"

"You're setting a dangerous precedent,"[1] said Mr. Gordon. "Next, people will be wanting to license wildcats and wolves."

"He eats marshmallows," I said.

[1] **precedent** (prĕs'ê·dĕnt): something done that may serve as an example for people's actions at a later time.

"We should not be afraid of setting precedents," said my father in the tone of voice that he used on customers at his store. "The motto for the state of Maine is 'Dirigo': 'I direct.'"

"Oratorical rhetoric will get you nowhere," said Mr. Gordon, wiping his glasses and peering at the bear. "There are no regulations in the community, or Oswego County, governing this situation. There may be a state law which applies. I'll have to write to Augusta. In the meantime you will be solely responsible for the bear's behavior or he will have to be shot as being hazardous to the public welfare."

My father seemed annoyed as we left the courthouse. He sat down on the bottom step and the bear and I sat beside him.

"Son, a man could come up right now, as things stand, murder this bear and the state would pay him money," said my father. "By George, if Theodore Roosevelt were still in office I bet you could get a bear license."

My mother didn't care for the bear. She would never permit me to bring the bear as far as the back porch. My brother George soon lost interest in the animal, but my father usually brought marshmallows home from his general store. Sometimes my father would sit on the back-porch steps, play his ukulele and sing, while the bear sat in front of him and listened. Nothing could distract the bear's attention while my father was singing.

During the day, while my father was at work in his store and my brother George and I were at school, the bear was tethered to one of the apple trees by a long rope attached to the leather collar my father bought for him.

"We'll tie him close enough to the house so he won't get lonesome," my father told me.

The brown bear slept much of the time on the lower branches of the apple trees, or tumbled about on the ground, or ate the apples he could shake to the ground by hugging the tree trunks with his forepaws. On Mondays I would lock the bear in the icehouse, because he would ordinarily sit and watch the hired girl hang the week's laundry on the clothesline in the back yard, something which seemed to disturb her so much that she kept dropping parts of the wash on the ground.

The town's sheriff, Shirley Jones, who lived next door to us, knocked on our door one morning while we were eating breakfast. He was breathing heavily.

"Look, Stephen," he said to my father, "you've got to get rid of that bear. You don't have a license for him and I've got to insist. Do you know where that animal is right now?"

"In the icehouse," said my father, looking worried.

"He's sitting in the back seat of my car," said the sheriff. "He won't get out. He must have opened the door himself."

My father and I followed the sheriff next door. The bear had his head and forepaws protruding from a side window of the car, opposite the opened door.

"Go get the marshmallows, son," said my father quietly.

"Yes, sir," I said.

When the bear saw the marshmallows he climbed out of the sheriff's car and sniffed at the box in my hand.

"I have enough to worry about without a bear loose in town, scaring people and maybe taking a swipe at children," said the sheriff.

"He's a good bear," said my father.

"Just let him pull one funny move

and I'll have him shot," said Sheriff Jones. "You'll have to get rid of him, anyway. You've heard about the bank robberies that have taken place north of here. We're expecting them to take a crack at the Farmers' Trust here in Fairfield any day now, and if I have to do any chasing of bank robbers I don't want a bear in my back seat breathing down my neck."

"We'll take him back to the woods this Saturday and lose him," said my father a little sadly.

"He'll be happier there," said my mother when we told her. She seemed cheerful about it. "It isn't really right to keep the poor animal in captivity, anyway."

When Saturday came my father hired an extra clerk for his store and got fishing rods out of the attic while I dug worms in the back yard. The brown bear made happy woofing sounds in his throat when we opened the rear door of our Essex for him.

"He likes to ride in cars, I guess," said my father, looking thoughtfully at the bear.

"He'll never be able to ride in cars if we leave him in the woods," I said.

"He won't mind," said my father. "He'll forget."

A few miles outside of town, tourists in a car with New York license plates blew their horn and started to pass us. The sound attracted the attention of the bear, who thrust his head out the left rear window just as the New York car was abreast of us. I heard a woman scream and the other car swerved off the road and shot up a grassy embankment, where it came to a stop. My father stopped the Essex and we walked back.

"Are you all right?" my father asked with some concern.

"Only a little shaken up," said the driver, a man in a white linen suit. "That animal frightened me. For a minute I thought he was driving."

"He's a tame bear," said my father. "I hope you aren't hurt."

"He eats marshmallows," I said. "We're taking him fishing."

"I see," said the man, looking from me to my father.

They waved at us as they passed us a few minutes later. My father waved back. He always made a point of being nice to out-of-state people so that they would think well of Maine. We kept the rear windows rolled up after that.

"Next they'll be saying this poor bear is a traffic hazard," my father explained.

We left the car on a farm road and walked several miles into the forest, the bear traipsing silently behind us. He gave no obvious acknowledgment of any change in environment. We fished for trout all that day in a clear water stream while the bear sat and watched us. At noon we ate

the lunch the hired girl had put up for us and fed the bear some meat bones.

"A wild bear would crouch on the bank of that stream and knock trout out of it with his paw," said my father. "This is the most helpless animal I ever saw."

"Maybe he doesn't like fish," I said. "Maybe all he can eat now will be meat bones, potatoes, and marsh-

mallows. Maybe he'll starve out here."

"No, he won't," said my father, eating a deviled-ham sandwich and looking at the bear. "He can eat berries and nuts like other bears. Maybe he'll find a mate and learn from her."

"He likes music," I said. "He likes to hear you sing."

"The woods are full of birds that sing," said my father.

"They can't play the ukulele," I said.

"There are times when I wish you

wouldn't talk to me," my father said. "I think you take after your mother at times. Please be quiet."

"Yes, sir," I said.

We fished for a while longer in the afternoon and the bear became tired of watching and wandered away into the woods.

"You mustn't feel badly about the bear, son," my father said, as we carried the fish baskets and rods back through the trees. He blew his nose in a large linen handkerchief.

"We didn't say good-by to him," I said.

"It's probably better that way," said my father. He was a theatrical man.

It was dusk when we reached the car and started for home. Neither of us spoke for a while. When we were on the state highway the lights of a car behind us threw a silhouette of a bear's head on the inside of our windshield.

"Is the bear in the back seat, son?" my father asked quietly.

I turned and looked at the bear in the back seat. He sat with his back to us, looking out the rear window.

"I think it's the bear," I said.

My mother locked herself in her room all the next day.

"I don't know why our home has to be turned into a zoo," she told my father tearfully.

"The circus will be passing through here in a few days," my father reassured her. "They'll be glad to have a tame bear."

The bear and I waited on the back steps that evening for my father to come out and sing, but he never did.

In late June the circus was playing Millinocket on its way north and my father wired the manager that he might have the bear if he called for it. One afternoon, a few days later, a man drove up in front of our house in a coupé with a large wire cage protruding from the half-opened trunk. I brought the bear around from the icehouse. The man looked at the bear.

"I knew it was Henry," he said, nodding his head thoughtfully.

"Is that the bear's name?" I asked.

"We lost him last summer up this way," the man explained. "He must have hibernated [1] in the woods all winter."

"He eats marshmallows," I said.

"It used to be jelly beans," the man said. "He's the most temperamental animal I ever saw. He wouldn't eat anything unless we gave him jelly beans once in a while. He has quite a sweet tooth. I wish we hadn't found him. He's such a nuisance."

He raised the gate of the cage and sprinkled a few jelly beans from his pocket on the floor of the cage.

"Let's go, Henry," he said to the bear.

The bear ambled inside the cage and began chewing the jelly beans. The man closed the gate after him.

"He likes to ride in cars," I said, looking at the bear through the wire.

"I know," the man answered. "That's all we could get him to do,

---

[1] **hibernated** (hī'bẽr·nāt·ĕd): spent the winter in his den, sleeping, as bears usually do.

ride in the back of an old jalopy that two clowns drove around the ring. He's the most useless bear I ever saw. He wouldn't learn to ride bicycles, or roller-skate, and he ran away when we tried to teach him to dance. We were all glad."

The man sighed and got into the car.

"Thank your folks for taking care of him, kid," the man said sadly.

"Yes, sir," I said.

He drove away with the brown bear sitting in the wire cage chewing jelly beans.

It was the first year my family didn't go to see the circus when it played Presque Isle.[1] My brother George threatened to run away from home, but my mother said she couldn't stand to look at another animal, and my father said he supposed it would make the bear unhappy if he saw us in the crowd.

"He rides in the back of an old car that two clowns drive," I told my father.

"He's probably very happy, then," said my father, patting me on the head. It was several weeks before he played his ukulele and sang on the steps of the back porch.

One morning my father was awakened by somebody throwing pebbles at his bedroom window. He got out of bed and went to the window. It was the hired girl. She told my father she didn't dare to come into the house because a bear was sitting on the front porch in front of the door. I followed my father downstairs and

[1] Presque Isle (prěsk' ĭl').

we looked at the bear through the curtains of the living-room windows.

"Look at the dust on his fur," said my father. "He must have walked twenty miles."

"Maybe he's mad at us for giving him to the circus," I said.

"No," my father replied. "He just got homesick for us."

I led the bear around to the icehouse and locked him in. When I got back my father was strumming on his ukulele.

"Son, Judge Holt told me he heard from Augusta that there's no legal protection for bears as pets," my father said. "I don't know what we'll do with him. We certainly can't keep him. Sheriff Jones and your mother just wouldn't stand for it."

My father went to work without telling my mother the bear was back, and it was about ten o'clock that morning when I discovered the bear had got out of the icehouse. I searched back of the orchard and finally started downtown to the store to tell my father the bear was loose in Fairfield. A block from the Farmers' Trust Building I saw the bear trudge out of an alley and climb into the front seat of a long black Pierce Arrow that was standing in front of the bank, its motor idling and the front door open. From the front seat the bear pushed himself over into the back and sat on the floor. I was looking at him through the car window when two men carrying guns and cloth sacks came running out of the bank and leaped into the car.

"The bear's in there," I told them,

pointing.

The men didn't hear me, apparently. They slouched in the front seat and the car roared away just as the burglar alarm went off outside the bank. In a few minutes I saw Sheriff Jones's Reo and two cars filled with deputies race down Main Street in the direction the Pierce Arrow had taken.

My father was in the office of his store, sitting at his roller-top desk.

"The bear got in a car and the people drove away and didn't see him," I told him.

My father buried his face in his hands.

"Son," he said after a while, "this is the end. Those poor innocent people will find a bear in their car, not know he is a tame bear, go off the road and kill themselves. The bear will be shot, if he gets out alive, and I'll be put in jail."

"Sheriff Jones is chasing the bear," I said.

"You and George will have to go with your mother to live with her family," said my father absently. "You must always be good to her,

son."

"Yes, sir," I said.

We drove slowly home in the Essex. He asked me not to talk to him for a while and I promised I wouldn't. A group of people were standing on the lawn in front of our house when we drove up.

"The bear is sitting in Sheriff Jones's car," I said.

"Those bank robbers didn't even get out of town," the sheriff told my father happily when we joined him. "The driver spotted that bear of yours in the rearview mirror, sitting on the back seat. They went over the edge of the culvert at the bottom of Mill Hill. Took them both without firing a shot. They're in the prison hospital."

My father sat down on the front steps to think.

"The bear likes to ride in cars," I said.

"He didn't get hurt a bit," said the sheriff. "We're going to give him part of the reward."

Several children gathered around the sheriff's car to look at the bear that had helped capture the bank robbers. The bear yawned and went to sleep on the back seat.

"He came back from the circus," I said, "but we can't keep him."

"I saw Judge Holt at the prison hospital," Sheriff Jones continued, sitting on the steps beside my father. "The judge doesn't see why the town can't give this bear a special license."

"By George!" said my father. "That's good of the judge. He's a good bear. We won't let him get loose again."

I shook the bear awake and led him back to the icehouse.

My mother was in a pleasant mood at supper that evening.

"With the two thousand dollars the sheriff is giving the bear," she said, "I think it would be a nice thing to build a comfortable enclosure for the animal in back of the orchard, with a little house for a shelter."

"We can buy him lots of marshmallows," I said.

"We might screen in the back porch too," my mother added. "I've always wanted that done."

"That might be arranged," my father said.

After supper the bear and I sat down on the steps of the back porch. After a while my father came out, carrying his ukulele. He patted the bear on the head.

"Son, tomorrow we'll get the bear a new collar with a shiny metal license tag," my father said.

"What will we do with him when winter comes?" I asked.

"He can sleep in the icehouse," said my father. "It will be dark and quiet in there. Fairfield is very proud of this bear and we must take good care of him."

"Yes, sir," I said.

Then my father began singing Oh, Dear, Are You Lonesome Tonight? while the bear and I sat and listened to him. My father had a pleasant voice to listen to, and I always knew he was happy when he sang.

A Bear Joins the Family

1. What is unusual about the way the bear's first appearance is described in the story? Point out other places in the story where you particularly enjoyed the author's "deadpan" tone in describing strange happenings.

2. When could you first tell that the father was in favor of keeping the bear? How did the rest of the family line up on this question?

3. Why did the father want a license for the bear? Why was it refused? Why did the judge later change his attitude?

4. When did you first learn that the bear liked to ride in cars? What importance does this fact have later in the story?

5. Twice the father tried to get rid of the bear. What were the occasions?

6. How did the father's ukulele playing reflect ups and downs in the bear's standing in the family and the community? What kind of person is this father? Illustrate your answer by pointing out examples of his behavior toward his young son, his wife, and the townspeople.

Explore the Full Meaning of Words

When the father and son took the bear into the woods, the bear ambled along quietly. The author says the bear "gave no obvious acknowledgment of any change in environment," that is, he did not seem to notice any change in his location. *Environment* is a common word, one that has more meaning than is sometimes recognized. *Environs* means "the surrounding parts." Most often the word is used to mean the outlying districts, or suburbs, of a city. But when this word is expanded into *environment*, it takes on a fuller meaning. A person's environment is made up of all the things, conditions, people, and events that surround (or influence) him. What is meant when we say that a young criminal came from a "bad environment"? How would you describe the environment of the boy in "The Lonesome Bear"?

Mr. Chairman

FRANK B. GILBRETH, JR., AND
ERNESTINE GILBRETH CAREY

When Dad and Mother decided to operate a family on democratic principles they opened the gate to twelve votes. For this was the famous Gilbreth family, whose story has become a national favorite through the book *Cheaper by the Dozen*. It was a family that had fun living together, though for the children life was sometimes complicated by their parents' new ideas. Dad was an efficiency expert. His specialty was to study the ways that jobs were performed in factories and then suggest faster, more efficient methods of work. Mother was a psychologist who advised employers how to help make their employees happier, healthier workers. Dad and Mother, as you'll see from this account, often tried out their ideas at home.

OUR house was too big for Tom Grieves, the handyman, and Mrs. Cunningham, the cook, to keep in order. Dad decided we children were going to have to help them, and he wanted us to offer the help of our own accord. He had found that the best way to get co-operation out of employees in a factory was to set up a joint employer–employee board, which would make work assignments on a basis of personal choice and aptitude. He and Mother set up a Family Council, patterned after an employer–employee board. The council met every Sunday afternoon, immediately after dinner.

At the first session, Dad got to his feet formally, poured a glass of ice water, and began a speech.

"You will notice," he said, "that I am installed here as your chairman. I assume there are no objections. The chair, hearing no objections, will . . ."

"Mr. Chairman," Anne interrupted. Being in high school, she knew something of parliamentary procedure,[1] and thought it might be a good idea to have the chairman represent the common people.

"Out of order," said Dad. "Very much out of order when the chair has the floor."

"But you said you heard no objections, and I want to object."

"Out of order means sit down, and you're out of order," Dad

[1] If you are not sure just what **parliamentary procedure** means, read "Words in Meetings" on page 107 before you go ahead with the story.

shouted. He took a swallow of ice water, and resumed his speech. " The first job of the Council is to apportion necessary work in the house and yard. Does the chair hear any suggestions? "

There were no suggestions. Dad forced a smile and attempted to radiate good humor.

" Come, come, fellow members of the Council," he said. " This is a democracy. Everybody has an equal voice. How do you want to divide the work? "

No one wanted to divide the work or otherwise be associated with it in any way, shape, or form. No one said anything.

" In a democracy everybody speaks," said Dad, " so, by jingo, start speaking." The Good Humor Man was gone now. " Jack, I recognize you. What do you think about dividing the work? I warn you, you'd better think something."

" I think," Jack said slowly, " that Mrs. Cunningham and Tom should do the work. They get paid for it."

" Sit down," Dad hollered. " You are no longer recognized."

Jack sat down amid general approval, except that of Dad and Mother.

" Hush, Jackie," Mother whispered. " They may hear you and leave. It's so hard to get servants when there are so many children in the house."

" I wish they would leave," said Jack. " They're too bossy."

Dan was next recognized by the chair.

" I think Tom and Mrs. Cunningham have enough to do," he said, as Dad and Mother beamed and nodded agreement. " I think we should hire more people to work for us."

" Out of order," Dad shouted. " Sit down and be quiet! "

Dad saw things weren't going right. Mother was the psychologist. Let her work them out.

" Your chairman recognizes the assistant chairman," he said, nodding to Mother to let her know he had just conferred that title upon her person.

" We could hire additional help," Mother said, " and that might be the answer."

We grinned and nudged each other.

" But," she continued, " that would mean cutting the budget somewhere else. If we cut out all desserts and allowances, we could afford a maid. And if we cut out moving pictures, ice cream sodas, and new clothes for a whole year, we could afford a gardener, too."

" Do I hear a motion to that effect? " Dad beamed. " Does anybody want to stop allowances? "

No one did. After some prodding by Dad, the motion on allotting work finally was introduced and passed. The boys would cut the grass and rake the leaves. The girls would sweep, dust, and do the supper dishes. Everyone except Dad would make his own bed and keep his room neat. When it came to apportioning work on an aptitude basis, the smaller girls were assigned to dust the legs and lower shelves of furniture; the older girls to dust table tops and upper shelves. The older boys would push the lawn mowers and carry leaves. The younger ones would do the raking and weeding.

The next Sunday, when Dad convened the second meeting of the Council, we sat self-consciously around the table, biding our time. The chairman knew something was in the air, and it tickled him. He had trouble keeping a straight face when he called for new business.

Martha, who had been carefully coached in private caucus,[1] arose.

"It has come to the attention of the membership," she began, "that the assistant chairman intends to buy a new rug for the dining room. Since the entire membership will be required to look upon, and sit in chairs resting upon, the rug, I move that the Council be consulted before any rug is purchased."

"Second the motion," said Anne.

Dad didn't know what to make of this one. "Any discussion?" he asked, in a move designed to kill time while he planned his counter-attack.

"Mr. Chairman," said Lillian. "We have to sweep it. We should be able to choose it."

"We want one with flowers on it," Martha put in. "When you have flowers, the crumbs don't show so easily, and you save motions by not having to sweep so often."

---

[1] caucus (kô′kŭs): a meeting of leaders to decide on policies before appearing before a general meeting.

"We want to know what sort of a rug the assistant chairman intends to buy," said Ernestine.

"We want to make sure the budget can afford it," Fred announced.

"I recognize the assistant chairman," said Dad. "This whole Council business was your idea anyway, Lillie. What do we do now?"

"Well," Mother said doubtfully, "I had planned to get a plain violet-colored rug, and I had planned to spend a hundred dollars. But if the children think that's too much, and if they want flowers, I'm willing to let the majority rule."

"I move," said Frank, "that not more than ninety-five dollars be spent."

Dad shrugged his shoulders. If Mother didn't care, he certainly didn't.

"So many as favor the motion to spend only ninety-five dollars, signify by saying aye."

The motion carried unanimously.

"Any more new business?"

"I move," said Bill, "that we spend the five dollars we have saved to buy a collie puppy."

"Hey, wait a minute," said Dad. The rug had been somewhat of a joke, but the dog question was serious. We had wanted a dog for years. Dad thought that any pet which didn't lay eggs was an extravagance that a man with twelve children could ill afford. He felt that if he surrendered on the dog question, there was no telling what the Council might vote next. He had a sickening mental picture of a barn full of ponies, a roadster for Anne, motorcycles, a swimming pool, and, ultimately, the poorhouse or a debtors' prison, if they still had such things.

"Second the motion," said Lillian, yanking Dad out of his reverie.

"A dog," said Jack, "would be a pet. Everyone in the family could pat him, and I would be his master."

"A dog," said Dan, "would be a friend. He could eat scraps of food. He would save us waste and would save motions for the garbage man."

"A dog," said Fred, "would keep burglars away. He would sleep on the foot of my bed, and I would wash him whenever he was dirty."

"A dog," Dad mimicked, "would be an accursed nuisance. He would be our master. He would eat me out of house and home. He would spread fleas from the garret to the porte-cochere.[1] He would be positive to sleep on the foot of *my* bed. Nobody would wash his filthy, dirty, flea-bitten carcass."

He looked pleadingly at Mother.

"Lillie, Lillie, open your eyes," he implored. "Don't you see where this is leading us? Ponies, roadsters, trips to Hawaii, silk stockings, rouge, and bobbed hair."

"I think, dear," said Mother, "that we must rely on the good sense of the children. A five-dollar dog is not a trip to Hawaii."

We voted, and there was only one negative ballot — Dad's. Mother ab-

stained.[2] In after years, as the collie grew older, shed hair on the furniture, bit the mailman, and did in fact try to appropriate[3] the foot of Dad's bed, the chairman was heard to remark on occasion to the assistant chairman:

"I give nightly praise to my Maker that I never cast a ballot to bring that lazy, disreputable, ill-tempered beast into what was once my home. I'm glad I had the courage to go on record as opposing that shameless flea-bag that now shares my bed and board. You abstainer, you!"

Family Council in Action

1. Where did Dad get the idea for a family council? What was the particular problem he hoped to solve by it?

2. Compare Dad's methods with Mother's during the first meeting of the council. Whose were more successful? Do you know what a psychologist is? How did Mother prove herself a good psychologist with her family?

3. When the household jobs were passed out it was done on an "aptitude basis," that is, each child did what he was best able to do. How did the jobs the Gilbreth children performed carry out this idea?

4. In the second meeting of the family council how did the children use their votes to obtain what they wanted? Why did they bring up the subject of the rug first?

Words in Meetings

If you have not already had some experience with holding meetings in proper parliamentary order, you will certainly have it in high school. All the most useful

[1] **porte-cochere** (pōrt′kō·shâr′): A porch under which a vehicle may be driven to protect the people going from it into the house.

[2] **abstained:** here, did not vote.

[3] **appropriate** (ă·prō′prĭ·āt) looks like a familiar adjective, but pronounced this way it is a verb meaning "to take over for one's own use."

terms used in meetings occur in this story of the Gilbreth family council. The *chairman* refers to himself as *the chair*. He *recognizes* a speaker and then the speaker *has the floor*. Anyone who interrupts that speaker is *out of order*. (Dad used this term too freely!) The chairman is supposed to ask whether there are any *objections* before he announces that there are none. When discussion leads toward a certain decision, the chairman asks, as Dad did, " *Do I hear a motion to that effect?* " The person who puts a motion before the meeting says properly " *I move that — ,*" not " *I make a motion — *" as careless peo-

ple sometimes do. Then someone else must *second* the motion, or it dies. After discussion, the chair puts the motion to a vote by asking those *in favor* to *signify by saying aye* (or *opposed, no*). If you do not want to vote either aye or no, you may *abstain* from voting, as Mother did on the motion to buy a dog.

For practice in using these terms, let different members of the class take the parts of the speakers and read the dialogue of the family council meetings aloud. Then try to use the correct terms in your next club meeting, or organize your English class and practice these procedures.

Maudie Tom, Jockey

GLADYS HASTY CARROLL

DIFFERENT — BUT ALIKE. It's easy to see that people are all different from each other. But it takes a little more understanding to realize that all people are alike in certain important ways. Probably you have never known anyone like the girl in this story, Maudie Tom, the wild, uneducated daughter of a lighthouse keeper. If you met her in real life, how well could you judge her as a person? Would you try to understand why she acted differently from other people your age? Would you try to discover what interests and what characteristics she had in common

with you and your friends?

Reading stories is one of the best ways to become a good judge of people. You meet all kinds of people in stories, most of them with hopes and feelings and problems like your own. To read this story skillfully — and many others that you run across in the years to come — learn to watch the actions of the characters closely. Perhaps you can quickly discover the key to Maudie Tom's problem, and the real reason why she wanted desperately to win the horse race against the summer visitors.

"Maudie Tom, Jockey" by Gladys Hasty Carroll from *St. Nicholas Magazine*, September 1931. Reprinted by permission of the author.

OVERNIGHT a great white placard had appeared on the blackboard at the corner of the village street. Pictures of horses were pasted all over it, and there was printing at the bottom. Maudie Tom, crouched low on Bess's back, stared at it for a long time. Then she tugged on her reins and cantered into the bustling, crowded square.

She was a strange figure among the thronging summer guests of the little town. College-girl waitresses, off duty for a few hours, hopped on bare pink feet toward the beach, pulling off blue-and-scarlet coats as they went. Ladies in soft-colored cotton dresses wandered in and out among the little gift shops. Clean, brown children stood in sun suits before the big show-window which revealed a gigantic candy machine in operation. Men in milk-white clothes strolled about, puffing expertly at fragrant cigars. People laughed and skipped and called across from one corner to another, and drank cloudy brown and rosy sodas from tall glasses. But Maudie Tom rode grim and dark and silent through the carnival of summer; a big, bony girl with ragged black hair, blue overalls, and a secure seat on her vicious, prancing horse.

When she attempted to draw up before the post office, the beast flung her head about and leaped forward. Maudie Tom sawed economically but inexorably [1] at the ugly, uplifted mouth.

"Stand, will you!" said Maudie Tom. "Hey, Bill!"

A man leaning against a building thrust his hat up from his eyes and looked at her. There was no friendliness between them — only recognition and a certain similarity of feature.

"They going to have the races again, ain't they?" called Maudie Tom, steady hands on the reins.

"Sure. What do you care?"

"When they going to have them?"

"Labor Day, of course."

"When's that?" persisted Maudie Tom. "You know I can't tell."

The man shifted his position and figured silently. Neither face had altered even faintly in expression.

"A week from Monday, that is," said the man.

Maudie Tom jerked on the reins. The horse had sagged in sleep and now awoke more irritable than ever. She reared slightly. Maudie Tom sat tight.

"How's Pa?" asked the man.

"Oh, he's all right," said Maudie Tom, laconically. [2]

A group of girls walking with linked arms down the boardwalk watched her gallop away. "How she can ride!" one of them said.

"I always wonder what goes on inside her head," another added.

"Hasn't she a marvelous build, though!" said a third. "Sinewy as an Indian."

Maudie Tom had seen them from

---

[1] **inexorably** (ĭn·ĕk′sō·rȧ·blĭ): without softening or yielding.

[2] **laconically** (lȧ·kŏn′ĭ·kȧl·ĭ): using no unnecessary words.

the corner of her eye, their crisp piqué dresses, their smooth hair knotted at their necks, but she did not know what they said of her. She only imagined, and imagining soon made her mouth grow hard with bitterness and sulking. She sat forward and urged her mount with a boot-heel sharp on a red hind quarter.

"We'll show them, you old fool of a horse," she growled, "come a week from Monday."

Fourteen years and a half ago, one December, Maudie Tom, the light-house keeper's daughter, had been born in the small, snugly built house on the island a half-mile off the coast. A storm raged at the time; the strip of water between the island and the mainland was too rough for doctors to cross. The mother died, but the baby lived, and was named Maudie Tom — nobody knew why.

She grew up on the island with her father and a lazy, surly brother who appeared occasionally, when no more convivial [1] roof would shelter him. She drank goat's milk and ate hen's eggs; she ran in the sun and grew as big and strong as a boy. The room where she slept looked out on the water, across the path of the signal light; she learned to trim the lamp herself. Fogs drifted in, storms blew out of the northeast. She heard distress signals, saw rocket flares, once made coffee for a rescued crew. Sometimes she lay all day on a shelf rock that nobody knew of but herself. Gray gulls dipped and soared; her fingers played with wet, dark

[1] convivial (kŏn·vĭv'ĭ·ǎl): festive, gay.

green seaweed; wind could not reach her; it grew warm, and she slept.

When she was nine, officials came to ask if she had been sent to school. She had not. The officials pursed their lips and shook their heads.

"She's got an aunt," her father said, "up to Portland. She can go up there to get her schooling. I been meaning to send her right along. A young one ain't much these days without an education."

But Maudie Tom was well past ten before she went, and then she stayed only two weeks. She did not like Portland. She could not find her way about; her aunt, and the teacher, too, had whipped her. She ran away home, and her father slapped her on the shoulder and they laughed together. When the officials came again, faintly seasick from their brief boat ride across the choppy sea, her father said that Maudie Tom was fourteen. It was not true, but she was large for her age, and after a fourteenth birthday education was not compulsory in Maine. Maudie Tom had come back to the island, and she meant to stay. It was part of her, and she loved it as she loved no other thing.

Her father, in his glee, bought her a horse and built a stable for it beside their little boat house on the mainland. Nearly every day when the weather was fine she rowed over, with short, rapid movements of her strong dark arms, and mounted Bess, to tear away through the village and up into the rocky, pine-covered hills, her hair blowing back in the wind, and salt water dripping off her boots. But she was not happy.

She was not happy because of the city people who came every summer. She saw perfumed women who looked to her like the brisk, neat little Portland teacher who had struck her with a ruler seven times on the hand. She saw men who lay, clean and smiling, on the sands, reading newspapers. Little children played games together — games that Maudie Tom had never played. But it seemed to her that more than half the people she saw in the village, summertimes, were girls of fourteen and fifteen. Even in the dead of winter, when storm winds rocked her bed, she could see the faces of the girls who came to the Cape in summer. Laughing faces with small, sunburned noses and cool, appraising eyes. She could see their figures in bathing suits, or in dresses that were sometimes rumpled but never soiled. She remembered the books and magazines old Aunt Maggie Dennis, from the fisher colony, found in their rooms when she cleaned the cottages at the end of the season. They had pictures, all of girls, and all beautiful. In the winter nights she thought of them.

"I hate them kids," thought Maudie Tom.

She did not hate them for being so different from herself, but only because of the opinion she imagined they had of her.

"They ain't so much," she told herself. "I can do a lot of things they can't. I'd like to see them ride a horse like me."

Two years ago the summer people had inaugurated the Labor Day races. Horses were bought and a community stable built. It was a friendly sport. Men practiced on the beach before breakfast, advising one another, admiring all the mounts. There were two girl riders among them, one in a brown leather jacket and tweed knickers, the other in a scarlet jockey suit with an absurd little visored cap. Maudie Tom had not gone across to town on the previous Labor Days, but she had seen the horses and their riders from her steps, where she sat ominously dour.[1]

"I could beat them," jeered Maudie Tom, "even if Bess balked, the old fool of a horse."

This year she meant to try. It had taken a tremendous amount of self-persuasion, for she feared these summer visitors as much as she envied and hated them.

The horses came, and a fine, rich scent of well-kept horseflesh made Bess lift her upper lip and prance and neigh.

"Never mind being so friendly," scolded Maudie Tom. "You've got them all to beat in the races!"

Now the poster had appeared, spattered with the heads of handsome horses and decorated with the complete outline of a beautiful bay mare at full stride, her neck stretched out in ecstasy of effort. It was time for the trial.

"You ain't got so much looks,"

[1] **ominously dour** (ŏm′ĭ·nŭs·lĭ dŏŏr): threateningly sullen in expression.

said Maudie Tom, buckling a strap about Bess's head, "but looks ain't everything."

Still, she trimmed the mane and tail of her mount on Labor Day morning. She brushed the straight back, rubbed down the wide, veined flanks and bulging joints, and even tied a bit of dirty ribbon on the thick black forelock. Maudie Tom herself wore a clean dress from the store — a cheap little print with the wild, glaring figures usually seen in smocks, which became her wonderfully well.

It was a cool, bright, windy day. Maudie Tom and Bess went out into the sun together, down along the coast, through the town, and up to the beach where the races were held. Men already stood about with flags and pistols; other horses had arrived, stepping high with dainty legs, twitching pleasurably with every thunderous crash of rolling breakers.

"I want to get into the races," said Maudie Tom to a man who held an open book.

"You want — "

He broke off and stepped aside to address another man. Only members of the Jockey Club were expected for the races, but Maudie Tom did not know this. Women and girls and children were approaching from all directions. The two girl jockeys, one in blue and white this year, and one in yellow leather, stared curiously.

"All right, miss," said the man of the notebook, returning. "Glad to have you. What's your name?"

"Maudie Tom."

"Maud — Well, what else?"

"I don't — Oh, Tibbetts."

"Maud Tibbetts. And the horse?"

"Huh?"

"The horse's name?"

"Bess."

"All right, Miss Tibbetts. We start the trial heats [1] in about half an hour. I'll let you know when you're listed. Stand just over there, will you, Miss Tibbetts?"

The recurrence of "Miss Tibbetts" annoyed Maudie Tom. She sat, big and glowering, on the folded blanket which served her as a saddle. When the other two girl jockeys came up with proffered sugar, both horse and rider waited with suspicion. Maudie Tom did not speak, and Bess snapped at their fingers.

"Ouch," said the girl in blue and white. She smiled at Maudie Tom. "Unfriendly beast you have."

"Leave her alone; she's all right," growled Maudie Tom.

Inside her another prouder, more fiercely wretched voice was saying: "You can leave me alone, too. You needn't try to make out you're so much. I'm going to beat you!"

What she was thinking showed in her face. The girls drew away. "Whew!" exclaimed one. "Isn't she marvelous, though? What wouldn't Miss Kincaid make out of her if she had a chance? That girl's got stuff!" And the other said: "She's a lot of pluck to turn up here with that beast. She fascinates me." But Maudie Tom

[1] **Trial heats** are preliminary races to determine which contestants may enter the main race.

did not hear what they said. She only saw their incredulous, faintly injured faces, and the curls escaping under their caps.

A broad, white strip of hard sand, the race track, divided the two streams of onlookers.

Nine horses were entered. The officials divided them into three groups for the trial heats, and Bess was number two of the first. A man with snow-white hair and pink cheeks pinned a great "2" on Maudie Tom's back. She headed Bess into line, her heart pounding under the huge flowers stamped on her dress. On one side of her was a grinning boy on a young sorrel horse, and on the other the leather-jacketed girl, riding a steed which looked as swift as ever Lochinvar's was. Both riders smiled at Maudie Tom and waved to friends on the sidelines, but Maudie Tom did not smile back and she had no friends to wave to.

She crouched low on Bess's high, unlovely back.

The pistol cracked. The horses leaped forward. At the sound Bess had pawed the air in nervousness and bad temper, and set out a length behind the others. Her gait was awkward and gangling. She threw out her feet like brown spray to each side of her step. She kicked her hind left ankle with her right and left a trail of blood in the sand. The other horses ran swift and straight, tails lifted, manes flying, noses in the air. But the girl in yellow leather let her mount break from his smooth trot into a gallop, and so was disqualified. The boy who grinned so engagingly was riding for the first time in a race; he did not know where to bear his weight or when to urge his horse. Maudie Tom rode like a part of Bess — two big, bony, untamed things together, the girl's face close to the corded red neck, her voice quick with unintelligible sounds, her boot heel a sharp, firm pressure. The red horse beat the sorrel by half a length.

"Two!" yelled the judges in good-humored amazement. What of their blooded stables now?

"Good!" cried the boy.

"Splendid!" sang out the yellow-jacketed girl, cantering up. " What *riding!* Simply magnificent! "

Clapping ran along the lines. To the summer people these races added a charming interest to their last day. Having the picturesque daughter of the lighthouse keeper entered gave new color to a familiar excitement. They rather hoped she would win the finals, and they clapped and smiled encouragement. Maudie Tom scarcely looked at them. She was now one of the three best. She had won the first race!

" You wait. I'll show you something yet," she told them under her breath. " You think you know it all."

Her heart thumped as if it would tear through her breast. She dismounted, led Bess far up the beach, and made her walk in the salt water, to cleanse the wounded ankle. The sound of other pistol shots and more clapping reached them. When they returned, the girl in blue and white, on a coal-black mare, and a fat, little bald-headed man on a fiery gray horse, had won the two other races. They sat waiting, a Number 1 and a Number 2. Some one changed Maudie Tom's number to a 3.

" You got to do it," choked Maudie Tom. " You go it, you old fool of a horse! You got to win! "

But she could not win — it was absurd! Dusky Dart was four years old, daughter of His Majesty, and had done six furlongs in 1:15 [1] many times. Gray Skies was a three-year-old with a pedigree that filled a

pigeonhole.[2] Bess was twenty, if a day — badly built, untrained, and nobody had ever dreamed of recording her parentage.

The pistol cracked — they were off! Maudie Tom rode as an eagle flies; her hair blew back, and her strong body held itself as light as a feather. But Dusky Dart went past and Gray Skies' tail flicked Bess's nose. The crowd roared, the breakers boiled and foamed, the tape broke — with Dusky Dart the winner, the blue-and-white girl on her back. Gray Skies had been a three-quarter length behind. Maudie Tom let Bess into a walk twenty paces back.

The white-haired, pink-faced man tied blue ribbons on Dusky Dart's mane and tail. Blue sky, blue water, blue ribbons, and laughter. Maudie Tom thought she could not bear it.

" Get up," she breathed in Bess's ear. " Get out of here before that leg goes lame. Get up! "

They galloped off together, as if making an escape. She heard hoofs behind, and urged Bess faster.

" Go on, you! "

But again Dusky Dart proved the better horse. The girl in blue and white overtook Maudie Tom and crossed before her, so that she had to stop.

" Where are you going? " she asked. She, too, had straight hair, but it was yellow, and her cheeks were soft. " You must come back and get your ribbon."

---

[1] **six furlongs in 1:15:** about three-fourths of a mile in one minute and fifteen seconds.

[2] **pigeonhole:** a small open compartment for papers in a desk.

"Ribbon?" echoed Maudie Tom dully.

"Yes, the green one. Third prize, you know. Come on."

The girl in blue and white reached for Bess's rein and turned her around. They rode back together, side by side.

"I'm Carolyn Kincaid," the girl said. "I think you're marvelous. I'd give anything in the world if I could ride the way you do."

Maudie Tom lifted her head and looked full at Carolyn. Her eyes were asking. She did not think she could have heard rightly.

"You live over at the lighthouse, don't you?" asked the other.

Maudie Tom nodded.

"Do you stay there all the time?"

Maudie Tom nodded again.

"Because I'm going to live here with my aunt until at least November. I'm supposed to stay outdoors a lot. My aunt's a teacher, but she's taking a leave of absence. I wonder — you know, you don't have to say you will — but I wonder if you'd want to teach me more about riding while I'm here. Would you?"

Maudie Tom swallowed. She wanted to speak, but she could think of no words to use. Finally she nodded once more.

Carolyn bounced up and down in glee.

"Oh, good! And listen, will you take me over to the island some time?"

This time Maudie Tom managed, "Sure!"

"Really? What fun! Do you know,

I'm beginning to be *glad* I'm staying. You must come and meet my aunt. About my riding lessons — we'll want to pay you, of course. Or — is there anything you want to learn that we could teach you?"

"Teach me?" said Maudie Tom with a comical, confidential movement of her eyebrows. "I don't know anything!"

They reached the judges, and the white-haired man replaced Bess's dirty ribbon with crisp green ones. He stroked the thin old nose and spoke gently. Bess did not snap at him, but looked up softly out of wondering, chastened eyes.

Understanding Characters in Stories

1. In the first part of the story, what was your feeling toward Maudie Tom? At what later point did your opinion of her change? What led to the change of opinion?

2. What did you learn about Maudie Tom's earlier life and her family that helped to explain why she was different from other girls?

3. Test your ability to understand a person who is "different" by figuring out why it seemed to Maudie Tom that most of the summer visitors were girls about her own age, and why she thought she hated them.

4. Was it partly Maudie Tom's own fault that she did not have friends? Point out incidents that support your answer.

5. Was Maudie Tom's attitude toward Bess different from her attitude toward people? What special meaning does Bess's response to the judge's stroking have in the story?

6. Would it have been better for Maudie Tom if she had won the race? Why do you think so? Is this ending a happy one for her?

First Flight

LOUISE McNEILL

When I was quite little and played on the hill
One wondrous evening — I dream of it still —
Mom called me to dinner — impatient, I knew —
So I lifted my arms up and flapped them and flew.

I lifted my arms up and flapped them, and, lo!   5
I was flying as fast as my short wings could go.
The hill swirled beneath me all golden and green.
I lit by the yard fence, and no one had seen.

I told them at dinner. I said, " I can fly."
They laughed, not believing. I started to cry   10
And ran from the table. I sobbed, " It is true.
You need not believe me; I flapped and I flew."

I told them next morning; I told them again.
For years I kept telling; they laughed and I ran.
No one would believe me; I stopped then, to tell;   15
But still I remembered, remember it well.

Believing in Dreams

1. Is this the way most families treat a small child's report of a vivid daydream? Explain why you think it is the right or wrong way.

2. Can you remember a dream of your own that seemed real? Did you tell it to your family? How did they treat your story? How did you feel? Suggest better ways to handle this situation.

"First Flight" by Louise McNeill from *The Saturday Evening Post*, December 10, 1949, Reprinted by permission of the author.

Family
and
Friends

Tailoring

Out of Knee Pants

EMILE C. SCHURMACHER

A generation ago boys wore knickers, or knee pants, until they were nearly as tall as their fathers. For them the change into long pants was a tremendous event, visible proof that at last a boy had become a young man. But only *one* suit of " longies " could leave a boy with a serious problem on his hands. You'll laugh at Emile's attempt to solve his problem, but you have a heart of stone if you do not sympathize with him, as well.

Herbie and I got our first longies about a week before we started high school. Father hadn't been easy to win over. He said that if Herbie's father wanted to get him longies that was his business and anyhow Herbie was at least a head taller than I. But Mother helped me. She told Father that there was just no telling when and where a fellow might need long pants when he went to high school.

As soon as Father yielded, Mother took me to Franklin Simon's store on Fifth Avenue. The clerk had to do considerable searching through his stock for sizes small enough to fit me. He was quick about it though. With the air of a magician pulling a rab-

bit out of a hat he removed a suit of gray worsted from a rack and held it out for our admiration.

Mother and I liked it on sight. It had a vest and two pairs of pants. The clerk rolled up the legs of one pair of pants and showed me where the dressing room was so that I could try the suit on.

When I came out of the dressing room Mother choked up and dabbed at her eyes with a handkerchief. The clerk nodded sympathetically and remarked that many of his customers reacted the same way. It took the first pair of long trousers to make mothers realize that their sons had grown up.

" He's starting high school this term," Mother said. " De Witt Clinton."

I tried to appear nonchalant [1] as the tailor went over me with tape, chalk, and pins. Herbie had advised me to instruct the tailor to pleat my pants like the Prince of Wales'. But the tailor was so busy tucking in and pulling up I thought I'd better not complicate matters.

[1] **nonchalant** (nŏn'shá·lănt): casual and unconcerned.

When he had finished, the clerk promised that the suit would be delivered in time for me to wear that Saturday. He asked Mother if he could show us some other suits. She said that the gray worsted would do for the present.

I could hardly wait for the suit to arrive. It came early on Saturday morning just as the clerk had promised. I put it on with my new necktie in college colors and a pair of socks I carefully selected from several that Mother had bought for me. Both of us had forgotten all about garters to hold up the socks but Mother gave me the extra pair she found in Father's bureau.

Father, himself, took a look at me between calls and said that I looked just fine even if some neighbors would think that he had taken in a midget for a boarder.

Herbie called for me and showed me how to arrange an extra handkerchief so that it would stick out of the breast pocket with three points. Then we took a walk down Fifth Avenue so that people could admire us.

Herbie told me that the blue serge suit of longies that he was wearing was only his Sunday suit. His father had also bought him a brown suit with extra pants to wear during the week when he would be attending Stuyvesant High School. He asked me about the color of my other suit. I told him that Mother had bought me only one suit of longies, the one I had on.

It was then that the terrible realization dawned on me. My parents hadn't bought me longies to wear for good. They had bought me a once-in-a-while suit. With it I could be a grown man on week ends and holidays. But when Monday and school rolled around I'd have to be a kid again.

That night I tried to convince my parents of the imminent tragedy of leading a double life in longies and in knee pants. Father was adamant and his arguments unanswerable. He pointed out that I had been pestering him for a long time to get me longies. He had promised to do so when I started going to high school. He had faithfully kept his promise.

But, he added, he was not made of money. I had several good knee-pants suits in my closet. When they began to wear out he would replace them with longies. But positively no more long-pants suits would be bought with his money until I wore out the others.

Father had me neatly trapped. I could wear my new gray worsted every day if I wished. That decision was up to me. If I wore it out, however, those knee-panters would still be waiting in the closet. Reluctantly I decided that the longies would have to be once-in-a-whilers. I started off to high school wearing knee pants.

De Witt Clinton was an adventurous distance from home. It was all the way over on Tenth Avenue and Fifty-ninth Street. There were several ways to get there. One was to take the Madison Avenue trolley down to Fifty-ninth Street and transfer to a crosstown trolley. Another was to take a trolley through the transverse in Central Park at Eighty-fifth Street and transfer at Eighth Avenue. Then I had to get out at Columbus Circle and walk two long blocks to Tenth Avenue.

I preferred the second way of going. Although the block between Ninth and Tenth Avenue was full of hospitals and uninteresting, the one between Columbus Circle and Ninth Avenue was one through which I enjoyed walking. It had several pawnshops in whose windows all sorts of fascinating objects were jumbled. It had a butcher shop which advertised odd food like " hog maw " and " chittlins " painted on the window in large white letters. It had little restaurants whose doorways emitted strange fried smells.

The change from grade to high school was in itself an exciting experience. A lot of the fellows wore long pants. But whether they did or didn't, the teachers all treated us as though we were really grown up. My biology teacher even called me " Mister."

Instead of sitting in one classroom as I had done in grade school I now moved around to different classes each period when the bell rang. This made me feel responsible to myself instead of to a teacher as I had at grade school.

It was a nice, independent feeling. I didn't have to go to the cafeteria on the top floor during my lunch period if I didn't want to. I could go to a restaurant outside of the building.

At first, delighted with this new-found freedom, I dined in splendor at Thompson's Cafeteria on Columbus Circle. Father had decided to give me an allowance of thirty-five cents a day for school days and an extra dollar to take care of movies and entertainment on Saturdays and Sundays.

This was ample. After deducting ten cents for carfare I could get a big meal at Thompson's. Frankfurters and beans, bread and butter and milk came to twenty cents. This left a nickel over for either dessert or coffee.

One morning on my way to school I was walking west from Columbus Circle looking into the store windows as usual when I noticed something new in the window of Mahoney's Pawnshop. It was a blue suit with long pants.

Somebody, evidently in a hurry, had hung it on the window curtain pole so that the neck of the banjo beneath it stuck up one leg. Pinned to it was a scrawled sign reading: " Natty-$7-Cridit."

I went up to it and made a closer examination. It wasn't just blue the way Herbie's blue serge suit was. Even on the shady side of the street it was a bright, vivid blue. The coat was thrown back so that I could see the vest beneath. The vest claimed my attention immediately. It had little lapels on it!

I stared at them. This, I told myself, was something that would really bowl over Herbie if he could see it. With all his talk about a Prince of Wales pleat in his pants he wasn't the snappiest dresser in the world. But I would be. When Father finally gave in and consented to buy me another suit of longies I'd ask for one with lapels on my vest.

Then an inspiration hit me. Why not get this one? Suppose I was able to buy it on credit out of my allowance and wear it every day to school? Then with my gray worsted for Saturdays and Sundays I'd be in longies for good.

Spurred with enthusiasm I went into the store and up to the man behind the pawnshop cage. He looked sleepy and in need of a shave. Before I could speak he shook his head.

"Minors,"[1] he said sternly, "ain't allowed to hock anything."

"I don't want to hock anything, Mr. Mahoney," I said.

"Mahoney, he calls me!" He said accusingly, "My name's Dill. There

---

[1] **Minors:** young people under the age of twenty-one.

ain't no Mahoney. What do you want?"

"I'd like to look at the suit you have in the window, Mr. Dill," I said.

"So why can't your poppa come?" he asked suspiciously.

I told him that I was thinking of buying the suit for myself. He got it out of the window and laid it on the counter. It looked very blue.

"Will it fit me?" I asked dubiously.

"Sure," said Mr. Dill with conviction.

"What about the pants?" I asked.

"Right from off'n the legs of a big bank president who was a natty dresser," he said.

122

I asked him what he meant by credit.

"I mean seven dollars," said Mr. Dill, "five dollars down and a dollar a week. I can't let this here suit especially imported from Paris, France, for a big bank president go for a penny less."

"Oh," I said disappointed, "I thought that maybe I could make other arrangements."

Now I knew why the vest had lapels. It was a French suit. I wondered who the bank president was for whom it had been imported and how it had come to be on sale in the store. Maybe the bank president needed money badly and had to pawn the suit.

It didn't do me any good to wonder. I started out of the store.

"Wait a minute," said Mr. Dill. "How much will you pay for this beautiful suit?"

I said that I thought I could give him fifty cents a week. He scratched his face reflectively. I looked at the clock on the wall behind him and saw that I'd have to hurry if I didn't want to be late to class.

"I have to go to school now, Mr. Dill," I said. "I'll be back to see you after school."

"Oh, a student," he said. "That makes a difference. In Odessa[1] onct I was a poor student too. Only I never got enough to eat. How much money you got on you now?"

I told Mr. Dill I hadn't expected to buy a suit when I started off for

---

[1] **Odessa** (ô·dĕs′ȧ): seaport on the Black Sea, in the U.S.S.R.

school that morning. All I had with me was my quarter for lunch money and a nickel for carfare home.

He showed his disappointment by making a face as if he had just sucked a lemon. I knew that he wanted to help me, however. He held me by the sleeve when I started to leave.

"Iff'n I put the suit back in the window again somebody'll snap it right up," he said. "You give me a quarter now for a deposit to hold it till after school. Then we'll figger a cridit for you and you can have the suit."

That sounded fair to me. I gave Mr. Dill my quarter and hurried to school tremendously pleased with myself.

The first period was biology. Our teacher, Mr. Tietz, spent it explaining about the stamen and pistil of flowers. While he was drawing a picture of a hollyhock and a bee on the blackboard I had a chance to do some figuring in my notebook. I estimated that by eating two hamburgers and a glass of milk, costing fifteen cents, for lunch for only fourteen weeks I could pay Mr. Dill fifty cents a week easy. It wasn't even a full fourteen weeks because I had already given him twenty-five cents. I could do it all on the weekday allowance without dipping into my week-end dollar at all.

When lunch period came I was hungry. I debated whether or not I should spend my remaining nickel on a candy bar and hitch home on a truck. I decided against it. If by good luck Mr. Dill would let me wear the suit it wouldn't look dignified to hitch on a truck or even the back of an automobile. Once I started wearing longies for good, I resolved, I'd give up all hitching.

I spent my lunch period in the study hall reading a book to avoid the temptation of buying a candy bar. I pretended to myself that I was a poor hungry student like Mr. Dill in Odessa without enough to eat.

I *was* a little hungry after lunch period when I attended classes. But as soon as school was over, in my excitement I forgot all about it and hurried off to the pawnshop.

Mr. Dill was waiting. The suit was still on the counter right where he had left it.

"I've been fixing up your cridit," he said. "I can allow you two dollars for the suit you have on. You paid me twenty-five cents down. So all you have to pay me is $5.25 or fifty cents every week."

"But that comes to $7.50, Mr. Dill," I said. "The suit is marked $7.00."

"Sure it's marked," he said, "but cridit costs too. It costs you fifty cents. Besides I'm losing heavy by allowing you two dollars on the old suit you're wearing because you remind me about the time I was a poor student. Try on the suit."

I went behind the counter and put it on. The waist of the pants came up to my armpits but the vest hid that when I put it on. The pants legs were much too long and so were the sleeves. Even Mr. Dill ad-

mitted that I couldn't wear the suit home.

"For another dollar," he said, "I can take the suit home and have my wife shorten the sleeves and pants tonight."

"Well," I said doubtfully, "it isn't just the sleeves and the pants. The suit is big on me all around."

I was getting into financial complications deeper than I had anticipated. Besides I suspected that Father would be angry if I sold my old suit to Mr. Dill for two dollars.

"Of course the suit is roomy all around," Mr. Dill exploded. "When you put on long pants you also start to put on weight. What kind of a guy would you think I am if you hadda come back here in six months or a year and say to me: 'Sam Dill, look what a tight suit you sold me.' I don't treat my customers like that!"

I saw that I had hurt Mr. Dill's feelings. Much as I wanted the suit, however, we had reached an impasse.[1] He would not let his wife shorten the pants and sleeves until I had paid him at least three dollars. At fifty cents a week this meant a wait of six weeks. I was too anxious to wait that long. It would be better to forget the whole thing.

I told Mr. Dill I was sorry I had caused him so much trouble. I explained to him that I couldn't let him have the suit I had on. I'd just have to start saving from my allowance and some day when I had enough

[1] **impasse** (ĭm·pàs'): a situation with no way out.

I'd come in and buy a suit from him.

Mr. Dill looked sad and thoughtful. He happened to look down and see the new Waterman fountain pen that Mother had given me when I started going to high school. He asked me to show it to him. Then he explained how to dissolve the impasse.

He would let me pay him fifty cents a week for seventeen weeks and meanwhile hold the fountain pen for security. At the end of that time I'd own the suit and he'd give me back my fountain pen. It was just as easy as that. He pinned up the sleeves and cuffs and promised to take the suit home to his wife that night.

On the following day after school I called at the pawnshop. Mr. Dill had the suit ready and I put it on. He nodded approvingly. " Just keep the bands on the vest tight and the coat open and you'll look wonderful, especially when you fill out a little," he told me.

I decided to wear the suit home and he tied up the one I had been wearing in newspapers.

I walked over to Columbus Circle slowly, casting sidelong glances at reflections of myself in store windows. The suit was even bluer than I had thought. In the sunlight it was sort of aquamarine, like Mother's scarf. It would be a nice contrast to my gray worsted. The pants flapped when I walked because they were so wide. But I know that Mrs. Dill couldn't have done anything about that. The bank president was probably a bigger man than she suspected.

When I got off the trolley car and started to walk down Eighty-seventh Street toward our house I suddenly felt a little panicky. How, I asked myself, was I going to explain this new suit of longies to my parents when they saw me wearing it?

I stopped in my tracks. Then I made for the nearest brownstone house, went into the areaway [1] and cautiously looked down the block. Father's car was not in sight. I walked briskly to our house, into the lobby, and to the recess behind the stairs. Our elevator boy slept there on a mattress at night. He was at the switchboard when I came in.

" Hey," he shouted, " what you want back there? "

He came around to take a look. In one hand he held the sawed-off baseball bat which he kept behind the switchboard to use against burglars.

" Oh," he said, " it's you. What you up to? "

" I want to change my clothes, Edward," I said as I opened my newspaper bundle.

" Mon! " he said, open mouthed. " Look at you all dressed up for a shindig. Where did you get that hot vest? "

" It's imported from Paris," I said. " Like my new suit? "

" Mon! "

I took Edward into my confidence and explained that I had bought the suit myself and I didn't want my

---

[1] **areaway:** an open place in a building providing air, light, and an entrance to a basement.

parents to find out about it. I told him that I wanted to leave it behind the stairs when I came home at night. In the morning before I left for school I'd change clothes and leave my knee-pants suit behind the stairs. Edward said that was all right with him so long as he wasn't responsible and I didn't stand on his mattress with muddy shoes.

For almost three weeks the system worked out fine. When I went to school in the morning I walked down the stairs and changed behind them. When I came home, instead of going through the lobby I went down the cellar through the delivery entrance and up the back stairs to the bunk. That way I was sure not to encounter my parents.

Then one day I came home as usual and went behind the staircase to change. My knee-pants suit wasn't there. I sneaked out into the lobby and called Edward.

"Where's my suit?" I asked.

"Ain't no suit," he said. "It's been swiped along with my best yaller shoes and the alarm clock that Mr. Moberly gave me to wake up early."

"Gee!" I said, shocked. "You're not fooling?"

"Somebody sneaked them off while I was up in the elevator," said Edward. "I've called the cops couple of hours ago."

"Gee!" I said again. "I better get upstairs and change before my folks come home."

"They're home," said Edward. "I took them up about half hour ago."

I went upstairs and I could hear my heart pounding as I rang the bell. Bertha answered it.

"Hello," she said. "You want milk and cookies or milk and bread with marmalade — *Donnerwetter!*[1] where did you get such a suit?"

"I'll tell you later, Bertha," I promised. "I've been robbed. I've got to change right away."

It was the wrong thing to say.

"Robbed?" Bertha shrieked. "You was held up by pandits?"

That brought Father out in the hall to see what the commotion was about. He saw me. He just stared for a few seconds. Then he told me to come into the parlor where Mother could see me too. There was a startled expression on her face.

"Now," Father said sternly, "suppose you explain the meaning of this masquerade."

"It isn't a masquerade," I protested. "It's an imported French suit of longies that I'm buying from Mr. Dill on cridit."

"Credit," Mother corrected automatically. "Who is Mr. Dill?"

I told them the whole story right from the beginning. Mother was considerably upset that I had gone into a pawnshop. For some reason or other she was positive that this would lead me into becoming a gambler.

"He's dressed like one all right," Father commented in a caustic voice. "Just look at that vest!"

"Emile isn't to blame," Mother said, rallying to my defense. "I really

[1] *Donnerwetter* (dŏn′ẽr·vĕt′ẽr): a German exclamation, "Thunder and lightning."

think that it is our fault."

"How do you mean, Jeanne?" Father asked in surprise.

"Well, after all, you can't expect a young man who goes to high school, to *De Witt Clinton,* to be a little boy one day and a man the next," Mother said. "Once he is allowed to wear long trousers, he should be allowed to wear them all the time."

"Hm!" said Father. "Before we talk about it further get out of those clothes. Send them down to the cellar for the janitor to burn. There's no telling who wore them before."

"A bank president wore them," I said. "That's what Mr. Dill told me."

"About your Mr. Dill," Father said, "he had no legal right to sell a minor anything on the installment plan. Or to take for security the good fountain pen Mother gave you. But you agreed to it. Now it's a debt of honor for you to pay off."

In addition to paying Mr. Dill fifty cents a week out of my allowance until I had paid it all and redeemed my fountain pen, Father made me promise never again to buy anything on the installment plan or pawn anything.

On the following Saturday, quite unexpectedly, Mother took me down to Franklin Simon's again. There she bought me two suits with long pants, a blue serge and a brown. The brown one had a Prince of Wales pleat in it, just like Herbie's.

I wore the gray worsted to school on Monday.

I was out of knee pants for good.

A Real "Clothes Problem"

1. Did Emile want long pants chiefly because he was going to high school, or because his friend Herbert already had them? Tell bits of the story to support your answer. How much are your tastes in clothes affected by what your friends wear?

2. When was Emile's joy in his new suit dimmed by a new problem? What was the problem? What was his first solution?

3. Why did Mr. Dill show so much interest in Emile? What deal for the blue suit did he finally work out? Explain whether you think Emile's father was right in making Emile stick to his bargain, even though the deal was illegal.

4. What parts of the story seemed funniest to you?

5. Who sympathized with Emile more, his mother or his father? Tell what they did or said that makes you think so.

6. How was high school different from Emile's earlier school? What new privileges are given to high school students in your school system? What responsibilities go with the privileges?

7. Suppose the elevator boy had not been robbed. Think of another way Emile's parents might have found out about his new suit and tell this incident to the class.

Names for Colors

The suit Emile bought from Mr. Dill seemed *aquamarine* in the sunlight. It was a bright blue. The name of this particular color is made from two Latin words, one meaning "sea" and the other "water." Think of other English words in which either *aqua* or *marine* appears, and then decide which of these Latin words means "sea" and which means "water."

Many names for particular tints and shades of color are taken from objects in nature, like gems and flowers. Think of three colors named for gems, three named for flowers, and three named for other natural objects or substances. Put the names on the blackboard with their correct spelling and pronunciation.

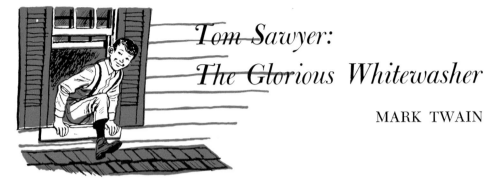

Tom Sawyer: The Glorious Whitewasher

MARK TWAIN

Adapted for Television by Alvin Sapinsley

BEHIND THE SCENES IN TELEVISION. Tom Sawyer and his friends Huck Finn and Jim are like real American boys to millions of readers. Their good times and bad scrapes in *The Adventures of Tom Sawyer* and *The Adventures of Huckleberry Finn* are such popular stories that these books have been adapted for the stage, movies, radio, and just recently, television. Here is a television version of Tom's famous whitewashing job.

Reading a television play is somewhat different from reading a play designed for the stage. Because television plays are filmed with a camera, the shifting of scenes is more flexible than on a stage. Certain terms indicate scene changes. When several scenes or pictures are presented, one directly after the other, the term DISSOLVE is used. One picture simply dissolves while another takes its place. When one scene of the play ends completely, the term CUT indicates the showing of a new scene. At the end of an act or at the end of the play, the term FADEOUT describes the gradual darkening of the screen. OFF SCREEN means just what you can guess: the voices of some characters are heard but they themselves are not seen on the screen.

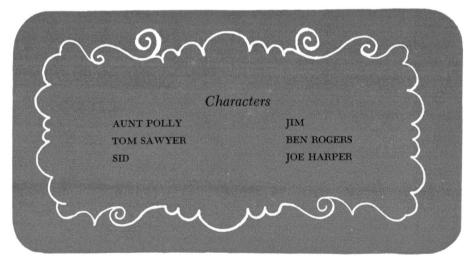

Characters

AUNT POLLY	JIM
TOM SAWYER	BEN ROGERS
SID	JOE HARPER

"Tom Sawyer: The Glorious Whitewasher" adapted by Alvin Sapinsley from *The Adventures of Tom Sawyer* by Mark Twain. Reprinted by permission of Alvin Sapinsley, the Trustees of the Mark Twain Estate, and Harper and Brothers.

ACT I

OFF SCREEN *we hear an old side-wheeler, slowly churning its way along the Mississippi. Birds are chirping, and the background music suggests a morning in spring. The opening scene is the interior of* TOM's *and* SID's *room, on the second floor of* AUNT POLLY's *house. It is a small room, made even smaller on one side by the sloping roof. The major piece of furniture in the room is a brass bedstead, in which* TOM *and* SID *are sleeping.*

Gradually, TOM *opens his eyes to greet the day. He looks toward the window, sees the sun streaming in, and hops nimbly out of bed. He goes to the window, and perches on the sill, looking out at the world. He looks downward.*

DISSOLVE *to the yard beneath the window. It is a small area, enclosed on one side by the fence, and the other by the house.* JIM, *a Negro boy of* TOM's *age, is sawing wood. He is humming to himself as he works.*

TOM *whistles — a peculiar, special sort of whistle, soft but compelling.*

JIM (*looks up, grins, waves his hand*). Gonna be powerful nice today, Tom.

TOM (*stretching*). Sure 'nuff is, Jim. Reckon a body could swim most half the day and not get enough.

JIM. Reckon he could — if'n they'd let him.

[AUNT POLLY *appears in the kitchen door, holding a skillet.*]

AUNT POLLY. When you're done with the wood, Jim, you can get the pail and fetch us some water.

JIM. Yes, Miss Polly.

[AUNT POLLY *returns to the kitchen. Her voice is heard calling,* "Sid — Tom! Get outen that bed and come eat your breakfast afore you're late for school!"]

DISSOLVE *to* TOM, *still in the window. His face falls like a plummet at mention of the word "school."*

TOM. School? A body's got to go to school on a day like this? (*He turns from the window, and crosses the room, crestfallen. He sits on the edge of the bed and looks toward the window at the bright spring day. His mind is working at top speed. He gets a sudden idea, and partly unwraps the small bandage around his big toe. He examines the toe closely, then binds up the bandage again, Deliberately and carefully, he climbs back into bed beside* SID, *arranges himself in what he considers to be an appropriate and realistic position of suffering, and lets loose a deep-throated groan. He looks at* SID. SID *sleeps on.* TOM *groans again, louder this time. Still* SID *doesn't respond. In great pain*) Oo-oo-ooh, my toe!

[SID *merely snores.* TOM *leans over and shakes him violently.*]

TOM. Sid! Sid! (*He groans heavily.*)

[SID *stirs,* TOM *shakes him again and returns to his misery.* SID *yawns, stretches, and brings himself to his elbow with a snort. He becomes conscious of* TOM's *suffering and stares at him.*]

SID (*worried*). Tom! Here, Tom, Tom! What's the matter? (*He shakes* TOM *slightly.*)

TOM (*moaning*). Oh, don't, Sid. Don't joggle me.

SID. What's the matter, Tom?

[TOM *groans some more.*]

I'll call Ma. (*He jumps out of bed.*)

TOM (*weakly*). No — never mind. Don't call Aunt Polly, Sid. It'll be over by and by, maybe. Don't call anybody.

SID. But I gotta! Don't groan so, Tom, it's awful. How long you been this way?

TOM. Hours. Ouch! Oh, don't stir, so, Sid, you'll kill me.

SID. Tom, why didn't you wake me sooner? Oh, Tom, don't! It makes my flesh crawl to hear you. Tom, what *is* the matter?

TOM. I forgive you everything, Sid. Everything (*groan*) you've ever done to me. When I'm gone —

SID. Oh, Tom, you ain't dying, are you? Don't, Tom — oh, don't. Maybe —

TOM. I forgive everybody, Sid. Tell 'em so, (*groan*) Sid. And, Sid, give my white marvel, and my —

[SID *leaps out of bed in his nightshirt, runs to the door, and exits. He can be heard off screen, running down the stairs into the kitchen.* TOM *opens one eye, studies the situation, and groans loudly, in an experimental fashion. He hears footsteps*

approaching, screws his face into a mask of utter pain, and groans even more loudly. AUNT POLLY *bursts into the room, and runs over to the bed.* TOM's *groans attain new heights.*]

AUNT POLLY (*gasping*). You, Tom! Tom, what's the matter with you?

TOM. Oh, Auntie — it hurts so terrible!

AUNT POLLY. What hurts, child?

TOM. Oh, it's so awful, Auntie. I can't hardly bear it, the pain's so fierce!

AUNT POLLY. What hurts, Tom? (*concerned*) Tom, Tom, what *is* the matter with you?

TOM. Oh, Auntie, my sore toe's mortified.

AUNT POLLY. Your sore toe's — oh, my lands!

[*She sits down on the edge of the bed and starts to laugh, almost helplessly.* TOM *opens his eyes and stares at her, crushed.*]

TOM. Auntie — !

AUNT POLLY (*laughing and crying*). Your sore toe's mortified! Land sakes, the things you can think of.

TOM (*very indignant for a dying man*). But, Auntie — it hurts so much I —

AUNT POLLY. What a turn you did give me for a minute. Now you shut up that nonsense and climb out of this. Now, get yourself into these clothes and come down for your breakfast. The school bell will be ringing in a minute, and here you are — not even half ready.

TOM. What good's going to school

on Friday? What can you learn in only one day?

AUNT POLLY. Tom, you'll be the death of me with these nonsensical notions.

TOM (*grumpily*). Sittin' in school on a day like this — it ain't nacheral, Aunt Polly — especially with tomorrow bein' Saturday, and all.

AUNT POLLY (*severely*). Now, you pay heed to me, Thomas Sawyer! You're goin' to school today, and you're staying *all day long* — or you'll spend your Saturday workin'.

TOM (*scandalized*). Workin', Auntie? On Saturday?

AUNT POLLY. You heard me, Tom. So you'd best make up your mind to goin' to school today, hear?

[*She exits and can be heard clumping down the stairs. Despondently,* TOM *begins to dress.*]

TOM. School — ! Ain't a body never gonna get some fun for himself afore he's a hundred years old? (*As he dresses*) Reckon the Lord didn't have but grownups in mind when he made Saturday comin' only one a week. Geeminy!

AUNT POLLY (*her voice sounding up from the kitchen*). Tom! (*Getting no reply*) Tom! What's gone with that boy now? You *Tom.* The school bell's a-ringin', and where are you? I never did see the beat of that boy. (*Raising her voice*) I 'low if I get hold of you I'll —

[TOM *is dressed, and in the act of leaving the room by the window. He throws one foot over the sill. Off screen,* AUNT POLLY's *footsteps are heard on the stairs.* TOM *quickly disappears out of the window.* AUNT POLLY *comes into the room, sees that it is empty, and stands for a moment with her hands on her hips, surveying the premises.*]

AUNT POLLY. Where's that boy got to now? I 'low as one of these days I'm going to give him a belting he'll remember till his dying day! (*She hears a noise from downstairs. Craftily she tiptoes to the door, and descends the stairs quietly.*)

DISSOLVE *to the kitchen.* TOM *is standing by the table, cramming food into his mouth. Unseen by him,* AUNT POLLY *appears at the bottom of the stairs. She watches him for a moment.*

AUNT POLLY (*in a voice of doom*). Tom Sawyer!

[TOM *leaps, tries to escape through the kitchen door, but* AUNT POLLY *is upon him, grasping him by the slack in his trousers and almost raising him completely off the floor by the violence of her thrust.*]

AUNT POLLY (*surveying the prisoner*). I might 'a' known you wouldn't be off 'thout stuffing yourself first. Now stand still!

TOM (*squirming*). Better let me down, Auntie. I'll be late for school.

AUNT POLLY. You're late already. Five more minutes isn't going to change the licking you're going to get from your teacher. Now, hold still while I sew up your collar. (*She takes a needle and thread from his lapel.*)

TOM. Aw, now, Auntie, don't sew it up.

AUNT POLLY. You ain't a-goin' to school 'thout your collar sewed. Now, stop whinin', Tom. Land alive, it's enough to drive a body to her grave the way you caterwaul at everything.

TOM. You're chokin' me, Auntie.

AUNT POLLY (*sewing*). You'll be the ruination of me yet, with your playin' hookey, and climbin' out of windows, and —

TOM. I didn't climb out of the window, Auntie.

AUNT POLLY. Don't lie to me, Tom. I reckon I almost don't care what you do — so long's you don't lie to me.

TOM. I ain't lyin' to you, Auntie.

AUNT POLLY. If you didn't climb out of the window, how'd you get down here 'thout usin' the stairs? (*She bites off the thread.*)

TOM. I — don't know.

AUNT POLLY. Well, *I* know. You climbed out the window. Forty times I've said if you did that again I'd skin you. Reckon it's high time I did what I set out to do! Hand me that switch.

[*She points an imperious finger at the switch, which hangs on the kitchen wall.* TOM *is desolate.*]

TOM. Aunt Polly —

AUNT POLLY (*sternly*). Hand me that switch!

[*Like a prisoner ascending to the scaffold,* TOM *goes to the switch, removes it from its moorings, and carries it forlornly to* AUNT POLLY. *Slowly* TOM *turns, presenting his back to* AUNT POLLY. *He watches her over his shoulder as she steps back, draws a bead, and raises the switch for the first blow. The switch hovers in the air, about to descend.*]

TOM (*suddenly*). My! Look behind you, Auntie!

AUNT POLLY. My lands!

[*She whirls, snatching up her skirts, alert to whatever danger is menacing her from behind.* TOM *makes a beeline for the garden door.*]

AUNT POLLY. Tom!

CUT *to the yard, as* TOM *comes flying through the door, traverses the path on the run, and leaps the old board fence at a single jump, vanishing on the other side.* AUNT POLLY *hurtles out of the house after him, brandishing the switch.*

AUNT POLLY. Tom Sawyer, come back here! (*She skids to a halt, confounded by the height of the fence and the absence of* TOM. *For a moment she stands in the middle of the garden, breathing heavily, and then she breaks into a gentle laugh.*) Hang the boy, can't I never learn anything? (*She raises her voice, just loud enough for* TOM *to hear, in case he is lurking on the other side of the fence.*) Mind you now — straight to school with you, and no playing hookey or you'll get what's comin' to you!

[FADEOUT]

ACT II

SCENE: AUNT POLLY, TOM, *and* SID *are sitting at the kitchen table, having their supper.* AUNT POLLY *presides over the meager board, ladling out* whatever there is to eat.

AUNT POLLY. What're you mindin' to do tomorrow, Sid?

SID. Reckon I'll go swimmin' with the rest of the boys, Ma. Leastwise until the ol' *Missouri* comes in.

AUNT POLLY. Land sakes, what you boys all want to go runnin' down to the levee to see that steamboat for, is more than I can see.

TOM. It's powerful gay when the *Big Mo*'s puttin' in, Aunt Polly. (*Making circles with his arms*) Ting-a-ling-ling! Stop the stabboard! Ting-a-ling-ling! Stop the labboard! Come ahead on the stabboard! Ting-a-ling-ling!

AUNT POLLY. Tom Sawyer, stop that right now! (*As he ceases*) When you ain't playin' at pirates or robbers, you're playin' at bein' a steamboat! Sakes alive, that old ship comes in to Saint Peterburg every Saturday but the whole town still rushes down to the levee as though they'd never seed a boat before. (*To* SID) Mind you take heed down there. You stand back from the water, hear?

SID. Yes, Ma.

TOM (*scornfully*). Me 'n' Joe Harper's gonna ride with the pilot far as Hannibal tomorrow.

AUNT POLLY. Tom, I forbid you to go on that boat!

TOM. Aunt Polly!

AUNT POLLY. I ain't a-goin' to allow it! It was your poor ma's dyin' wish that I take keer of you like you was my own son, and I ain't a-goin' to have you messin' around them boats, and like as not get brought home all drowned some night.

TOM. But, it's the *Big Missouri,* Aunt Polly! Nobody ever gets drowned on the *Big Mo!*

AUNT POLLY. I ain't talkin' about it no more! If Miz Harper don't care what happens to her Joe, *I* care what happens to you. There now! (*With an air of finality she turns to* SID) What did you learn in school today, Sid?

SID (*his mouth full*). About Christopher Columbus.

AUNT POLLY (*interested*). Christopher Columbus? Land sakes! That sounds powerful enlightenin'! (*To* TOM) What did *you* learn today in school?

TOM (*a little fussed*). Me, Auntie?

AUNT POLLY. You, Tom.

TOM (*groping*). Why — the same thing as Sid learned.

SID. Ma, he's lying! How could he learn the same thing, Ma, when he's a grade behind me?

TOM (*jumping up*). Anyone who'll call me a liar — Why, Auntie, next thing he'll be sayin' I never was in school today, at all.

AUNT POLLY. Which ain't so, is it, Tom?

TOM. Sure 'nuff ain't!

AUNT POLLY (*looking at him craftily*). Must have been middling warm in school, warn't it, Tom?

TOM. Yes'm.

AUNT POLLY. Powerful warm, wasn't it? (*Craftily, she reaches out her hand and feels* TOM's *shirt.*) But you ain't too warm now, though.

TOM (*A ghost of a smile crosses his face*). Some of us pumped on our heads — mine's damp yet, see?

[*He presents his tousled head for inspection.* AUNT POLLY *feels the damp locks, a little vexed.*]

AUNT POLLY. I see —

[*She bends to her food, momentarily withdrawing her forces while she plans a new attack. Warily,* TOM *goes on eating, his eyes fixed on her face. Suddenly,* AUNT POLLY *has a new inspiration.*]

AUNT POLLY (*probing*). Tom, you didn't have to undo your shirt collar where I sewed it — just to pump on your head, did you?

TOM. No'm —

AUNT POLLY. Open your jacket, Tom. (*As he hesitates*) Open it —

[*Slowly* TOM *smiles. He opens his jacket, revealing his shirt collar to be securely sewed.*]

TOM (*grinning*). It ain't been undone, Auntie.

[AUNT POLLY *looks at the shirt collar, at* TOM, *at* SID, *and back to the shirt collar. She smiles, and then laughs, giving* TOM *a playful box on the ear.*]

AUNT POLLY. Bother! Well, go 'long with you. I'd made sure you'd played hookey and been a-swimming. But I forgive ye, Tom. I reckon you're a kind of a singed cat, as the sayin' is — better'n you look. *This* time. Run along with you if you've et all you've a mind to.

[TOM *jumps down from the table and starts to go.*]

SID (*with malicious gentleness*).

Well, now, if I hadn't 'a' thought you sewed his collar with white thread this morning, same as mine. (*Shows his collar.*)

AUNT POLLY. Why, I did sew it with white. (*As* TOM *makes a dash for the door*) Tom! (TOM *stops.*) Turn around, Tom. (*Slowly* TOM *turns.*)

SID. 'Pears an awful lot like black thread from here.

TOM. I'll belt you for this, Siddy — just see if I don't.

AUNT POLLY. Come here, Tom.

TOM. Aw, Auntie —

AUNT POLLY. Stand still, Tom. (*She takes two needles from under the lapel of his jacket. One needle has white thread, the other black. She shows them to* TOM.) White and black, white and black. Now you see what comes of lyin' and cheatin'?

TOM (*sullenly*). Why'n't you stick to one or t'other, Auntie? I can't keep the run of 'em.

AUNT POLLY. And now you know why I change 'em. Well, Tom, I said you'd get it if you played hookey today — and you're getting it. You couldn't wait one more day for your holiday — so now you're losin' it.

TOM. What are you gonna do to me, Auntie?

AUNT POLLY. I'm tellin' you now. Tomorrow you're to whitewash the fence out front.

TOM (*scandalized*). Whitewash the fence? Auntie — on Saturday? You can't make a body work on *Saturday!* Not when the boys are goin' swimmin' — and — and the *Big Mo's* comin' in!

AUNT POLLY. Land sakes, I know it's hard workin' when all the other boys is havin' holiday, Tom — but I knows you hates work more than you hates anythin' else, and I've got to do my duty by you, or it'll be your ruination! So you can weep and wail at me for as long's you got a mind to — tomorrow you're whitewashin' that fence out there!

TOM (*in a panic*) Auntie — it's thirty yards long!

AUNT POLLY. If'n you put your mind to it you could have it done by the middle of the afternoon.

TOM, Auntie — it's nine feet high! Geeminy Christmas, it'll take most a year to whitewash that old fence!

AUNT POLLY. Then you'll spend a year on it! Tom Sawyer, I'm at the end of my patience with you! If it's the last thing I do I'll learn you not to lie to me! Now, get along out of here, the two of you, while I clear up!

[*She starts to clear the table angrily.* TOM *looks at* SID *hatefully.* SID *returns the glance indifferently.*]

TOM (*muttering*). Workin' on a Saturday. The whole town'll be standin' 'round hootin' an' hollerin'.

[*He looks to see if* AUNT POLLY *is watching, sees she is not, and picks up a crust of bread, which he flings at* SID, *hitting him in the eye.* SID *lets out a yell,* AUNT POLLY *turns, and* TOM *heads for the kitchen door on the run. He exits.* AUNT POLLY *shakes her head dolorously, and returns to her dishwashing.*]

[FADEOUT]

ACT III

SCENE: *The sidewalk outside the fence. It is morning, and a few boys skip by, laughing, shouting, playing tag. They leave and another boy hurries along the sidewalk, a fishing rod slung over his shoulder. Two more boys play leap-frog across the sidewalk, going off.* SID *comes through the gate from the yard onto the sidewalk, rolling a hoop. He goes off happily.*

Then TOM *enters through the gate. He carries a large bucket of whitewash and a broad brush. He sets the bucket down and mournfully gazes at the long expanse of unwhitewashed fence. He is a picture of misery and despair. Sighing, he dips his brush and passes it along a section of the topmost plank. He steps back and surveys the insignificant white streak, comparing it to the far-reaching continent of unpainted wood. Dejectedly, he sits down on an upturned barrel.*

JIM *comes through the gate, bearing an empty pail.*

TOM. Where you goin' to, Jim?

JIM. To the pump for to fetch the water. If'n I get the chores done early, Miz Polly gone let me go down to the levee to watch *Big Mo* draw up. (*Grinning*) Man, that there's a sight to see!

TOM (*peers guardedly around the corner of the fence*). Say, Jim, I'll fetch the water if you'll whitewash some.

JIM (*shakes his head and retreats a pace*). Can't do it, Tom. Miz Polly, she told me I got to go an' get this water an' not stop foolin' 'round with anybody. She says she spec' you'll ask me to whitewash, an' she told me to go 'long an' tend to my own business.

[TOM *produces a marble from his pocket, and shows it to* JIM, *as if to bribe him.* JIM *begins to waver. He examines the marble with reverence.*]

JIM. My! That's a mighty gay marvel, I tell you!

TOM (*crooning*). A white alley, Jim. An' for you if you'll just do a little whitewashin' while I —

JIM. But, Tom, I's powerful afraid Miz Polly'll —

TOM. She won't ever know!

JIM (*dubiously*). Seems like she always finds out, Tom.

TOM. Before you know it I'll be back!

JIM. I'd like to help you, Tom, you knows that, but —

TOM (*intensely*). Jim — I'll show you my sore toe!

JIM (*breathily*). Sure 'nuff?

TOM. Sure n'uff!

[*After a second's hesitation* JIM *sets down his pail. He collects the marble from* TOM *and bends over the sore toe, his eyes wide with interest, as* TOM *proceeds to unwind the bandage.* AUNT POLLY's *arm and hand, clutching a slipper, descend into the picture, fetching* JIM *a hefty wallop.* JIM *grabs his pail and with a startled shriek exits quickly, and* TOM *leaps to the fence and begins whitewashing with vigor.* AUNT POLLY *retires from the field triumphantly.* TOM *continues to whitewash rapidly. In the distance is heard the long-drawn, mournful blast of the* Big Missouri's *whistle.* TOM's *eyes widen, and he looks longingly in the direction of the sound. He sighs. The whistle is repeated.*]

CUT *to view of* BEN ROGERS, *a stout young man of* TOM's *age, approaching on the sidewalk. He is eating an apple and imitating the sounds and movements of a steamboat.*

BEN. Stop her, sir! Ting-a-ling-ling! (*His headway runs almost out, and he draws slowly toward the edge of the sidewalk.*) Ship up to back! Ting-a-ling-ling! (*His right hand begins to describe stately circles.*) Set her back on the stabboard! Ting-a-ling-ling! Chow! Ch-chow-wow!

[TOM *looks down at* BEN, *then he looks at his brush, and thence to the fence. An idea seems to be forming in his mind. Quickly, he dips the brush, and turns to the unpainted boards, commencing to work resolutely.*]

BEN (*suiting the action to the word*). Come — out with your spring-line — what're you about there? Take a turn 'round that stump, with the bight of it! Stand by the stage, now — let her go! Done with the engines, sir! Ting-a-ling-ling! Try the gauge cocks! Sh-h-h-! (*Having successfully moored himself to the barrel,* BEN *descends his imaginary gangplank. He catches sight of* TOM.) Hi-*yi!* You're up a stump, ain't you?

[TOM *doesn't hear. He surveys his last touch with the eye of an artist, then gives his brush another gentle sweep and surveys the result as before.* BEN *ranges up alongside of him, sucking deliciously on his apple.*]

Hey, you gotta work, hey?

TOM (*turning, surprised*). Why, it's you, Ben! I warn't noticin'.

BEN. Say — I'm goin' in a-swimmin', I am, till *Big Mo* pulls in. You hear it just now, whistlin' away? You can hear it most half way to Cairo. Don't you wish you could come along with us? (*Satirically*) But of course you'd druther *work* — wouldn't you? Course you would.

[*He chuckles and takes another bite out of his apple.* TOM *stares at the apple, as though entranced, but he forces his eyes away from it and looks at* BEN *with an air of tolerant amusement.*]

TOM. What do you call work?

BEN. Why, ain't *that* work?

TOM (*frowning*). You mean — whitewashing this fence?

BEN (*impatient*). Course I mean whitewashing that old fence! Ain't that work, standing there whitewashing an old fence when it's Saturday and *Big Mo's* comin' in?

TOM (*carelessly*). Well, maybe it is, and maybe it ain't. All I know is it suits Tom Sawyer.

[*He resumes his whitewashing, using*

careful, artistic strokes. BEN *watches for a moment, puzzled.*]

BEN. Hey! You meanin' to let on you *like* it?

TOM. Like it? Well, I don't see why I oughtn't to like it. Does a boy get a chance to whitewash a fence every day?

[BEN *stops nibbling his apple to consider the logic of this remark. He watches* TOM *work.* TOM *sweeps his brush daintily back and forth, steps back to note the effect, adds a touch here and there, criticizes the effect again.* BEN *watches, getting more and more absorbed.* TOM *pretends not to notice him.*]

BEN (*finally*). Say, Tom —

[TOM'S *brush stops.*]

Let *me* whitewash a little.

[TOM *whirls, about to pounce. Then he changes his mind.*]

TOM (*shaking his head*). No — no — I reckon it wouldn't hardly do, Ben.

BEN. Aw, now, Tom —

TOM. I'm sorry, Ben. You see, Aunt Polly's awful particular about this fence — right here on the street, you know — but if it was the back fence I wouldn't mind and *she* wouldn't.

BEN. I'd be careful, Tom.

TOM (*dubiously*). She's awful particular, Ben. It's got to be done very careful; I reckon there ain't one boy in a thousand, maybe two thousand, that can do it the way it's got to be done.

BEN (*impressed*). No — is that so?

TOM. Sorry, Ben.

[*He returns to his work. Now* BEN *is feverish with desire.*]

BEN. Oh, come on now, hey, Tom — lemme just try. Say — I'll give you the core of my apple!

TOM (*starting to hand over the brush*). Well, here —

[BEN *grabs,* TOM *changes his mind.*]

No, Ben, now don't! I'm afeard —

BEN (*desperately*). I'll give *you* all of it!

TOM (*after a long pause*). Well —

[*With seeming reluctance he gives up the brush and takes the half-eaten apple.* BEN *takes up his quarters by the fence and proceeds to whitewash.* TOM *seats himself on the upturned barrel and takes a luxurious bite from the apple.*]

TOM (*warningly*). Now, be powerful careful, Ben. I'm resking an awful lot just lettin' you do that.

BEN (*reverently*). I'll be careful, Tom. I'll do it just like I saw you doin' it. (*He makes a stroke.*) Shucks a'mighty, watchin' that old *Missouri* come in ain't beans compared to this!

[*And he whitewashes, very delicately. Once more, in the distance, the* Big Missouri *sounds its whistle.* TOM *looks up anxiously.* BEN *doesn't even notice. Soon* JOE HARPER *races in, carrying a kite.*]

JOE. Hey, say, Tom, you hear *Big Mo*? She's roundin' Potter's landing — s'pose we cut across the hill, and foller her up along the shore?

TOM. Some other time, Joe. Me'n

Ben's got more important things to do than watchin' steamboats.

JOE (*scandalized*). Tom! *Big Mo!*

TOM. I heard you, Joe. You can watch *Big Mo* any old Saturday you want.

JOE (*puzzled*). Well — what're you doin' that's so important?

TOM (*quietly*). Whitewashin'.

JOE. Whitewashin'? What do you want to go doin' that for — on a Saturday?

BEN (*proudly*). When else can you get a chance to whitewash a fence?

JOE. Who wants to whitewash a fence, nohow?

TOM. That's all you know, Joe Harper. You ever whitewash one?

JOE (*frowning*). No. What's so particular gay about whitewashin' a fence? Tom — we was gonna cadge a ride to Hannibal with Mister Clemens.

TOM (*airily*). Oh — I reckon I'll get around to that one of these days, Joe. Right now I gotta watch Ben an' make sure he does it right.

BEN. I can do it right, I guess!

JOE (*looking from* BEN *to* TOM). How come Ben's whitewashin' your fence for you? You *payin'* him?

TOM. Payin' him? Why, Joe, he begged me so hard I just had to let him for awhile. I don't even know as I shoulda done it, though. Even for the apple he give me.

JOE. Why not?

TOM. Why, Joe, it ain't everybody as can whitewash a fence.

JOE. I can whitewash a fence as good as Ben can!

TOM. Well — I don't know, Joe —

JOE. I know.

TOM. Besides, I just now told Ben he could do it awhile. I can't turn around and take the brush away from him, can I?

JOE. Hey, say, listen, Tom — I could run home and get a brush — Pap's got one.

TOM (*dubiously*). I don't know, Joe — I ain't sure you could do it like it ought to be done. Aunt Polly —

JOE. Tom — I'll give you my kite!

TOM. Well —

[*The camera moves in close to the kite in* JOE's *hands. Big Mo whistles off screen. Camera draws back, showing* TOM *again, sitting on the barrel holding the kite.* JOE *and* BEN *stand side by side whitewashing the fence. Big Mo sounds again.* TOM *looks anxiously at the still largely unpainted fence, and searches the sidewalk for more victims. Another boy of* TOM's *age and size comes down the sidewalk, swinging a dead rat by a string.*]

CUT *to the kitchen.* AUNT POLLY *sits before the open window, rocking back and forth as she knits. Her glasses are way down on her nose. She is almost sleeping. Big Mo whistles in the distance.* AUNT POLLY *stirs slightly.*

CUT *to closeup of the barrel. Besides the kite and the dead rat, the barrel now holds a window sash, six marbles, a piece of chalk, a glass stopper from a decanter, a tin soldier, a couple of tadpoles, six firecrackers, a kitten with only one eye, a brass doorknob, a dog collar, a knife handle. In addition to* JOE *and* BEN, *a veritable host of boys are gathered around the fence, some whitewashing, some mixing more whitewash, some waiting their turns at the brushes or mixing buckets.* TOM *leans indolently against the barrel, surrounded by his booty, idly watching the working, sweating group.*

TOM. All right, Joe, Billy, Johnny — that's enough. (*Through their chorus of protests*) Sam, Jonah, Chuck — your turn.

BEN. Ain't it time for me again, Tom? There's only one more board left, and I aim to have a lick at it!

JOE. If Ben's gonna whitewash that last plank — I gotta right, too. My kite's wuth more'n an old apple!

[*The other boys gather around, demanding a chance at the final board.*]

TOM. Now, hold on there, all of you!

(*They stop squabbling*) I'm aimin' to be fair 'bout it. Reckon you can all have a lick at the last board. (*There is a burst of cheering from the boys.*) Jest line up, an' each of you take *one* stroke at it. But no cheatin', or I'll lam you!

JOE. First!

[*He leaps to the unpainted board, and stands in front of it. Yelling and pushing, the other boys line up behind him.* TOM *hands the brush to* JOE.]

TOM. Only one lick, Joe! Then pass it along.

CUT *to the kitchen.* AUNT POLLY *is sitting with her knitting. She rises.*

AUNT POLLY (*muttering to herself*). Reckon I'd best get out there and see how much the child did afore desertin'. Reckon if he's done *one quarter* of it I ought to be satisfied. (*She goes out the kitchen door.*)

CUT *to the sidewalk.* TOM *is sitting on the barrel, arranging his newfound wealth. The other boys have gone,* AUNT POLLY *comes through the gate, spies* TOM *there, and descends on him, without looking at the fence.*

AUNT POLLY. Is this the way you whitewash a fence — lollin' about in the sun, playin' with gee-gaws? (*She is about to slap him.*)

TOM (*skipping away nimbly*). But it's all done, Auntie!

AUNT POLLY. Tom, don't lie to me — I can't bear it. You ain't been out here long enough to do half of it. (*She turns to look at the fence as she talks, and is dumbfounded. She stares at it.*) Well, tan me if it ain't! (*Looks at* TOM) There's no gettin' 'round it, you *can* work when you've a mind to — but it's powerful seldom you've a mind to, I'm bound to say. (*Suspiciously*) How come you to do it so fast, Tom?

TOM. Why, Auntie, I jest worked away at it, 'thout stoppin'. Jest like you told me to.

AUNT POLLY. Tom — I'm most ready to believe you're tellin' me the truth for once. Come back into the house and I'll give you a doughnut. (*She takes his wrist, and leads him into the yard.*) Reckon you're due for a little treat, and jest see how much better it'll taste when you know you've earned it through virtuous effort and far away from the paths of sin and damnation. Wait here. (*She goes into the kitchen, continuing to talk off screen*) Remember what the Scripture says, Tom: There's six things the Lord ain't got no love for — haughty eyes, lyin' tongues, an' hands that shed innocent blood; a heart that's forever devisin' wicked imaginations, feet that're swift in runnin' to mischief, a false witness that uttereth lies and soweth discord among brethren.

[*While she talks, off screen,* SID *comes through the gate into the yard. He sees* TOM *and stops. A wicked gleam appears in* TOM's *eyes, he grabs up a clod of earth and heaves it at* SID, *hitting him in the face.*]

TOM. I said I'd fix you for tellin' on me!

[SID *yells, and runs around the corner of the house, just as* AUNT POLLY *appears in the kitchen door, holding a doughnut.*]

AUNT POLLY. What was that noise, Tom?

TOM (*quickly*). Nothin', Auntie! Mayn't I go and play now?

[*He grabs the doughnut and takes a bite of it.* SID *comes around the corner of the house, bawling.*]

SID. Ma! He throwed dirt in my eyes!

AUNT POLLY. Tom!

[TOM *heads for the fence, leaps over it, and is gone.*]

AUNT POLLY. Tom! Come back here! (*But* TOM *is gone.* AUNT POLLY *shakes her head.*) I might 'a' known he couldn't stay out of devilment more'n a minute. The good Lord knows what I'm gonna do 'bout that boy. (*To the sniffling* SID) Oh, stop your bawlin', child. You can't be hurt that bad! (*She goes back into the kitchen. Off screen, Big Mo whistles again, very near.*)

[FADEOUT: THE END]

Enjoying a Television Story

1. What effect did the fine spring day have on Tom? How did he try to make the most of it?

2. How did the sewing thread Aunt Polly used trap Tom in a fib? What part did Sid play in this?

3. Compare Tom and Sid as boys you would like to have for friends. What offsets Tom's bad habits?

4. Point out places in the play that show Aunt Polly's real feeling for Tom. Tell if she is like anyone you know, a person who nags and scolds but still is warmhearted.

5. Why is the sound of the *Big Mo* so important in Tom's actions? Do you remember Joe's saying he was going to catch a ride with " Mister Clemens "? Mark Twain's real name was Samuel L. Clemens. Look up his life story to discover the meaning behind Joe's remark.

6. How does Tom get his friends to fight over the privilege of whitewashing the fence? Do you think the boys really enjoyed the work or just *thought* they did? What do you do for fun that seems like work to other people?

7. Discuss why reading a television play is different from reading a radio or stage play. How is it possible in a television play to tell parts of the story without having any characters speak? Point out such parts in this play. If you were performing *Tom Sawyer* for the school assembly — a good idea! — what tricks would you use in place of the camera's " dissolve," " cut," and "off screen "?

Word Parts

At dinner Aunt Polly tries to find some way to trap Tom into admitting he was not at school: " She bends to her food, *momentarily* withdrawing her forces while she plans a new attack." If you look at the word *momentarily* you can see " moment " as its main part, and you can guess that the word means " for a short time " or " for a minute." There are many long words that are built, like this one, from simple parts whose separate meanings you know.

In the following list, first define the *italicized* part of the word and then try to get from it the meaning of the whole word: extra*ordinary*, *percent*ile, *season*able, en*mesh*ed, *labor*atory. For this list do the same thing, only this time you will have to spot the " inside " part yourself: infantile, secretive, grammatical, criminology, picturesque, entanglement.

Roundup

Comparing Families and Friends

1. If you could pay a week's visit to one of these families, which one would you choose? Why?

2. Who was the best father in this group of families? Who was the best mother? Discuss your answers.

3. What character in these stories would be the most satisfactory friend to have? Explain the reasons for your choice by stating first what qualities you expect in a friend.

4. Did your reading about " family and friends " suggest any good ways for parents to treat their children — or bad ways to avoid? Make a class list of " Do's and Don't's " for parents.

Have an " Only Child " Debate

Arrange a class debate on the subject " It is better to be an only child than to be a member of a large family." Divide the class into two sections, one to argue for the advantages of having brothers and sisters and the other for the advantages of being an only child.

As far as possible, let each student take the side he prefers, but make the groups equal, even if some have to argue for the side they do not really agree with. (Debaters must be ready to take either side of a question!) Let each speaker make one definite point in favor of his side.

Reserve two speakers on each side to make the " rebuttal," answering the arguments of the other side after they have been presented. Have the best speaker on each team make the final talk, summing up all the points his side has made. Invite your principal or supervisor to serve as judge.

Adopted Jane, by Helen F. Daringer (Harcourt, Brace, 1947)

A summer of visiting real families brings an orphan girl a home.

Binnie Latches On, by Marie McSwigan (Dutton, 1951)

Binnie was the odd one in her family until she made her own place in the circle.

Carol from the Country, by Frieda Friedman (Morrow, 1950)

Life in the city was difficult until she made new friends.

Crown Fire, by Eloise Jarvis McGraw (Coward-McCann, 1951)

Friends help a young logger to control his temper.

Ghost Town Cowboy, by Genevieve Torrey Eames (Messner, 1951)

He won a family on a ranch.

The Growing Human Family, by Minoo Masani (Oxford, 1951)

How groups for living developed from tribes to an international community.

Hidden Harbor, by Kathrene Pinkerton (Harcourt, Brace, 1951)

Family conflicts and loyalty on the coast of Alaska.

Holiday Mountain, by Lloid and Juanita Jones (Westminster, 1949)

A family makes fun from hardships running a tourist camp in Colorado.

Jeb Ellis of Candlemas Bay, by Ruth Moore (Morrow, 1952)

After his fisherman father is drowned, Jeb is the man of the family.

Little Women, by Louisa May Alcott, new ed. (Grosset, 1947)

A great old favorite family story.

Loblolly Farm, by Madye Lee Chastain (Harcourt, Brace, 1950)

A girl makes odd new friends on a Texas farm.

Margaret, by Janette Sebring Lowrey (Harper, 1951)

A story with good pointers on getting along with people.

A Nickel for Alice, by Frances Saloman Murphy (Crowell, 1951)

An orphan girl finally gets a family that loves her.

Peeps Elliot & Family, by Andrew Hall (Dodd, Mead, 1950)

A sports-loving boy in an entertaining family. Try also *Like Father, Like Fun* (1948) by the same author about the same folks.

People Are Important, by Eva Knox Evans (Capitol, 1951)

Help in understanding all kinds. This author's novel *Tim's Place* (Putnam, 1950) shows the ideas in action.

Penrod, His Complete Story, by Booth Tarkington (Doubleday, 1914)

A typical American boy, with his family, his friends, and his dog.

Rusty at Rams Horn Ranch, by Shannon Garst (Abingdon, 1951)

All the world seemed to be against Rusty and his dog until they found a home on a sheep ranch.

The Swiss Family Robinson, by Johann David Wyss, new ed. (Grosset, 1949)

When they were shipwrecked on a desert island, they learned the value of family teamwork.

Uncle Andy's Island, by Anne Malloy (Houghton Mifflin, 1950)

A boy curbs his love of mischief to win the respect of his war-hero uncle.

Ways to Improve Your Personality, by Virginia Ballard and Ruth Strang (Whittlesey, 1951)

Good definite advice illustrated with anecdotes from real life.

Young Razzle, by John R. Tunis (Morrow, 1949)

Rivalry of father and son in big-league baseball.

Scene from RKO–Sol Lesser production, " Under the Red Sea." Photographed by Dr. Hans Haas.

The World Around Us

Inside a Hurricane

WILLIAM J. LEDERER

You might think that peacetime duty for a Navy flier is actually a peaceful job. Yet if his assignment is scouting the weather in a hurricane area, he may long for the good old days when he was fighting only enemy planes. Get ready for rough going. You are about to join the weather-reconnaissance patrol on a flight right into the middle of a hurricane!

I NVADING our shores as no enemy has ever dared, hurricanes since 1900 have killed more than a thousand people and have destroyed more than a billion dollars' worth of valuable property.

To find out exactly what happens in the middle of the roaring violence of a hurricane, the Navy and Air Force are sending weather-reconnaissance planes to make on-the-spot investigations. Under the command of aerologists,[1] these planes battle their way through shattering winds into the very " eye " of the hurricane — and back again.

This is the inside story of what happens on one of these exploratory flights. Here, in the crew's own conversation, reactions, and observations, you will see how lifesaving weather data is obtained.

[1] **aerologists** (ā'ĕr·ŏl'ô·jĭsts): specialists in the study of the atmosphere and its behavior.

Last September a tramp steamer en route to Panama reported a hurricane brewing north of Puerto Rico. Storm warnings were hoisted immediately on 3,000 miles of American coastline, from Charleston to Galveston. And a four-motored Privateer, a Navy flying weather bureau, took off from Roosevelt Roads, Puerto Rico.

The Navy plane, with gas for 20 hours, flew directly toward the storm. Air conditions were still fairly calm as the slender, sunburned aerologist, Lieutenant Commander Archie Fields, gave last-minute instructions to his nine-man crew.

"We have two missions on this flight: one, to locate the center of the hurricane and two, to bring back a detailed description of everything — wind, rain, clouds, barometric pressure,[1] temperatures, and state of the sea. In order to give an accurate report of the highest winds, we will go in at low altitude and maintain contact with the surface as much as possible."

He tested the two microphones. One went to the wire recorder on which Fields kept a running account of the flight. The other plugged into the ship's intercommunication system.

Fields spoke into the wire recorder: "This is Plane No. 1, Navy Weather

Reconnaissance Squadron. The plane is at 6,000 feet on course 348. The wind is from 235 at 20 knots.[2] Sea is calm. Time: 1820.[3] There are no storm indications yet."

Throughout the plane, gear was put in motion. There was a dummy run on the radar [4] camera. Readings were taken on the wet and dry bulb thermometers and the altimeters.[5]

The assistant aerologist handed Fields a note: "First weather report went out."

"Pilot from weather," Fields called on the intercom. "Everything's set. Recommend you stay on present course."

"O.K.," answered the pilot, blond, stocky Lieutenant Commander Janeshek, veteran of World War II.

Forty minutes later Fields recorded again.

"Time is 1900. We are on the fringe of the storm. Surface wind has increased to fifty knots and we are passing through intermittent rain. Visibility has reduced and we have come down to 1,000 feet to keep the surface in sight. These early storm

---

[1] barometric (băr'ō·mĕt'rĭk) pressure: the weight of the atmosphere.

[2] knots: nautical miles, which are 800 feet longer than land miles.

[3] 1820: In Navy time, which is counted in one cycle of twenty-four hours beginning with midnight, 1820 is 6:20 P.M.

[4] radar: a device used to locate surrounding objects by reflection of an electronic beam.

[5] altimeters (ăl'tĭm'ê·têrz): instruments that measure altitude.

conditions are 40 miles ahead of where we expected them."

He switched to the intercom.

"Pilot from weather. Recommend you change course to 320; that'll keep the wind slightly forward of the port beam." [1]

"O.K.," said Janeshek.

The wind heightened and the Privateer bounced roughly. "1915," Fields spoke into the recorder. "Wind has increased to 60 knots. There are low clouds and rain. We are at 800 feet and can hardly see the water."

The radioman called Fields on the intercom.

"I've lost contact."

"Keep trying."

"Aye, aye, sir."

"The time is 1923," Fields continued. "We have lost radio contact with the base. Wind is 70 knots. Heavy rain. Visibility almost zero. We are at 600 feet and can see the surface only from time to time — huge green and white waves about 40 feet high."

Janeshek strapped on his shoulder harness to keep steady hands on the controls. Violent cross winds made the ship roller-coast and jolt; she needed constant babying.

"1928," Fields went on in his cool, unhurried voice. "Because of the low barometric pressure the cockpit altim-

eters are 2,000 feet in error. We're almost skimming the waves but the altimeters say we're a half a mile high. Janeshek is depending on radar readings."

"Mr. Fields, this is radio," came a voice on the intercom. "I've got contact with an amateur in Texas. He's relaying our reports on."

"Nice going, Sparks," [2] cut in Janeshek.

The hurricane was becoming more and more angry. Rain, driven by frenzied wind, battered the plane, making a noise like a thousand kettledrummers.

"1930," said Fields loudly into the recorder, "we are rapidly approaching the center. Wind is 90 knots and we're in the worst turbulence I've ever experienced. The plane is jumping up and down 50 or 60 feet at a time. It is absolutely dark."

The motors screamed in tune with the shrieking storm and the plane shuddered violently.

"Fields!" called Janeshek over the intercom. "The rain has cooled the motors down to 100 degrees. I'm increasing the manifold pressure. If they don't warm up in about a minute — you know what!"

A moment later Janeshek's relieved voice came back.

<hr />

[1] **port beam:** a direction exactly toward the left side of the plane.

[2] **Sparks:** the usual Navy nickname for a radioman.

"Fields, service temperature is O.K. now."

"Time is 1932," shouted Fields into the recorder. "We must be almost there. Wind about 100 knots. Equipment is shaking loose from its stowage. The wing tips are fluttering and there are tearing noises in the fuselage."

"Do you think it will get any worse, Fields?" called Janeshek. "I don't believe she can stand much more punishment."

Rain flooded through the cockpit and Janeshek hunched his blond head forward to keep the water out of his eyes.

"Sir, this is radar!" came an excited voice on the intercom. "It's here! I got the eye on the radar scope! Distance six miles."

"O.K.," said Janeshek, "good work."

Fields spoke into the recorder again.

"It is now 1933 and we are approaching the eye of the hurricane. The wind is buffeting the plane so hard I can only estimate the velocity — possibly 110 knots. But we're almost there! I can see the eye now. A faint glow. It's like being in a long black tunnel and seeing the opening ahead."

The photographer, bracing against the turbulence, tried to take pictures.

The fury of the storm became almost unbearable, when suddenly — as if shot out of a gun — the plane catapulted into the eye of the hurricane.

Fields gasped, then went on recording:

"It is 1934 and we are inside the eye. The air is smooth. The sun is shining through a thin high overcast. The light blinded us all momentarily. This eye is sort of a circular weather oasis about thirty miles in diameter."

"What's that strange cloud column ahead?" asked Janeshek.

"It's an eye inside the eye, sir," interrupted the radar operator.

"Ahead of us," continued Fields, "is a column of ragged gray clouds, about eight miles in diameter, starting at the surface and merging with the thin overcast. If that is the true eye of the storm, then we are witnessing a phenomena never before reported. It's the formation of a new, larger eye around the small, original eye when the storm has increased to such a size that the small eye will not accommodate the greater volume of subsiding [1] air.

"We are now in the inner eye. We experienced the highest winds of the trip in a narrow one-half-mile-thick ring. Going through them bashed the plane badly. I don't like the way she rattles. Something has broken loose.

"We are turning within the inner eye. It is hazy and the air is smooth. The navigator has determined our position and the photographer is taking pictures . . ."

The recording stopped as the plane abruptly plunged downward. Everyone and everything lurched against the overhead. Equipment tore loose; Fields crashed against the dome. The left wing had been caught by an unexpected wind in the wall of the eye and the plane flipped over. It hurtled

[1] **subsiding**: sinking, falling.

almost to the water before the momentum carried it into the wall of wind, which lifted it on an uncontrollable 45-degree climb. A few seconds later the plane broke out into the calm outer eye.

"Fields, are you through getting data?" demanded the easygoing Janeshek. "I'm ready to get out of here."

"We're ready," said the shaken-up Fields.

In a short time the plane had left the outer eye and was battling its way home. It was a repetition of the flight in, except that to the darkness of the storm was added night. As the plane struggled toward Miami, the raging core of the hurricane gradually was left behind and the weather improved. An enlisted man managed to fry steaks on the electric stove. Two men at a time ate.

Six hours later, Fields spoke into the recorder again:

"It is now 0115. We have been checking the position of the hurricane's center and place it as 22-15N, 66-37W,[1] about 900 miles east of Florida. It appears as if the storm is moving westerly at a speed of about 15 knots."

The Privateer approached the wet runway at Miami and dropped slowly, like a tired eagle. The cowlings on her four motors were pushed in and bruised. The paint was stripped from her wings and raw metal showed. She taxied to the ramp and the crew disembarked. Fields headed for the

aerology office to make a detailed report. From knowledge such as he brought back, hurricanes will some day be controlled.

Lieutenant Commander Janeshek lighted a black cigar and strolled into the Operations Room.

The radio was blaring out:

". . . intrepid Navy fliers have valiantly fought their plane through the 140-mile-per-hour winds of the hurricane. From what they've learned we now know positively that the storm will not reach here for two days . . ."

Janeshek puffed on his cigar and wrote in the Operations Book:

"Plane No. 1," he wrote, "returned from weather reconnaissance flight.

"*Comments:* No comments. Flight was routine.

"*Signed:* William Janeshek."

Routine Flight

1. What were the two aims or missions of the flight? How were both accomplished?

2. Two other members of the crew besides the pilot and the aerologist speak in this account of the flight. What were their jobs? What news did they report to the aerologist?

3. When were the plane and its crew in greatest danger? Why couldn't the crew "wait out" the storm by staying inside the "eye"?

4. What is meant by the term "eye" in speaking of a hurricane? What was surprising about this particular eye? Can you explain the reason for the rough air around the eye and the smooth air inside?

5. Compare the radio report of the flight with the pilot's written report. Which one seems to you to be more accurate? Explain why both reports could seem quite accurate to the person reporting.

[1] **22-15N, 66-37W:** the position in degrees of latitude north and longitude west.

Know Your Meters

The ending -meter on a word always means "measure," particularly a mechanism that measures whatever the first part of the word means. It is easy to tell what a speedometer measures. In thermometer, the exact meaning of "thermo" is not so easy. Can you guess its meaning? Barometer and altimeter were explained in footnotes. What does the first part of each mean?

A clock is a chronometer. What is the meaning of chrono? Judging from the way the other -meter words are pronounced, how do you think you should say chronometer? Check with the dictionary to see if your guess is right.

The Voyage
of the Raft Kon-Tiki

THOR HEYERDAHL

ADVENTURE WITH A PURPOSE. When six young men shoved off from the coast of South America on a log raft to drift across thousands of miles of the Pacific Ocean, they embarked upon one of the most thrilling adventures of modern times. But it was not primarily adventure they were seeking. The leader of the expedition was a scientist, and he had a serious purpose in making the strange voyage. Many of the greatest tales of adventure tell of the exploits of scientists and explorers seeking to learn more about the world around us and its people and its history.

In this account of a now-famous journey, you will find many interesting details that are important to the big question behind the trip: Did the ancient Peruvian Indians sail across the Pacific and settle the far-off Polynesian is-lands?[1] The idea had been discussed by scientists for many years, impossible though it sounded to some, but there was no detailed evidence to support it. Thor Heyerdahl set out to find facts to prove the theory. He paid attention to all kinds of details, such as using only primitive materials in the raft, and never forgot them even in the midst of great excitement and danger. As you read, see how many important details you can notice in this tale of modern adventure.

U SUALLY men who have embarked on an ocean raft in modern times have been shipwrecked sailors whose sole desire was to escape the perils of the open sea and reach the nearest

[1] The **Polynesian** (pŏl'ĭ·nē'zhǎn) **islands** are in the central Pacific Ocean.

"The Voyage of the Raft Kon-Tiki" by Thor Heyerdahl from *Natural History*, June 1948. Reprinted by permission of the author.

coast. But this was not the case in April, 1947, when the tugboat *Guardian Rio* towed a clumsy raft away from the sheltered docks of the Peruvian port of Callao [1] and left it adrift well outside the harbor entrance. The six of us that were left aboard the raft were filled with one single hope — that the wind and current would push our primitive craft far away from the South American mainland and right into the wide-open span of the vast Pacific Ocean.

Our purpose was not to flee the Republic of Peru. Leading officials of many nations had bidden us hearty farewell at the dock as the Peruvian Navy tugged us to our point of departure. Nor did we possess any desire to establish a world record in hazardous ocean drift. Yet the betting went high at the docks when we left.

Some claimed that we would be picked up off the coast in a few days or would never be seen again. The nine logs of porous balsa wood upon which we floated were too fragile and would break asunder in the heavy coastal swells, or they would at least be waterlogged and sink underneath us far short of the halfway mark to Polynesia, whose nearest islands lay some 4000 miles from Peru. With a foot and a half of freeboard [2] at the highest section of the bamboo deck, and with an open bamboo hut with thatched roof as our only shelter, we would be at the constant mercy of the waves and the weather and be lost in the first storm.

Others claimed that ropes were no good in the tropic sun and in the sea water and that the complete absence of nails, pegs, and wire in our raft would allow it to tear to pieces as soon as the constant movements of the logs started to chafe the hemprope lashings. And if a balsa-wood raft, against all the warnings of the experts, should prove to be seaworthy, it would still not be navigable with its clumsy, square sail and primitive steering oar. How, then, could we possibly expect to hit one of the tiny, farflung islands? The distance ahead was twice the journey of Columbus and the clumsy raft not even comparable.

All these SINISTER [3] but well-meant warnings were haunting my mind the first night after the last smoke of the tugboat had dissolved behind the horizon. When I was relieved from watch and tried to sleep, I realized how everything was in motion, not so much the pitching and rolling, as the restlessly undulating movement of the bamboo matting on which we lay on top of the great logs. Each time the stern was lifted by the seas, I saw dancing black hills of water, silhouetted against the stars as they chased along both sides of our raft, with whitecaps hissing at us as they passed. I listened to the squeaking and gnawing of a hundred ropes and the splashing and hammering of water everywhere. At regular intervals heavy seas

---

[1] Callao (kä·yä′ō).

[2] freeboard: the sides of a vessel above water.

[3] In this selection you will find several words printed THIS WAY to suggest that you figure out their meaning from context, that is, from the other words and the sentences that surround them.

thundered on board astern, but I noticed with comfort how the water, after whirling up to the waists of the two steersmen, instantly DWINDLED by falling between the open logs or over the sides of the raft. The seas fell in a pit before they could reach the unprotected bamboo hut lashed on deck a few feet from the stern. Therefore, we struggled to hold the stern to the weather and never let the seas in from the sides.

Gradually I felt happy and proud of our peculiar craft. But I could not quite get away from the complaining music of all the light and heavy ropes as everything aboard moved slowly up and down and even sideways as far as the ropes would permit.

What would the future bring us? How would the raft behave after a week, a month, or perhaps a year at sea?

I was not a sailor, and only one of my companions was experienced in handling an ordinary boat at sea. I had not been able, word by word, to answer the pessimistic warnings of naval authorities and other experts before we put out to sea. I was, nevertheless, firmly convinced that our raft could float across the ocean and bring us safely to some distant Polynesian shore. The secret of my stubborn confidence was that I felt certain that this same ocean route had been covered before by prehistoric men on the very same type of craft.

Already in 1937, after leaving the University of Oslo,[1] I had made a

zoological-ethnological[2] survey on the lonely Marquesas[3] Islands in the Southeast Pacific. What I found led me to suspect that an influence from early Central or South America had somehow preceded the present Polynesian culture in this area. It is well known that a number of striking similarities in the culture of South America and Polynesia have been noted. These include two of the important cultivated plants — the sweet potato and the bottle gourd — and many cultural features. The theory has therefore frequently been advanced — and again as frequently rejected — that there must have been a prehistoric contact between these two areas.

There can be no possibility of any land bridge having existed in human times, for a comparative study of the animal life of Polynesia proves its hoary isolation. The island people, when first discovered by Europeans, possessed good seagoing canoes, whereas the natives of Peru had only clumsy balsa rafts for their coastal navigation. Because of this, it has usually been assumed by the few who believe there was a cultural transfer that the South American cultures were influenced by the island people rather than vice versa. This view has never been fully accepted and is even doubted by competent scholars of the present day. It is too obvious that some of the Peruvian constructions,

[1] Oslo: the capital of Norway.

[2] zoological-ethnological (zō'ō·lŏj'ĭ·kăl-ĕth'nō-lŏj'ĭ·kăl): Zoology is the study of animal life. Ethnology is the study of the customs, habits, and beliefs of different races or peoples.

[3] Marquesas (mär·kā'sȧs).

artifacts,[1] and food plants in question date from an earlier period in America than A.D. 500, which is commonly accepted, through comparative genealogy,[2] as the approximate date when the first Polynesians spread into the East Pacific.

Thus I had found myself inescapably drawn toward the alternative theory to explain the striking parallels between Peru and Polynesia — namely, that an offshoot from the amazing cultures of early Peru drifted, intentionally or otherwise, into the Pacific.

I was instantly met by one killing argument: How could the Peruvians have covered the thousands of miles of intermediate ocean when their only means of navigation in prehistoric times was an open balsa raft?

To me, there was only one satisfactory answer, and that was to build such a balsa raft and see if it could survive this journey.

I selected five dependable men who volunteered to join me on the experimental voyage. One of them, Herman Watzinger, was a technical engineer, and he directed the building of the balsa raft, guided by detailed accounts and sketches left in the earliest records after the conquest of Peru. First we had to get into the heart of the Ecuadorian jungle to find present-day balsa trees that would match the dimensions of the prehistoric rafts. We cut down nine giant trees, and floated on them down a jungle river to the Pacific coast. With the blessings of the President of Peru and his Naval Minister, the prehistoric type of craft was built in the main naval harbor of Callao under our own supervision.

The nine balsa logs were lashed together side by side with many separate pieces of hemp rope. The bow of the raft took an organ-pipe design, with the longest log in the middle measuring 45 feet and projecting beyond the others both in the front and in the stern. In the stern it supported a big chunk of balsa holding tholepins for the steering oar. Of the two-foot cross section of these logs, more than half was submerged in the water, but nine smaller crossbeams of light balsa covered with bamboo lifted the highest portion of the deck (including the floor of the open hut upon which we slept) eighteen inches above the sea. The little plaited bamboo hut with thatched roof; two hardwood masts side by side, with a square sail; five centerboards two feet wide and six feet deep, inserted at irregular intervals between the logs; and a long wooden steering oar astern completed our REPLICA of the colorful prehistoric craft.

We named our raft *Kon-Tiki* in honor of the mythical sun king who the Incas [3] claim built the enormous stone constructions near Lake Titicaca [4] before he was defeated in war

---

[1] **artifacts:** things made by people, such as tools, furniture, jewelry. The term is usually used for ancient or primitive products.

[2] **genealogy** (jĕn′ê·ăl′ô·jĭ): the study of the descent of families or peoples.

[3] The **Incas** were the leading tribe of Indians in the highlands of Peru when the Spaniards conquered the country.

[4] **Lake Titicaca** (tĭt′ĭ·kä′kȧ) is high in the Andes Mountains between Peru and Bolivia.

by local tribes. After the defeat, according to legend, he fled with his light-colored people down to the coast and then westward into the Pacific Ocean, never again to return to Peru. Throughout the Polynesian islands, Tiki is remembered as the mythical hero who was first in the line of aboriginal chiefs to settle the islands and to claim direct descent from the sun. The Peruvian prefix " Kon " means Sun.

The six of us went aboard on April 28 and were left at the mercy of the elements in the old Inca fishing grounds outside the port of Callao. Our ages ranged from twenty-five to thirty-two. Herman Watzinger, second in command, was in charge of testing and hydrographic and meteorologic [1] measurements. Erik Hesselberg, an artist, was responsible for plotting our drift. Our radio operators were Knut Haugland and Torstein Raaby, both famous for their sabotage activities during the recent war (instrumental, respectively, in the important sabotage of the German Heavy-Water Plant and the battleship *Tirpitz*). Bengt Danielsson, lonely Swede on our Norwegian expedition, was an ethnologist from the University of Upsala who joined us in South America after an expedition in the jungles of Brazil.

Our voyage would carry us through a vast span of ocean that was very little known, since it was outside all the usual shipping lanes. We had

therefore been requested to make continuous observations and transfer them via the amateur radio network to the United States Weather Bureau. But unless we should use the radio for calling help, it would not alter the primitive conditions of our experiment in any way.

The first weeks at sea were hard. One man was seasick for several days and confined to the hut; consequently, with the ocean breaking over us, two of us at a time constantly had to battle with the clumsy steering oar, trying to hold our stern against the short, racing seas of the Humboldt Current. [2] We were soon caught by the offshore trade winds [3] and were then only able to sail before the wind. We now realized that we had cut all our bridges and that there was no road back to the coast.

We had been at sea only a couple of days when an airplane flew out to bring us a last farewell. We never saw the plane (our horizons were narrowly fenced in with watery hills on all sides), nor did they see us, but we spoke to them for several hours with our little radio.

After the first weeks we came into calmer seas with long, rolling swells. The great blue ocean was dotted with whitecaps, and trade wind clouds drifted across the blue sky. We had soft days with swimming and rest, and we traveled along in comfort.

---

[1] **hydrographic** (hǐ′drǒ·grăf′ĭk): concerning bodies of water; **meteorologic** (mē′tě·ŏr·ō·lǒj′ĭk): pertaining to the atmosphere and its behavior.

[2] **Humboldt Current:** a cold stream of water that flows north along the coast of Peru and Chile.

[3] The **trade winds** blow almost continually toward the equator, from an easterly direction.

Our drift turned from northwest to west as we left the green and cold Humboldt Current and entered the blue and increasingly warm South Equatorial Current. We made as much progress as 72 miles in one day, with a daily average of 42 miles for the entire voyage. The surface drift exceeded the current drift and occasionally blew us out of the main sweep of the central current.

We found little wearing on the ropes and learned the reason why. The balsa was too soft to chafe them. In case of friction, a rope would soon work itself into the waterlogged surface of the balsa logs and thus remain protected. It was more discomforting to observe that splinters cut from the surface of the logs had become waterlogged and sank when thrown overboard. It had been common opinion in Peru that the logs would be completely submerged before we sighted the islands.

Archaeologists [1] no longer doubt that the prehistoric Peruvians used sails: Not only are there good historical descriptions of rafts equipped with sails, but centerboards of late pre-European date have been found. Our testings with centerboards clearly proved that they are useless on a raft if it is merely paddled or carried along by the current.

The first real excitement we ran into after entering the South Equatorial Current was the largest monster of the seas — the rare but famous whale shark. Accompanied by a shoal of pilot fish, this giant among all fishes slowly caught up with us from astern, and the water splashed around its enormous, white-speckled back as though on a small reef. The fish bumped into the steering oar and placed its huge, froglike head, with tiny eyes and a five-foot mouth, right up against the raft. The whale shark has been measured to a length of 45 feet and undoubtedly grows larger. We would never have dared such an estimate, but while the head appeared on one side of the raft, the tail SIMULTANEOUSLY appeared on the other.

The whale shark kept us company for several hours, and the excitement on board was great, with everybody prepared with spears, hand harpoons, and motion picture camera. The peaceful visit ended when the excited navigator ran his harpoon with all his strength down between his legs and into the cartilaginous [2] head of the monster. During the terrific commotion the whale shark dived, broke the harpoon, snapped the rope, and disappeared.

Only at one other time were we visited by what we suspected to be whale sharks. It was during a fairly calm night when three immensely large and phosphorescent [3] bodies swam in circles under us. But occasionally we ran into schools of whales. The huge, snorting animals rolled

[1] **Archaeologists** (är′kē·ŏl′ō·jĭsts) study human life of earlier times by discovering and reconstructing monuments and relics.

[2] **cartilaginous** (kär′tĭ·lăj′ĭ·nŭs): like cartilage, the tough, elastic substance that makes up most of the framework of the body of young animals.

[3] **phosphorescent** (fŏs′fō·rĕs′ĕnt): gleaming with light, especially in the dark.

right up beside us without the slightest fear. They could have splintered our raft with a single blow of their mighty tails, but after an exhibition of their swimming ability, they left us behind.

Some 600 miles southwest of the Galápagos [1] we were twice visited by giant sea turtles. One was under constant attack by a dozen furious dolphins which tried to snap at the turtle's neck and fins. After sighting the raft, the turtle made its way right up to our side but swam away as soon as it saw us. Three of our men, equipped with rope, pursued the turtle in a tiny, inflatable rubber float, but our visitor escaped while the bewildered dolphins concentrated all their attention on the bouncing little float.

Weather permitting, we often got into our rubber float, two or three at a time, and took a " vacation " from our sturdy log raft to study our craft from a distance. We could imagine the sight that early Peruvian seafarers must have had when they sailed their FLOTILLAS of rafts side by side along the coast — or into the ocean like Inca Tupac Yupanqui,[2] who according to legend discovered some East Pacific islands before the Spanish Conquest. Particularly at night, we experienced an unforgettable sight. Night-black seas, billowing on all sides, and twinkling stars formed our entire world.

The year 1947 — A.D. or B.C. — what did it mean? We were at least alive.

[1] Galápagos (gȧ·lä′pȧ·gŭs).
[2] Inca Tupac Yupanqui (tōō·päk′ yōō·päng′-kē) ruled Peru in the middle of the fifteenth century.

Time had little meaning; we were lost in the endless dark. Ahead of us *Kon-Tiki* rose and then sank between the seas. In moonlight there was an unbelievable atmosphere around the raft. The huge, wet logs fringed with seaweed, the square contour of the sail, the bushy jungle hut with a petrol lamp astern looked like something cut from a fairy tale rather than from reality. Now and then the raft would disappear entirely behind the black sea; then, with water pouring from the logs, it would rise high to be silhouetted against the stars.

Although we spent 101 days and nights drifting on our raft, we never sighted a ship or any floating DEBRIS left by mankind. If a ship had crossed our path during an average day at sea, it would have found us slowly dancing up and down over great rolling swells dotted with minor waves that were stirred up by the trade winds, which constantly blow from the New World into the island domain. A tanned and bearded man, devoid of clothing, would have been sighted at the stern of the raft, either desperately struggling with the ropes of a long steering oar or, if the wind were steady, sitting and dozing in the sun. Bengt would be found on his stomach in the doorway of the hut reading one of his 73 sociological books. Herman would be seen busily occupied anywhere, at the top of the mast, underneath the logs, or running around with instruments to measure wind and water. Knut and Torstein were always struggling with the weather-beaten radio sets, repairing damage and sending our reports at night to the amateur stations that could hear our signals. Erik was always mending sail and splicing rope and sketching fishes and bearded men alike. And each noon he grabbed his sextant and gazed at the sun to determine how far we had moved since the day before. As to myself, I was writing logs,[1] collecting plankton[2] for food experimentation, and fishing or filming.

The day started with a glorious sunrise over the sea, the cook being relieved by the last night watchman to collect the flying fish that had flown on board during the night. These were fried on a small primus stove and devoured at the edge of the raft after a quick morning dip in the sea. Extra flying fish were used as bait for the great colorful dolphin fish that followed the raft day in and day out across the ocean. Dolphins that we did

not eat were used as bait for the great sharks that calmly swam around us day and night. When the sea was high, we could see them sideways as though through a perpendicular glass wall raised high above the level of the raft. Then the raft tipped up and let the water and the slowly moving sharks pass beneath us. They never seemed treacherous except when we cleaned fish, and they scented blood. Then they would wake up in a fury. Yet we never quite trusted them, and in one day we pulled aboard nine six- to ten-foot sharks just to dispose of their intimate company.

When we slid the sharks up onto our shallow and slippery logs, the remoras,[3] clinging to the sharks' skin by suction, would jump off and attach

[1] logs: daily records of a ship's voyage.
[2] plankton: small plants and animals floating or swimming weakly in the water.

[3] Both remoras and pilot fish habitually accompany sharks and eat scraps of food from the prey of the larger fish, but they are never attacked by the sharks.

themselves to the side of the raft; and the pilot fish, having lost their king and master, would find a substitute in *Kon-Tiki*, joining us in nice formation before the bow or between the centerboards. If a big blue shark passed, they would occasionally follow him away, but more than 40 of them tailed us right across the ocean until our raft was shattered on the reef.

Although we carried our rations lashed to the logs beneath the bamboo deck, it was still of great importance to me to find out whether primitive man, accustomed to hardship as he was, would have been able to renew his supply of food and water on such a long-lasting drift. The answer was affirmative. After the fourth day at sea, there was not a single day throughout the journey when we were not accompanied by numbers of dolphin fish. They kept to the side of the raft or beneath us and could be fished, speared, or hooked whenever we desired. EDIBLE barnacles and seaweeds grew all over the huge logs and could be picked like garden greens. And they often housed tiny, edible pelagic crabs or very small fishes. A dozen or more flying fish, often accompanied by baby squids, came aboard almost every night, sailing through the air in schools right above the surface, if pursued by dolphins or sharks. Twice in mid-ocean on dark nights, a long snakelike fish with huge eyes and carnivorous jaws jumped right into our sleeping bags inside the bamboo hut and caused a great commotion. It was probably the *Gempylus,* which was seen this way by

man for the first time, only a couple of skeletons having previously been found on South American shores. Soaked shark meat, delicious bonito, and yellow-fin tuna completed our seafood menu and made it clear enough that early, hardy raftsmen were not menaced by hunger.

We carried 200 coconuts and samples of the Peruvian sweet potato and gourd, which were important food plants that the aborigines of Peru shared with those of Polynesia. Those not eaten en route were successfully planted upon our arrival on the islands, to prove that they could be carried on a raft without loss of GERMINATING power. These prehistoric food plants could never have drifted across the ocean without the aid and care of human hands, and the aboriginal name for sweet potato was *Kumara* — both in Peru and on the Polynesian islands.

The early raftsmen along the dry South American coast carried their water supply in gourds or pottery containers and in huge canes of bamboo with the joints pierced out. Left in the shade underneath the bamboo deck, where they were constantly washed by the seas, we found that our plain Peruvian spring water was preserved for more than two months before the first samples began to rot. At that time we had already entered a part of the ocean where drizzles were frequent and rains occasional, and we were able to collect sufficient rain water for our daily needs. We consumed a ton of water on the journey, along with more than ample rations, and the buoyancy of the balsa logs would have permitted us to double our water supply in easily stored bamboo canes under the deck. With the warm climate creating a demand for salt, we could mix up to 40 per cent of sea water with our drinking water without evil effects. Like our early PREDECESSORS and many sailors shipwrecked during the war, we found several simple methods of abstracting the thirst-quenching juice from raw fish, a supply that never ran short.

In this way, with the days full of testings and practical experiments, we found ourselves carried across the ocean bit by bit. By the forty-fifth day we had drifted from the seventy-eighth meridian to the one hundred-eighth and were exactly halfway to the first islands. During those days we were more than 2,000 miles away from the nearest shore in any direction. When the ocean was smoothly rolling, we could leave our raft in the little float and row away into the blue space between eternal sea and sky. As we watched our grotesque craft growing smaller and smaller in the distance, an oppressive sense of loneliness came over us. It was as though we were suspended in space, like disembodied spirits. When we rowed back to our distant raft, we felt a strange feeling of relief and were happy to crawl on board our precious, weather-beaten logs and find shade from the glaring sun inside the bamboo hut. The now familiar scent of bamboo and thatched roof made us feel that we were back in our earthly

home again, inside a jungle dwelling that was far away from the limitless sea.

We enjoyed our evening meals as the glorious sun sank into the sea before our bow, while sky and water became a dream of colors. Small, striped pilot fish would rush to the surface to snap at our crumbs, and they were occasionally followed by a lazy shark, like kittens by a bulldog.

As darkness came we would light our petrol lamp, and Erik would fetch his guitar. Then merry song and music from the raft spread with the dim light over the nearest waves of a trackless, endless ocean. We would soon roll up on the bamboo matting inside the hut, leaving the watchman alone with the stars and the steering oar.

We hit two storms when we approached the end of the journey. The first lasted one day and the second five. With sail down and ropes shrieking, *Kon-Tiki* rode the breaking ocean like a duck. A raft in high seas with wet and slippery logs and no railing requires careful stepping. The second storm had just begun when Herman went overboard. When visible again, he was seen struggling behind the stern. He struck for the blade of the steering oar, but a strong wind pushed us ahead, and he missed. We could not turn our raft around to go back a single inch. There was no possibility of even stopping our stubborn craft in its reckless trek to the west. The airy float would blow like a feather ahead of the raft if put to sea in such a wind. We threw out a life belt, once, twice, but it blew right back on board. We became desperate as Herman, our best swimmer, was left farther and farther behind. With a line in one hand Knut leaped into the sea, and slowly the two friends worked their way toward each other. Thirty yards behind the raft they joined hands, and the four of us on board pulled them in.

We had a green parrot as ship's pet. It was a perfect sailor and a joyous companion, until a big sea stole it on the sixtieth day.

At the end of the third month, we were constantly visited by Polynesian frigate birds and boobies in increasing numbers. Then we sighted a rising cumulo-nimbus cloud,[1] revealing the existence of some hidden, sun-baked isle beneath the western horizon. We steered for the cloud as best we could, and as the golden sun rose from the sea on the ninety-third day, the blue haze of land was outlined against a reddish sky. We were passing the tiny atoll of Pukapuka, but wind and current would not permit us to turn around. We had covered 4,000 miles of ocean heading west, and yet we could not force ourselves 4 miles to the east to reach the island. More than ever was this a plain and unmistakable lesson, stressing the fact that in this ocean a drifting craft and a natural migration would inevitably be pushed to the west. And it was with strange feelings that we sat quietly down on our raft and saw the little, solid speck of land — the first

and only for twelve weeks — slide away on our port stern. For a moment the wind carried a mild whiff of verdant tropical foliage and smoky native household odors, and we filled our salty lungs before the fata morgana [2] — the mirage of our hopes — sank into the sea.

On the ninety-seventh day, another island grew up out of the ocean, straight ahead of us in line with the bow. As we approached, we saw from the top of the mast that a roaring reef was twisted like a submerged snake all around the island, blocking the approach to the palm-clad beaches behind. All day long we struggled in the current alongside the island to keep clear of the boiling reef and yet be close enough to attempt a landfall wherever an opening might be seen.

Late in the afternoon we sighted the first natives on a beach, and we hoisted all our flags in joy. A great commotion was seen on the beach, and shortly after, the first Polynesians in small outrigger canoes slid through a passage in the reef and swarmed aboard the *Kon-Tiki*. A strong wind blew up, and our ocean raft struggled away from land as the sun went down in the sea. There was a desperate fight against the elements, in which we were assisted by all the friendly natives who were able to get out and join us in the open sea. As the dark night engulfed the island and the sea, a great campfire was lit on shore to show us the direction of the entrance

---

[1] cumulo-nimbus cloud: a cloud with the form of a mountainous billowy mass.

[2] The term fata morgana (fä'tä môr·gä'nä) comes from the name of a legendary fairy who created illusions, or mirages, to deceive men.

through the reef. But the wind increased its grip and won another battle. When the glare of the great fire dwindled like a spark in the distance and the roar of the reef was no longer heard, our excited native friends jumped into their canoes to return to their homes on Angatau for fear of drifting with some crazy strangers into the open sea. And we drifted farther into the heart of the Tuamotu,[1] or Dangerous Archipelago.

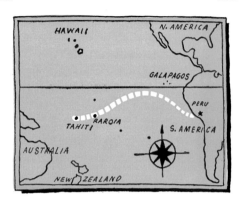

One night an unusual motion of the raft awakened me, and I suspected land ahead. Next morning, our one hundred-first at sea, we were alarmed by the watchman on the top of the mast, who had sighted an enormous reef that spanned the entire horizon ahead of us. It was the treacherous 20-mile reef of Raroia Atoll.[2] With white spray shooting high into the air, the surf battered the endless reef in fury.

As we rode directly into this boiling inferno, we had three hours to prepare for all EVENTUALITIES. We lowered the sail and threw out an improvised anchor on a long rope that kept sliding along the bottom. We carried valuable cargo into the hut and lashed it fast in watertight bags. We cut off all ropes holding the centerboards in position and pulled them up to get a shallow draft. With shoes on for the first time in 100 days, we concentrated on the last order: Hang

on — hang onto the raft whatever happens!

The first walls of thundering water broke down upon us from above as soon as our logs ran against the solid coral reef. Tons of crashing water tore up the deck, flattened the hut, broke the hardwood mast like a match, and splintered the steering oar and stern crossbeam, while we were thrown in and dragged out, thrown in and dragged out, by the furious ocean. During these minutes, when we cramped every existing muscle to withhold the deadly grasp of the passing seas, we made up for all the leisure of the average ocean day. I felt the last of my strength giving away when a wave larger than the others lifted *Kon-Tiki* free of the water and tossed us high up on the reef. Other waves pushed us closer to shore, until we could jump off the raft and wade the shallow coral reef to a tiny, uninhabited coconut island. Never did any tiny piece of land embody paradise so perfectly to me as this verdant, palm-clad isle with its white and shiny beach facing a crystal-clear lagoon, calm as green glass.

---

[1] **Tuamotu** (tōō′ä·mō′tōō) . . . **Archipelago** (är′kĭ·pĕl′á·gō): a group of small islands.

[2] **Raroia Atoll** (rä·roi′yá ăt′ŏl): An atoll is an island, or group of islands, made up of a coral reef surrounding a lagoon.

A week later we were found by natives who had detected from another island six miles across the lagoon the drift wreckage and the light from our campfire. And about the same time *Kon-Tiki* was carried by high seas right across the solid reef and left becalmed inside the lagoon. The nine main logs that had carried us 4,300 miles across the ocean in 101 days were still INTACT, and after an unforgettable two-week Polynesian welcome party on lonely Raroia, our battered raft was towed to Tahiti [1] by the French Government schooner *Tamara,* which was sent expressly to pick us up.

We shall never forget the welcome on these Polynesian islands.

From Tahiti the *Kon-Tiki* was carried as deck cargo back to the Norwegian Museum of Navigation in Oslo.

Noticing Important Details

1. What riddle about the inhabitants of the Polynesian islands was the writer trying to solve? What was his idea? Why were the prevailing winds important in his idea?

2. Behind this true story of an exciting adventure is a scientific experiment. Did you keep the experiment clear in your mind? To check up, tell which of the following details are necessary to the experiment and *why* they are necessary.

   a. avoiding the use of nails, pegs, and wire in building the raft

   b. the visit of the whale shark

   c. carrying water in bamboo canes

   d. finding edible barnacles and seaweeds attached to the raft logs

[1] **Tahiti** (tȧ·hē′tê): the largest of the Windward Islands and the chief port of call for ships on the South Central Pacific.

   e. finding a strange fish in the cabin

   f. catching fish to eat

   g. using a radio to transmit weather reports

   h. carrying sweet potatoes, coconuts, and gourds in the raft to plant on the islands

3. Where did Heyerdahl get the name " Kon-Tiki "? What myths of both the Peruvians and the Polynesians concerned Tiki? Would a scientist accept this similarity in name as *proof* that the Peruvians crossed the Pacific?

Adventure on a Raft

1. Describe the sounds and movements that made sleeping on the raft the first night seem strange. Describe one of the views of the sea that seemed most interesting to you.

2. How did the different members of the crew spend their time? What kinds of scientific information did they record?

3. Divide the class into groups to carry out these projects for a Kon-Tiki exhibit and program:

   a. Read parts of Heyerdahl's book *Kon-Tiki* (Rand McNally, 1950) and tell about interesting happenings or things not covered by this short account.

   b. Make a model of the raft.

   c. If you have an opaque projector, show photographs of the voyage from the book *Kon-Tiki* or from the June 1948 issue of *Natural History.*

Understanding Word Meanings from Context

Here are the words that were suggested for exercise in gaining the meaning of words from context. See if you can remember how each word was used and what meaning you guessed for it.

sinister	flotillas	predecessors
dwindled	debris	eventualities
replica	edible	intact
simultaneously	germinating	

Now check the words in the glossary to see how near you came to the exact meaning, and use each word in a new sentence.

THE
WORLD
AROUND
US

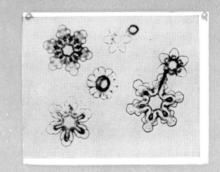

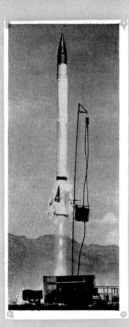

That Mysterious Stuff Called Snow

NORMAN CARLISLE

Strange and faraway places have no monopoly on the wonders of the world. Things that are near enough for your hand to touch have their own mysteries. One man finds a marvel in a single snowflake under a microscope. Another finds the answers he seeks in dealing with thousands and even millions of tons of snow. In this short essay you can share the discoveries of both explorers, and of others, too.

IF SOMEONE who had never seen snow should ask you to define it, you might say it is light, cold, pure, and definitely white. But you could be wrong on all points. The truth is, snow is fantastic stuff, at times so unsnowlike that it flabbergasts even scientists who have spent years studying it.

You may agree with the poets who sing about its beauties, yet snow can actually be a ruthless killer. You may, like the harried officials charged with clearing it from streets and highways, term it a nuisance. However, snow happens to be so enormously valuable that, far from trying to get rid of it, scientists are busy figuring out ways to *save* it. Add up all the contradic-

tory facts and you have one of nature's most fascinating paradoxes.[1]

Take the business of weight. A handful of snow seems light, but get enough of it in one spot and it becomes enormously heavy. A weather forecaster, who left a large galvanized pail lying on its side when the first snowfall of the season came, discovered in the spring that the snow had crushed it flat.

On the other hand, snow is one of the world's best insulating materials. At Milton, Massachusetts, a scientist took a thermometer reading of 19 below zero at three feet above the snow's surface. He next held the thermometer directly above the snow and the mercury dived to 27 below. Then he pushed the thermometer into the snow for seven inches. The reading showed 24 *above* zero! Those seven inches of fluffy white made a difference of 51 degrees!

Scientists have given truth to the old saying "pure as the driven

[1] A **paradox** (păr′a̲·dŏks) is a statement that seems to contradict itself, or a situation containing contradictory elements. Many riddles are paradoxes, for example, "The more it dries the wetter it gets. What is it?" (A towel.)

snow" by proving that only one-billionth of the average flake is made up of impurities. But sometimes a snowstorm gets mixed up with a cloud of dust and produces strange results. One of the most recent phenomena occurred in Chicago in 1947, when a January snow astonished citizens by its dark brown color.

Surprisingly enough, even snow free from dust is not always white. In 1911 a group of mountain climbers in Yosemite National Park were amazed to discover that their pack animals were leaving red tracks. At first they thought the mules must have been injured; then one man picked up a handful of snow and squeezed. It turned to red!

Red snow has been observed in many parts of the world, and yellow as well. The explanation is simple: tiny colored plants contained in the flakes, though sometimes snow has to be compressed before the color can been seen.

A Hungarian woman scientist, Erzsebet Kol, explored mountains in Alaska to find out more about these plants, and discovered at least 50 varities that seemed to "grow" in snow. The strangest effect she found was "polka-dot" snow — an area dotted with splotches of red plants.

Snow is probably at its most fascinating state as individual flakes. The knowledge that no two are exactly alike can be traced to a man who devoted his life to studying snow crystals.

In Vermont, in the eighties, a farmer reluctantly paid $100 for a micro-scope and camera for his son who wanted, of all things, to take pictures of snowflakes. The boy was Wilson Bentley, later to become world-famous as "The Snowflake Man."

Bentley took his first picture when he was 19, and kept on photographing flakes for 12 years before he received recognition. Scientists scoffed at the strange shapes of the crystals: they claimed that he, not nature, had arranged the flakes in such fantastic forms as hexagons with scalloped edges. But gradually their skepticism changed to wonder, and from all over America they began asking Bentley for prints of his marvelous photographs.

Despite his scrutiny, however, there is something in a snowflake that Bentley never saw — a tiny electrical charge. Air pilots notice its effect on their radios when they encounter a snowstorm. Scientists were puzzled by the fact that snow caused static during flight yet didn't affect planes on the ground.

To solve the mystery, Vincent Schaefer, General Electric's wizard of snow, measured the electric charges of individual flakes and found them so slight that even billions of crystals could hardly create the static. Then he tried hurling flakes against a metal plate at high speeds, in much the manner that they would strike a plane in flight.

Sure enough, he got the static, and found the answer when he examined the particles that had smashed against the metal. They had been shattered into as many as 500 fragments, and somehow this process had increased their electrical charge as much as 100 times!

To New York City authorities, snow is just a multimillion-dollar headache. They live in fear of another snowfall like that of December, 1947, when 90,000,000 tons fell in the New York City area. It took more than 30,000 men and cost $6,000,000 to remove it from Manhattan alone.

Yet the storm of '47 falls far short of being the champ among snowfalls. The all-time whopper, if old reports can be believed, occurred February 4, 1798, at Norfolk, Virginia, when 60 inches fell! Incredible as it seems, another 40 inches fell a few days later.

For seasonal snowfalls, Tamarack, California, holds the all-time record. There, during the winter of 1906–07, astonished snow surveyors discovered that the fall for the season totaled 884 inches, or almost 74 feet!

In the mountains of the West, snow is regarded not as a menace but as a " billion-dollar crop." For what happens in the lofty ranges of the Sierras and the Rockies during the winter months represents the difference between disaster and prosperity for millions of people in 11 Western states.

Will melting snows yield enough water to fill streams and reservoirs? Getting the answer to that question costs state governments a million a year for snow surveying. On skis, snowshoes, and aboard a curious gasoline-powered vehicle called the Sno-Cat, the surveyors venture far beyond civilization to take readings on 1,000 snow courses.

What they find out by thrusting pipes into the snow makes big news when they emerge from the wilderness. Their predictions are miracles of accuracy. They can tell, for instance, that there will be a drought in August because the snow isn't deep enough in March.

The surveyor may go armed with scientific apparatus, but the thing he needs most is plain courage, for he has one of the most hazardous jobs on earth.

One surveyor and his partner were skiing along their survey route in the Nevada mountains. They had reached the base of a steep slope when suddenly, with a terrifying roar, tons of snow swept down, burying them both.

When he came to, the surveyor saw a faint gleam above and realized he was beside a tree against which the snow had piled loosely. Agonizing pain shot through his leg, telling him it must be broken, but he pulled himself up from branch to branch until he reached the surface. Nearby he found his partner's dead body.

The surveyor was alone in the wilderness, miles from the nearest settlement, yet somehow — just how, he never knew — he managed to make his way to a cabin where he received aid. Doctors found no less than six broken bones, but he was back on the job the next season.

In Canada, a scientist has made a striking discovery about snow conservation that opens breath-taking possibilities for increasing our food supply. T. C. Aylwin, Ottawa engineer, became increasingly concerned about the great prairies of western Canada. They are vast and fertile, but they do not raise anything like the crops they could because the few summer rains do not provide enough moisture. And even though snow blankets them in the winter, most of the snow evaporates. What is left in the spring quickly runs off because the ground is frozen too hard to absorb water.

Agricultural scientists figure that loss at more than four inches — the difference between lush crops and scanty ones. Couldn't something be done to save that precious moisture?

First, Aylwin had to find the reason why so much snow evaporated. He prowled around snow-covered fields, probing, testing, taking temperature readings. The answer, he found, was that the snow presented too much surface to the air. In addition to the spaces between the granules, there were fissures through which currents of air moved, carrying the moisture with them into the atmosphere.

Now it was necessary to cut down that exposed surface by packing those granules together and closing the fissures. To accomplish this, Aylwin worked out a kind of sled which was really a stove on runners. This contraption, pulled across the surface of the snow, melted it and formed a thin coating of ice.

That worked all right. There was virtually no evaporation. Instead, the water trickled through the granules of snow, softening the ground and soaking into it. But Aylwin couldn't pull heated sleds across millions of acres of prairie.

What about the sun? Why not let it do the work? True, the winter temperature of the prairies stayed well below freezing, but if Aylwin could put a *black* surface on the snow, it would absorb enough sunlight to melt it and form a protective crust of ice.

Aylwin tinkered until he produced a smoke-making machine which, mounted on a sled, quickly sprays a thin coating of carbon. Adapted to use in a helicopter, the machine might be utilized to spray large areas.

More experiments are needed, but optimistic agriculturists believe the kinks can be ironed out in the near future. Within a few years they visualize fabulous yields from rich, virginal soil that has simply been awaiting the magic of science to make it add millions of tons to the world's food supply.

Some Puzzling Pairs

1. Most of the facts about snow in this article are paired off in contradictions that make a paradox, like " light, but heavy." Make a list of all the contradictions about snow that you found in your reading. Then explain why both parts of each paradox are true.

2. You can think of other contradictory views of snow besides those the writer mentions. Try writing a short sketch of the thoughts and feelings of a busy mother when she wakes to find snow falling outside, and another from the point of view of her ten-year-old son. Or you might choose another pair of contrasting viewpoints you think of yourself.

3. Describe the experiment being conducted in Canada. Why is the moisture

from the snow largely lost at present? Can you see a connection between the engineer's use of a black covering and the fact that people often become " sunburned " in snowy country?

Fitting Words to the Occasion

In an informal, chatty essay like this one, a writer may use words like *flabbergast* and *whopper,* and even slang like *champ* for *champion.* How would he probably change the first two words in making a serious report to a meeting of scientists?

Words that are acceptable in conversation or informal writing but not on formal occasions are called *colloquialisms.* In a dictionary they are labeled with the abbreviation *colloq.* Find in your dictionary three other colloquialisms. Tell occasions when they could properly be used and still other occasions when more formal terms would be needed. What formal terms would be good substitutes for them?

Snow

ELIZABETH COATSWORTH

A snow can come as quietly
as cats can walk across a floor.
It hangs its curtains in the air
and piles its weight against the door.
It fills old nests with whiter down   5
than any swan has ever known,
and then as silent as it came,
you find the pale snow bird has flown.

But snow can come quite otherwise,
with windy uproar and commotion,   10
with shaken trees and banging blinds,
still salty from a touch of ocean.
Such storms will wrestle with strong boys
and set the girls' skirts wildly blowing
until it throws its cap in air   15
and shouts, " Well, good-by now! I'm going! "

First of the Menfish

JAMES DUGAN

Sometime or other everybody has wished that he could fly through the air like a bird or cruise about under water like a fish. We still have to get inside a sizable machine to fly, but a French inventor has figured out a simple way to make the second wish come true.

IN THE clear, warm waters of the French Riviera[1] a new species of large fish have been observed in the last few years — one-eyed monsters shaped and colored like nude human beings with green rubber tail fins, gills of metal, and tubular scales on their backs.

They are divers who swim around sportively at hundred-foot depths, examining sunken ships, taking photographs, and harpooning big fish. They are the first of the menfish, a new order of marine life invented by Lieutenant Cousteau[2] of the French Navy.

Commander Cousteau, to use his equivalent rank in the U.S. Navy, has

[1] **Riviera** (rĭv′ĭ·âr′à): the region along the Mediterranean seacoast.

[2] **Cousteau** (kōōs′tō′).

developed a 35-pound diving lung which allows ordinary human beings to descend into the sea and swim around freely for a couple of hours without diving suits or lines to the surface. "We are simply naked men in the sea, carrying the breathing apparatus and fins of a fish," Cousteau says.

The arrival of menfish in the zoological table does not have to be believed on the Commander's word. He has filmed in color three magnificent motion pictures under water, showing Cousteau divers at work and play, *Sixty Feet Down, Sunken Ships,* and *Landscape of Silence.*

The revolutionary Cousteau diving lung consists of three parallel compressed air tanks strapped to the back. Flexible metal air hoses cross the swimmer's shoulders to a rubber face mask with an eight-inch circular glass window. Exhaled air passes out behind the head. The diver wears only bathing trunks and rubber foot fins in addition to the lung. The lung allows a swimmer to cruise 100 feet down for nearly three hours before surfacing. Cousteau has gone down 210 feet with his invention.

The magical component of the lung is the Cousteau-Gagnan valve. It was named for the diver and a colleague, who produced a demand valve which automatically releases just the amount of compressed air required by the human lung.

Since the compressed air is bottled at 300 atmospheres of pressure,[1] the valve is something of an engineering marvel. It makes a Cousteau Diver as superior to the rubber-suited and lead-weighted salvage diver as the airplane is superior to the captive balloon. For the first time, man has been enabled to move around freely under the sea without cords tying him to his air element.

The human lung is capable of withstanding water pressure over 300 feet down. The real danger of depth is the effect of pressure on the mental processes. The U.S. Navy finds that divers using compressed air become irrational at about 200 feet below. Cousteau, on the other hand, says that lungs using oxygen from which most of the other air elements have been removed (which the U.S. Navy prefers) black a man out at 60 feet down.

Twice in his early experiments, Cousteau suffered the giddy elation of anoxia (oxygen deficiency) while breathing oxygen at ten fathoms (60 feet); so he feels much safer with compressed air when he has occasion

to shoot a movie sequence 20 fathoms deep. Both Cousteau and the Navy agree that mixing helium[2] into the air supply helps a man keep his wits about him down below. This may be an important element in his survival.

Cousteau is not interested in depths over 100 feet for the simple reason that it becomes too dark to make movies. The entire motive for the 15 years of work he has put into his lung was to make films under water. He bought his first movie camera when he was 14 and began his persistent efforts to make movies under water. After he joined the Navy his experiments occupied all his off time. His first film, *Sixty Feet Down*, 1940, depicts goggle-divers hunting fish.

His lung was not ready until 1942 when Hitler unwittingly gave him the time off to produce the submarine masterpiece, *Sunken Ships*. Cousteau helped scuttle the French fleet at Toulon when Hitler moved into Southern France to counter the Allied invasion of North Africa. Cousteau was demobilized and, with the consent of the Resistance committee in the Navy, began an intensive series of dives in a 35-mile stretch of sea floor near Marseilles.[3]

The Germans patrolled the coast diligently for Allied landings. But they forgot to look under the water for Cousteau and his original divers, Captain Philippe Tailliez and Frederic Dumas,[4] who made 170 camera dives in 1943, spending a total of ten

[1] **300 atmospheres of pressure:** 300 times the weight of air at sea level.

[2] **helium** (hē′lĭ·ŭm): a very light, colorless gas.
[3] **Marseilles** (mär·sālz′).
[4] **Philippe Tailliez** (fē′lēp′ tä′yā′). **Dumas** (dōō·mä′).

days in the depths of the Mediterranean. They explored 15 sunken ships, impaled hundreds of fish with their *arbalètes* [1] or harpoon guns, and produced a four-reel movie.

The occupying Germans would have given anything for the diving equipment Cousteau was using under their noses. Their navy was feverishly financing submarine research trying to evolve free-diving equipment for military purposes. One of the Nazi experimenters was lowering his ponderous diving bells in the very waters the menfish dominated.

Cousteau carried an order from the Natural History Museum in Paris, certifying that he was a marine biologist crazy about sponges, in case the Nazis asked him any questions. They never did. It was beyond credulity to suspect that three lean holidayers with equipment no larger than a picnic hamper who were slipping into the sea from rockheads, jetties, [2] and fishing boats, were masters of a new diving system.

A Cousteau diver swims under

[1] *arbalètes* (är·bȧ·lĕtz′).
[2] jetties: structures like piers, built out into the ocean to protect harbors.

water as easily up and down as he does sideways because of a unique breathing technique perfected by Cousteau. The diver has exact suspension in the water, without weights or buoys. When he enters the water with tanks full, he weighs about four pounds more than a like amount of salt water. He cancels out the pull of gravity by taking systematic deep breaths. As the dive progresses and the compressed air is expended, breathing becomes less in volume and quicker, until at the end of a two-and-one-half-hour dive, the swimmer — and his depleted air tanks — weighs four pounds less than his displacement of water, and he is taking short rapid breaths to maintain his suspension.

The Cousteau diver swims at the speed of a walk using only his foot fins. His hands are used as rudders and are free to handle objects under water.

The film shows Captain Tailliez and Dumas exploring the shipwrecks, swimming lightly through the ruins of ships, brushing familiarly past the shimmering leaves of the sea floor. The diver is accepted by the fish, who

do not flee as he stirs up little gusts of seadust and exhales his silver trail of breath.

The oldest shipwreck filmed in *Sunken Ships* is that of a paddle-wheel steamer which sank in 1880. Since then, Commander Cousteau has looked into a Greek galley sunk in the first century B.C.; and last year he swam down in the ancient port of Carthage off Tunisia to see if there were anything the Romans had not destroyed in their total obliteration [1] of the Carthaginians.

The largest and most interesting wreck was that of the Greek steamer *Dalton,* sunk off Planier Island in the Gulf of Lions on Christmas Eve of 1928. The film shows Dumas flipping around the weed-grown hulk of the *Dalton* and disappearing gracefully down an open hatch. The camera follows Dumas down a companionway, watches him open stateroom doors, and sit prankishly in a very full bath tub. He selects a couple of souvenir china plates. Long immersion had given the white plates delicate rainbow hues. Cousteau keeps them on the mantelpiece of his home, along with a brass ship's wheel handsawed from another sunken derelict. They are his only mementoes of the deep. He has never found a coin. Cousteau is convinced there is not much money lying around the bottom.

As the divers glide below decks in the sepulchral [2] ships, keen suspense comes to those who see Cousteau's film: When will they find a skeleton in Davy Jones' locker? They never do. Cousteau has found no human remains in the several dozen shipwrecks he has explored during his years of diving.

He felt the absence of this standard romantic prop when making *Sunken Ships;* so he hired himself a medical skeleton and carried it down under his arm to plant in the *Dalton.* " It made beautiful film," he said, " but we did not use the sequence. It was fake. I have no untruths in my pictures."

Cousteau says there isn't anything to be afraid of " downstairs," as he refers to the domain of the Cousteau diver. Sharks, barracudas, and octopuses he views as everyday passersby in the deep. Man-eaters are intimidated by the streaming exhalations of the submarine swimmer. The principal dangers are sea urchins and coral, which can inflict severe cuts that may let a lot of blood [3] before the swimmer gets upstairs.

Cousteau divers always swim in pairs. " When you lose the hue of the surface," he says, " then all depends on your friend."

At 90 feet down, the sea world has no orientation of sunlight, and exists of itself in a gray-green gloom. One day on the Mediterranean floor, Dumas was prospecting a lost freighter when he innocently allowed a torn deckrail to pass between his naked shoulder and his air hose. He had swum a distance along the rail before Cousteau sounded an alarm on his

[1] **obliteration** (ŏb·lĭt′ēr·ā′shŭn): complete wiping out, destruction.
[2] **sepulchral** (sē·pŭl′krăl): suggesting a tomb.

[3] **let . . . blood:** cause it to be lost.

handbell. Dumas stopped and Cousteau swam to him. The hose had not been punctured, but Dumas was looped 15 feet down the jagged rail.

The divers put their face-plates together and discussed the situation — underwater swimmers can hear speech up to two feet apart. Cousteau could not wrench the rail loose without endangering Dumas' air hose. They decided on the only thing: Cousteau wrapped his hands around the hose and Dumas swam backwards with skillful kicks of his flippers, and finally freed himself. " We shook hands," said Cousteau, " and surfaced. We stopped diving until we had replaced the rubber air hoses with flexible metal."

Cousteau made many clandestine [1] dives from fishing boats during the enemy occupation. At the time, certain fishermen had taken to dynamiting fish. Cousteau saw what they were doing to the sea floor; the explosions made a wasteland of the marine vegetation, driving the fish off their pasturage. He went downstairs one day and filmed an acre of rich bottomland. When he surfaced he had the fishermen detonate a charge over the area. Then he dived again and recorded the destruction. When he showed the before-and-after lesson to the fishing syndicate, public opinion put an end to dynamiting. Cousteau's draggermen [2] cronies were fascinated when he showed them films of their otter trawls snaking across the sea prairie like paper dragons in a Chinese New Year's parade. They knew the performance only in theory.

He made a camera dive from a dragger during a wailing mistral.[3] The apprehensive fishermen saw him consumed by six-foot whitecaps and prayed for a miracle to cast up the demented artist. In a half-hour his Cyclopean [4] mask popped out of the trough and he was hauled aboard. His films showed them the astonishing life of the sea in storm; six feet under the wind-lashed waves the sea was calm and sleepy. The stems of marine grass stirred languidly in the agitated prisms of light cast down from the waves, and little fish lazed in the turbid water.

Cousteau offered his short subject as proof that fisherfolk could go in after a man swept overboard in a gale and have good odds of bringing him in alive. The Cousteau lung is ideal equipment for lifesaving at sea and on bathing beaches. A Cousteau-equipped lifeguard could go out in the undertow after any swimmer who had been drawn away.

As the first of the menfish, Commander Cousteau merely wants to be the poet of the new realm he has claimed for men. He sighs when he tries to describe what it is like to live in the sea. " I cannot tell you how much better than the imagination it is downstairs," he says.

---

[1] **clandestine** (klăn·dĕs′tĭn): conducted with care for secrecy.

[2] **draggermen**: fishermen who drag large nets, called trawls, behind their boats.

[3] **mistral** (mĭs′trăl): a violent wind.

[4] **Cyclopean** (sī′klŏ·pē′ăn): The round glass in the front of the mask made it look like the giant Cyclops, who had only one large eye.

Exploring the Underwater World

1. Why did Commander Cousteau want to find a way to move about freely under water? How did he solve the problem?

2. When did the Cousteau divers try out their equipment? Why didn't the Germans discover what they were doing?

3. How did Cousteau's demonstrations affect the practices of French fishermen? What did his films teach them?

4. What did the divers discover in sunken ships? What did they fail to find?

Can We Survive in Space?

HEINZ HABER

BIG IDEAS ABOUT A BIG SUBJECT. Not so long ago talk of a trip to the moon was in a class with tales of flying carpets and seven-league boots. Now space travel is a subject for serious discussion by scientists. Some are at work on designs for rocket ships and even satellite space stations that will revolve around the earth like another moon. The chief uncertainty left is how to keep man alive in outer space. That problem is discussed here by a doctor in the United States Air Force School of Aviation Medicine.

Like all scientists, or anyone else who is trying to put information into a clear order, this author clusters his facts and opinions around several main ideas. By this arrangement he keeps related information neatly together so that the reader can recognize the central ideas quickly. To help you spot them, the editors have printed certain statements that express the main point of each part of the article in italic type, *like this.* Notice how the rest of the paragraph, or even several paragraphs that follow, will fill in the details that make these italicized statements clear and definite. Be on the lookout for summary sentences like these in your other reading. Locating the central ideas and relating the details to them will make it easy for you to remember new information in an orderly fashion.

A̲LL day long, the frail little man attending the forum had listened to the engineers and scientists discuss the conquest of the heavens with huge rocket ships and space stations. Now he had a question.

" Mr. Chairman," he said, " you fellows seem to have worked out all the details. You know how your rocket ships should be designed, you even have plans on paper for machines to reach the moon and other planets. But as an ordinary layman who knows little about these matters, I would like to ask this one question:

"Who is going to design the crew?"

The questioner had put his finger on the greatest difficulty facing the engineers, scientists, and doctors in reaching space — man himself.

If the jet plane, guided missile, or rocket ship is not perfect, the engineer can redesign the machine over and over until all the kinks have been ironed out. He has a great variety of materials and devices at his disposal. He may eventually succeed in developing a flawless machine. The same cannot be said for man. He is the most important link, and yet the weakest one, in any attempt to conquer space. And he cannot be redesigned.

True, man can adapt himself to extraordinary conditions — he manages to survive anywhere on the face of this globe. But what will happen to him if he ventures into the alien [1] environment known as space — the void beyond the atmosphere?

There is no oxygen for breathing.

The lack of atmospheric pressure can cause his blood to boil.

Dangerous radiation (ultraviolet rays) from the sun hits him with full force and can broil him within minutes.

Atomic bullets, called cosmic rays, plow through his body.

He will be weightless, floating helplessly about, with no up or down.

In short, man was not made to survive in the "hostile territory of space." *It becomes the problem of the engineers, therefore, to create a high-*

ly mobile, self-contained, "packaged" environment for space-faring man. In other words, he needs an airtight shell to produce and preserve earthly conditions as nearly as possible.

Man is extremely hard to please in his demands, but the engineers can lick the problem and supply the crew of a rocket ship or space station with all the necessities for survival. Neither rocket ship nor space station will have the snug comfort of Mother Earth, the flying through space will be a rough job that will call for healthy, tough, and physically well-trained individuals. But it can be done.

Some pessimists [2] maintain that the crew members of a rocket ship wouldn't live to experience space, because they wouldn't even survive the tremendous stresses placed upon them during the ascent. The thrust of the operating rocket motors exerts strong forces upon the ship and its passengers. A motorist gets an inkling of one of these forces: if he steps on the accelerator, he is gently pressed against the back of the automobile seat. But this soft pressure in a car becomes a crushing force in a fast-rising rocket ship. As the space vehicle is whipped forward by the fiery jet of its escaping gases, the force increases in a slowly rising, irresistible surge. To the passenger, it will appear as though several men his own weight are standing on his chest. He will find it difficult to breathe. The acceleration will distend his features into a grotesque mask.

[1] alien (āl′yĕn): foreign, strange.

[2] pessimists (pĕs′ĭ·mĭsts): people who tend to take the least hopeful view of a situation.

The stress of acceleration is not, of course, the only hazard man will encounter as he leaves the friendly atmosphere of the earth. *A continuously flowing supply of breathing air is a necessity in the emptiness of space.* Man can live without food or water for a considerable length of time. But without oxygen he can live only a few minutes. The crew of the space station must not be allowed to run low on oxygen at any time. Rocket ships will replenish the oxygen containers of the satellites [1] at regular intervals.

Another problem, also tied up with the elementary fact that man cannot live without oxygen, is created by the existence of *meteorites.*[2] *They are the most important single danger to all space-travel projects.*

Unfortunately, " empty " space beyond the atmosphere is by no means completely empty. In fact, you might call it a " no man's land " in which ultra-high-speed cosmic " bullets " fly about at random. Hundreds of millions of these " bullets " of various sizes enter the earth's atmosphere every day and often can be seen as meteors or shooting stars. When a cosmic pebble the size of a pea strikes the upper atmosphere, the air resistance heats it until it burns away. This can be seen hundreds of miles distant as a bright streak or flare. Such a meteor hurtling through space at 25 miles a second would puncture more than an inch of armor plate. Very small meteors, the size of large grains of sand, could riddle the thin walls of the space station, permitting the air to escape.

However, engineering can do something even about the meteoric menace. One device, suggested by Dr. Fred L. Whipple of Harvard University's Department of Astronomy, is called a " meteor bumper " and consists of a thin secondary wall placed an inch or so outside the main wall of the space station or rocket ship. Incoming meteors would shatter on the outer wall, leaving the inner wall intact. If properly constructed of heavy enough materials, the meteor bumper could reduce the hazards very considerably, stopping 99 out of 100 meteors.

But even with these safety measures, there remains a probability that once every few years a relatively large meteor will smash through both walls of the space station. What would happen to the crew in that compartment?

The air would whistle out, and

---

[1] satellites (săt′ĕ·lĭts): that is, the space stations on the satellites. Any body that revolves around a larger body (like the moon around the earth) is a satellite.

[2] meteorites (mē′tē·ẽr·īts): stony or metallic bodies moving through outer space.

there would be a rapid drop in pressure. The crew would have exactly fifteen seconds left to restore their oxygen supply before losing consciousness. Without the oxygen they would die in a few minutes. In the early days of space exploration, it may be found safest to wear a pressure suit even in the pressurized cabin of the rocket ship. But because of the protective devices inside the space station, pressure suits might be worn there only in times of emergency.

Pressure suits for use by the crew outside the space station can be made of several layers of rubberized nylon topped by a sturdy metal helmet. The helmet's window would have to be made with a darkened piece of transparent material to ward off the sun's excessive ultraviolet rays. Of course the crew members will carry their own oxygen, and the suits will be equipped with a small air-conditioning unit for removing the exhaled stale gases.

In venturing into space, man abandons the powerful shield or filter of the atmosphere which protects him on earth from the hazards of the little-known effects of cosmic rays. These atomic bullets — which, like the meteors, crisscross space at enormous speeds — are one of the great mysteries of the region beyond our atmosphere. Scientists know they exist and

have measured their biological effectiveness. They may be dangerous.

Cosmic rays are potentially dangerous because they are related to some of the types of rays produced in atomic explosions and in the manufacture of the A-bomb. Civil defense has made the public conscious of the term " radiation sickness." Will exposure in space cause radiation sickness?

We have no clear-cut answer to this question. Cosmic rays are so powerful that they cannot be reproduced artificially in the laboratory. But, although we do not know where they come from, we do know that they are extremely rare. We can conclude, therefore, that short trips through the thin rain of cosmic rays will almost certainly be harmless affairs. A round-the-moon trip can be made without getting radiation sickness.

Of course, long before man ventures into space, animals will be sent up in small rocket ships for the study of radiation effects over extended periods of time. A sheep, a rooster, and a duck were the first living beings to take to the air in a balloon, more than 150 years ago. And it seems that more such honors are in store for the animal kingdom. But, in the final analysis, the exploration of space must await the arrival of man.

It will be, needless to say, a strange experience. And one of its strangest

aspects will be the absence of gravity (except within the space station, which will provide its own "synthetic gravity" by spinning slowly to produce centrifugal force [1]). *The result of the lack of gravitational pull will be weightlessness — and there can be no doubt that weightlessness will be the most unearthly and unforgettable experience shared by those who venture beyond the earth's atmosphere.* Space and weightlessness will become synonymous, like desert and thirst, or arctic and cold.

While the machinery of the body will go on operating in an orderly fashion even if it is weightless, man will possibly encounter trouble when he attempts to go about his daily routine. Weightless man may well find himself in this position:

Imagine a muscular weight lifter taking a good grip on what he thinks is a solid 300-pound weight, but is actually a much lighter contraption made of wood. His anticipation is utterly deceived, and the ill-adjusted strength he applies, to his great surprise, throws the fake weight violently upward.

Space-faring man will consistently experience much the same thing: he will find that his co-ordination, based on a lifelong experience with gravity, suddenly fails him in this new environment. A simple movement on earth, such as rising from his chair, will, in space, jerk him across the cabin toward the opposite wall. The co-ordination of the body, which is so automatic here on earth that we take it for granted, will have to be acquired all over again.

Since the customary effects of gravity are absent, there is no "up" or "down" — a factor certain to prove confusing. Normally, we rely to a great extent on gravity for orientation.[2] But in a rocket ship, all orientation will depend on the eyes. It probably can be acquired, but until it has been learned, there exists the possibility of "space sickness," which will reduce efficiency even if it does not completely incapacitate [3] the crew.

Not only the men will float around aimlessly in the weightlessness of a coasting rocket ship — objects will do the same, and this will cause trouble if careful thought is not given to the design beforehand.

In space, we must use other forces to substitute for gravity. Every metal object must be made of steel, or at least have a steel strip inlaid somewhere on it. Such tools can be kept in place with magnets, along the lines of the magnetic knife board in use in many of today's kitchens. Where magnetism cannot do the job, as with papers, friction will have to substitute for gravity — the clip-board is an everyday example of such a device.

As for eating utensils, the function of the knife and fork will remain the same. The knife still cuts and the fork utilizes friction to hold food after it

---

[1] **centrifugal** (sĕn·trĭf′ŭ·găl) **force:** the force that tends to thrust a body outward from a rotating center.

[2] **orientation** (ō′rĭ·ĕn·tā′shŭn): the sense of one's position in relation to surroundings or specific objects.

[3] **incapacitate** (ĭn′ka·păs′i·tāt): disable, put out of action.

has been speared. The spoon, however, is useless aboard a rocket ship (and so is the fork when used like a spoon), so the well-planned table in space will include some offspring of the sugar tongs, something which will hold food by friction.

Liquids will be especially annoying; any liquid from milk to Burgundy is likely to imitate what any bottled heavy sauce does on the ground. If you tilt a bottle in space nothing will come out, for, since the liquid does not weigh anything, there is no reason for it to pour. But when you shake the bottle, all the contents will come out in one splash. The solution to that particular problem is a very old invention: the drinking straw, which does not rely on gravity but on air pressure. Another method: plastic bottles, which, when squeezed, eject liquid.

Cooking aboard the space station will not be too difficult, because the satellite enjoys synthetic gravity. However, in rocket ships it will be quite different from the same process on the ground. Open pots or pans are useless, for boiling water will simply erupt from an open pot because of the steam bubbles which form at the bottom. Likewise, the first explosive sizzle of a steak's fat will send the meat floating across the cabin. Only closed cooking pots can be used and the ideal broiler is the so-called electronic range which cooks by short wave. (Naturally, if the crew members of the rocket ship are wearing pressure suits, they will have to open the visors of their helmets to eat.)

In long rocket-ship trips from the space station to other planets, seasoned space travelers may enjoy sleeping literally on an air cushion, just floating in air, possibly with a string tied to their wrists or ankles so that the reaction of their breathing will not "float" them away.

So far, we don't know whether the familiar pressure of a bed against the body is necessary for falling asleep. If it is, it can be "faked" during the weightless state by having a set of rubber straps force the body against a board or other flat surface. Beginners, however, will have to sleep in special bunks. These will look like six-foot lengths of pipe, upholstered inside and equipped with wire mesh covers at both ends. These wire mesh covers — the "wire" would probably be nylon string and the mesh widely spaced — would keep the sleeper inside his "bed." Without them, he might push himself out of it by unconscious movements or even be sucked over to the outlet end of the air-conditioning system.

For most of us, weightlessness will hardly be an agreeable and welcome feeling, and learning to live with it may prove a painful lesson. However, man has an astonishing ability to adjust himself to extreme conditions. A few individuals may even get to enjoy weightlessness, after a fashion. The crew members will probably be able to master its intricacies and go about their daily chores with ease.

We can be reasonably certain that man will be able to survive in space because we have sufficient knowledge of what will happen to the rocket ship or space station and to man himself. We can plan intelligently for his survival. Unlike the earth's early explorers, the pioneers of space know pretty well what they are headed for, and they know that they will be equipped adequately.

The conquest of space hinges on man's survival in space. And the crews of rocket ships and space stations, while they can never be completely protected against hazards such as meteors, will probably be safer than pedestrians crossing a busy street at a rush hour.

Relating Facts to the Main Ideas

1. See if you can set down from memory the main points of this article contained in the italicized sentences. Then see how many detailed facts you can recall to support each main point.

2. Like most well-written articles, this one has a distinct introduction and conclusion. Either of these sections would be out of place in the middle of the article. Find one sentence in the first part, and one in the last part, that you would italicize as the main statements of the introduction and conclusion. Can you find one central idea that covers all the main ideas of the various parts of the discussion?

3. One good test of whether a statement expresses a main idea is to see if it is broad enough to cover all the details relating to it. How does the italicized statement on page 178 dealing with gravity cover all the details about the eating, cooking, and sleeping that follow it?

4. Why does the author suggest it will be harder to adapt man to life in space than to design rocket ships to take him there?

5. Have one member of the class read briefly on gravity in the encyclopedia and explain why man will be weightless when he travels in space. Let others who are space-travel fans explain the basic design of space rockets and of the satellite space station. You can find descriptions and pictures in *Collier's* for March 22, 1952.

Quest for the Lost City

DANA AND GINGER LAMB

The desire to know more about how people lived in past ages often leads to strange adventures. The husband and wife in this story, Dana and Ginger Lamb, set out to search for the lost city of the Maya [1] Indians in the jungles of Guatemala in Central America.

[1] **Maya** (mä′yä).

More than four hundred years ago, when Cortes and other Spanish conquerors invaded the New World, they destroyed the native Indian cities and civilization. The Maya Indians were supposed to have fled into a remote, impassable jungle called the Forbidden Land. Here, the legends say, they built a new capital city, with many temples. The group finally died out, leaving behind the "Lost City," and the legend that hidden underground somewhere in the ruins were eleven gold plates. Besides being valuable works of art, the plates recorded the history of the once-proud Mayas.

You are about to read part of the Lambs' story of their quest. It begins just as they have reached the edge of the Forbidden Land. They have come over rocky roads and trails down the western coast of Mexico to Guatemala; they have canoed up rivers and across lakes, they have been lost in an underground cavern, and they have fought through tropical jungles and heat and mud and insects. Now they are in great suspense. Will they find native Indians, perhaps a Lost Tribe of the Mayas, and will the natives help them — or kill them?

AT LONG last, from the top of a hill, we saw, off toward the horizon, a table-topped mountain. The mountain of the pyramid! The key to the Lost Tribe and to the Lost City!

Turning to Ginger, I said, " From here on, we have to think out every step in advance."

" Haven't we always? " she asked.

I nodded. " Only now, we're close to a tribe that has probably never seen a white man. They may hate and fear us because of tales handed down from their ancestors who fought Cortes [1] and his captains. Maybe they know we've arrived, maybe they don't. Let's find a nice, open camp site with nothing hidden or secret about it; and set up a permanent camp."

" Why? " Ginger asked.

" Because I believe it's more important that the Lost Tribe *find us* than for *us* to find the Lost Tribe."

That night we were a long time getting to sleep, but we awakened before daylight and waited restlessly for the sun to rise. That morning we stayed in plain sight of whoever might be watching, and kept busy. Ginger did some mending and patching. I found a large log, hacked it in half, and rolled the two sections into camp to serve as a table of sorts.

It was Ginger's idea that we consider our camp a stage set, where we could be viewed from all sides. We spent the day as actors playing to an invisible audience. After supper we sat in the bright firelight and played ticktacktoe in the dust between us. When we at last retired, we did so with the hope that we had raised a great deal of curiosity and also managed to appear friendly and harmless.

The next day we went on playing the part of simple souls. We decided to play a game of toss-the-ring. I pounded two stakes into the ground about fifteen feet apart, and made some rings from lianas. [2] As we started our jungle version of horseshoes, Ginger laughed and said, " I hope the

[1] **Cortes** (kôr′tĕz): Spanish conqueror of Mexico (1485–1547).

[2] **lianas** (lē·ä′nàz): woody climbing plants that grow in tropical rain forests.

local population doesn't have anything that passes for an insane asylum, or we may find ourselves in it."

For several days we continued our charades and pantomimes.[1] Nothing happened. Time dragged. Now and then we had the uneasy feeling of being watched, but we were never certain that there was any reason for the sensation.

One morning while Ginger prepared breakfast, I began to stow our gear. We had finished eating when I saw him. He was high in a tree at the edge of the clearing and armed with a longer bow than any I had ever seen in the hands of an Indian.

Casually I moved my eyes away from him. After a moment of concentrating on the campfire to suppress my excitement, I said quietly, " O.K. We're on stage in earnest."

" Where are they? " Ginger's voice was tense.

" Not *they*," I told her. " One man. But let's not stare at him, though he must have wanted us to see him, or he wouldn't have shown himself."

She nodded, " I get the point, but it's not helping my nerves any."

" Fiddle around with your mess kit," I suggested. " Make it flash in the sun. That should whet his curiosity."

Ginger made her shiny cooking-ware flash bright spots of light into the shadows at the edge of the glade. Occasionally, when I felt that my glances would appear natural, I took quick looks at the figure in the tree. He was pretending to shoot at some-

thing above his head. Faintly I could hear the sound of his arrows as they flicked through the foliage. The sight was comforting. If he was content to waste his arrows in that fashion, it did not seem probable that we would end up as human pincushions.

We smiled and gestured for the man to join us. My smile seemed absolutely frozen on my face. It must have resembled the idiotic grin of a show-window dummy. The Indian pointed his half-drawn bow in our direction as we walked slowly forward.

As we neared the tree in which he was standing, he did not draw his bowstring taut, and on his intelligent features a questioning smile hovered. Long black hair hung to his shoulders and partially obscured his forehead and cheeks. He wore a long sacklike garment sewn up each side.

For a while we regarded each other in silence, all three of us continuing to smile. Then I murmured to Ginger, " Let's go back to camp, and see what happens."

While I went in search of firewood, Ginger busied herself preparing some lunch. I brought two armloads of wood into camp and was returning with the third when I stopped dead in my tracks. Ten feet away stood a silent figure, so still that his dark skin, black hair, and tan garment seemed to blend with the jungle surrounding him. Two things were apparent. His bow was unstrung, and I could have sworn he was very close to smiling.

I smiled in return, nodded toward camp as though I wanted him to fol-

---

[1] **pantomimes** (păn'tṓ·mīmz): acting without speaking.

low, turned my back on him, and delivered the firewood. How were we to receive him when he arrived? I decided we would go on being ourselves. "Put some more water in the soup, Ginger. It looks as if we're going to have company for lunch."

She nodded and continued her cooking. A woman doing woman's work, and the fact that I had spoken to her and then let her go on about ordinary tasks seemed to reassure the Indian. He was in the open now. The bow hung loosely in his hand. He took a couple of steps forward. I spoke to Ginger. "Let's greet our guest."

Ginger arose and stood by my side. Together we smiled and gestured for him to join us at the campfire. Hesitantly, he approached and squatted upon his heels beside the fire. We followed suit.

I spoke to him in English, not with the hope that we could converse, but simply to give us an identity other than Spanish. The most important thing, I knew, was my *tone* of voice. If I could keep it warm and friendly, the meaning of the individual words might not be too important.

With smiles and gestures I moved to my pack, rummaged through our small stock of gifts, and returned with a hunting knife. This I presented to him hilt foremost, indicating it was a present. He accepted it, examined its blade with sharp-eyed interest, and then burst into speech. His words were completely unintelligible, but we could not miss the friendliness of them.

I wondered what he thought of the steel blade. I was certain he had never seen one like it before.

Finished with the examination of his present, the Indian laid it aside and selected an arrow. He presented it to me, feathered end first, accompanied by an outburst of words and some odd, graceful gestures of his hands. The arrow was perfectly made, four feet long, slim and straight, with a finely chipped flint head.

We almost forgot our guest, so astonishing was his collection of arrows. Some had heads of blunt, heavy wood. These, I assumed, were for stunning small birds and squirrels. Another type had a barbed foot with flint points. These, as we later learned, were for shooting monkeys; the reason for the multiple barbs being that they prevented the monkeys from pulling the arrows from their bodies.

Apparently I had been right about the meaning behind the presentation of the arrow. The Indian was all smiles as we chatted back and forth, saying a very great deal which neither of us understood.

Eventually we got down to Step Number One in understanding. "Dan," I said, tapping my chest. Then I pointed to Ginger. "Ginger," I said, "Ginger."

The Indian smiled and tapped his own chest. "Kintun." He pointed at me. "Dan," he managed without much trouble. Ginger gave him more difficulty, the "ger" not being familiar to him.

"Kintun," we repeated. He nodded, satisfied.

We "talked" some more, using each other's names. From time to time Kintun's eyes wandered to Ginger's mess kit. I picked up one of the aluminum cups and handed it to him for his inspection. He laughed with surprised pleasure at its light weight, tapped the metal with his thumbnail, and then raised the cup in a pantomime of drinking. I offered him some water from the canteen. He studied the canteen with interest, but shook his head. He did not wish a drink of water, only to show us that he understood what the cup was for.

When it was completely dark, Kintun arose, picked up his bow and arrows, and with a wave of his hand, vanished into the jungle night as though he were part of its eternal rhythm and beauty and mystery.

Though we were in a strange country, a land of the past where a dead language and a dying people lived, we felt secure and content. Before I

fell asleep, I meditated what would be in Kintun's report and to whom it might be delivered.

The next morning, as our fire blazed up, we heard a shrill cackle from a nearby tree. Looking up, we saw Kintun squatting upon a branch, his huipil [1] draped about him from chin to feet. All that was visible was his grinning face.

Ginger was smiling and waving, and I joined her. Kintun arose with graceful ease and ran out along the limb. As it bent under his weight, he stepped nimbly to the ground.

From a woven bag he produced three fat yams, nodding and motioning for me to accept them. That he had brought a yam for each of us was like the breaking of bread.

Kintun could not keep his eyes from the aluminum cup which hung on one side of the forked uprights supporting the crossbar over our fireplace. Ginger handed it to him. He began to fondle it like a youngster with a new toy.

When breakfast was ready, Ginger held out her hand for the cup. Reluctantly, he released it. She filled it to the brim with scalding hot tea. Kintun pointed to himself. Ginger nodded. The Indian smiled and reached for the cup.

I tried to warn him, pointing from the fire to the tea and back again. I knew he had never experienced anything that absorbs heat like aluminum. He shook his head and smiled politely.

---

[1] **huipil** (wē·pēl′): a rectangle of cotton worn as a garment.

Ginger handed him some food.

He nibbled at the venison and then turned his attention to the cup, picking it up by the handle.

" Live and learn," I muttered.

He put the metal rim to his lips, let out a surprised yip, set the cup on the ground, and snapped his fingers at it.

Laughingly, I said, " We'll have to remember that gesture. It must mean disapproval."

Cautiously, Kintun tried the cup again. I snapped my fingers at it. He nodded, his eyes questioning. I showed him how to test the heat along the rim with his fingertips.

When we were through eating, Kintun made the motions of washing out his cup. I turned to Ginger, " He's got our routine down pat. I'll bet he's watched our every move since the day we first arrived."

When we returned to camp, he sat upon one of the logs I had rolled into the glade, and with sly amusement pointed to where I had obtained it. Then he strode over to one of the two stakes we had left in the ground and made motions of throwing rings.

" It's fortunate we did the right things while we were camped here," I commented to Ginger. " When you consider how long we were being watched without knowing it . . . why, we could have been wiped out without a glimpse of our attackers."

One of our camp operations in particular intrigued Kintun. It was our custom to cut a sapling, lop off its branches, leaving six-inch stubs, and use this hatrack affair as a hanger for our grub bags, mess pots, cups, and

such. Kintun laughed, delighted at the finished product, and lifted his favorite cup from the stub on the " grub tree " as though he were plucking fruit.

When the sun had reached the middle of the sky, Kintun pointed to the bag into which Ginger had put his gift of three yams. Besides yams and tea, there was venison from our supply of dried meat.

When Ginger handed us spoons, Kintun lost all interest in the food. Here, like the cup, was something new. He turned it over and over and glanced questioningly at me. I spread

open the steaming yam to hold gravy from the stew. Kintun followed suit. Then he held up his spoon once more as though I had been avoiding the issue. I dipped some gravy from the stew pot. Clumsily Kintun followed my lead, delighted that he had discovered at last the function of this new toy. He mixed his gravy into the yam as I did. He watched me lift a mouthful to my lips. Clearly, the spoon was a wonderful instrument, equal in wonder to the aluminum cup.

When we were through eating, it was Kintun who led us to a water hole, carrying Ginger's stew kettle. As he knelt with it at the edge of the water, I whispered to Ginger, " and they call them ' dirty savages ' ! "

Returning to camp, Kintun stretched out on the grass, yawned, patted his stomach, and fell asleep.

" Sunday dinner anywhere," I said to Ginger, as we also stretched out for a nap. This, then, I thought, is what we spent two years getting to, by flivver, by plane, and heaven knew how many hundreds of miles on foot: to have Sunday dinner and a nap with " one of the family," just as we might have back home. I didn't think about it long. Like Kintun, I fell asleep. So did Ginger. When we awakened, Kintun was gone.

We wondered why he had left without waking us. I felt that what we had been through could be called Test Number Two, and that Kintun was now sitting at some council fire turning in a full report. I wondered if we had passed our second examination.

We had finished breakfast the next morning and were tidying camp when off in the distance we heard the voices of several people.

Kintun appeared first, and immediately behind him followed a striking figure of a man. Well-built and sedate, he carried himself with dignity. From a frame of shining black hair cut in bangs across his forehead and flowing down to his shoulders, he surveyed us with intelligent, observant black eyes. There was no doubt that he was a leader, a chief, receiving and deserving respect, for he had the " look of eagles."

The next man in line was also impressive, but about the corners of his lips were lines which showed that he was given to quick and easy smiles. Ambling behind came a man with jovial features. There's one of them in every crowd: the jester, the clown, the life of the party; the guy who loves a good story, a practical joke, a full-bellied laugh any time, anywhere.

The four men entered our camp site as though they were expected. Kintun smiled, and indicated each of his friends, introducing them at length. All we were able to understand were their names. Chan, we assumed, was the chief, Cayon was a priest, but Chilon was still the comic.

Kintun glanced at Ginger for permission, then walked over to our " grub tree," plucked his favorite aluminum cup, and displayed it to his three companions. Chan inspected it gravely, passed it on to Cayon, who examined it with mild interest. It was Chilon who lived up to expectations. When he received the cup, he grinned, shook it upside down to indicate it was empty, then bit the rim gently with his strong white teeth to prove it was not edible. Afterward he returned it to Kintun, who hung it upon its proper prong.

Then Ginger and I were invited into the act. Through a barrage of words and gestures, we gathered that Kintun wanted us to demonstrate how the house-that-walked-with-us worked. So we struck the tent, folded it, and then set it up again. Our visitors smiled gravely and nodded approvingly.

Ginger giggled, " I'm beginning to feel like a trained seal. I wonder what we'll be asked to do next? "

Kintun walked over to where we had driven the two stakes in the ground, picked up the woven rings, and held them out to Ginger and me. We gave a command performance of toss-the-ring.

Within a short time, to our amazement, there were two teams facing each other, playing our jungle variety of horseshoes. Ginger, Chan, and Chilon were tossing rings against Kintun, Cayon, and me. Kintun kept score with an involved series of hieroglyphics [1] scratched upon the ground.

Returning to camp after the game, only Chan deigned to seat himself upon one of our logs. The other three squatted about the fire. It was obvious from Kintun's actions that he was in charge of preparing the meal.

I started to go down upon my heels when Chan indicated a seat on the log. Before joining him, however, I secured my ditty kit, as something that would give us a basis for conversation. We developed a lively " chat " over such amazing articles as a plastic comb, my razor, and the red-handled toothbrush, all strange and fascinating to Chan.

Chan showed no interest in the activities around the fire. He liked the business of exchanging words for the names of common objects. Quick as Kintun had been, Chan was even more facile in the handling of new words and phrases.

Cayon and Chilon by now had put together an elaborate stew of tuberous roots, wild tomatoes, and legumes [2] which were new to us. To this they added meat and some crumbled, tangy herbs. Kintun unwrapped a package done up in banana leaves, displaying a pile of large, thick tortillas, and started them to toasting.

We were ready to eat, but not before each of us washed. Even among the conquistadors,[3] the Mayas had a reputation as a clean people. Now we were seeing it in the way they handled their food and kept themselves clean.

If Kintun had found our spoons a puzzle, we had even more difficulty using their thick, toasted tortillas as a scoop for the juicy stew. Fortunate-

---

[1] **hieroglyphics** (hī′ĕr·ô·glĭf′ĭks): signs, often pictures, used in writing.

[2] **legumes** (lĕg′ūmz): vegetables of the family to which peas and beans belong.

[3] **conquistadors** (kŏn·kwĭs′tȧ·dôrz): the Spaniards who conquered the Mayas.

ly, our accidents struck our hosts as hilariously funny, and I think it was the sloppiest "good-will tour" on record.

We spent the afternoon showing the Indians a fire-by-friction set and our versions of snares, figure-4 traps, pitfalls, and the like. In exchange, we learned variations employed by them. Whenever the method involved capturing a larger animal, Chilon always volunteered to be the victim. We had pegged him correctly as the "court jester."

The afternoon ended with a final game of toss-the-ring, and then as abruptly as they had arrived that morning, they departed.

Ginger said, as I dropped down by the fire, "They're swell people. Look at our camp. We've played games, eaten, put on a regular Scout's jamboree, and yet there's not a thing out of place. Every piece of equipment we used is back where it belongs. No dirt has been kicked into our open tent. Moreover, not one of our visitors coughed or spit or spilled food while they were here. Can you remember any callers who have treated us so thoughtfully?"

"Well," I said, "tomorrow they'll be back. What do we do to entertain them?"

"Entertain," Ginger repeated. "That gives me an idea. How about a joke of some sort?"

We talked it over and decided it was a good idea.

After breakfast the next morning, I took the aluminum cup of which Kintun was so fond and placed it on a log by the fire. Between the cup and log I slid an odd-shaped chip of bark, balancing the cup precariously.[1]

Remembering Chilon, the clown, I said to Ginger, "I'm going to try a joke which all of them will understand." I whittled a new spindle for our fire-by-friction set, purposely cutting the point so that it was off center. To make a fire with such a spindle would be like trying to drive a car smoothly with three flat tires.

They came quietly from the jungle in single file. The first thing Kintun did was to pick up his pet cup. As he lifted it, he eyed the chip of bark, and then shot a quizzical glance at me.

With some to-do, I handed my fire-by-friction set to Chilon. The comic examined the fire block and tinder, and upon turning the spindle about in his hand, he suddenly leaned back, let out a whoop of laughter, and slapped his knee. Sobering to a threatening scowl, he pointed his finger at me accusingly, and once more he roared with laughter.

Ginger and I were pleased. We had not been wrong in keying this meeting to good humor. If nations, like simple people, I thought, could only meet in the spirit of fun.

After Kintun and Chan had hit a target with bow and arrow, Chilon stepped forward and presented me with his long bow and four-foot arrow. Obviously, he was enjoying the situation.

"So you think I can't shoot one of these gadgets," I said in English.

---

[1] **precariously** (prē·kâr′ĭ·ŭs·lĭ): uncertainly, not securely.

Chilon's grin broadened. Even Chan's usually grave eyes were twinkling. "Well, my friends," I added, "you're in for a little surprise."

With considerable confidence I fitted the arrow and began to draw on the target. Then it happened. The cord snapped, sending the arrow gyrating crazily over my shoulder. Laughter exploded around me. Chilon and Kintun pounded their thighs with merriment. I was, it appeared, the joke of the century.

From then on the spirit of high good humor ruled the day. As we sat down to lunch, Kintun presented his favorite cup filled with steaming hot tea to Chilon. Unsuspecting, the comic lifted the burning hot edge of the aluminum cup to his lips. He let out a yell. Kintun howled with laughter.

Afterward, when we were ready to wash dishes, Chilon picked up the pot of warm water and calmly poured it over Kintun's head. These were the "savages" we had been afraid of. Later we had some swimming contests, and a tussle of seeing who could hold his breath longest under water.

Back in camp, Kintun put our things in order. Carefully, he hung the cooking utensils in their proper places, reserving his favorite cup for the last. While I waited for him to hang it upon the "grub tree" with the others, he surprised me. I had quite forgotten the little balancing trick of the morning. But not Kintun. Carrying the cup over to the log, he studied the chip of bark. Kneeling and taking the cup in both hands, he balanced it at the same angle at which I had purposely placed it.

"Kintun and the elephants," Ginger murmured. "They never forget."

Then silently as they had come, the Indians disappeared into the jungle.

Inside, I could feel a warm glow of pleasure, and I wondered what the history of the new world might have been had the conquistadors met the Mayas as we had done: with patience, with an exchange of gifts, with a discussion of kitchen utensils, by feeding the fire and eating together, and with jokes and good humor.

People from Another Time

1. In what ways might Kintun and his people be called "people from another time"?

2. Why did Dana Lamb believe that it would be better for the people of the Lost Tribe to "find" them, rather than for them to search out the Lost Tribe?

3. How did the Lambs inspire trust and confidence in the Indians?

4. Often when we meet people of another group that is strange to us, we think of them as members of that group rather than as individuals with definite and different personalities. The Lambs make us see each of these people as a distinct individual. Which of the four Indians did you like best? Which one stands out most clearly in your imagination? Did each have a sense of humor?

5. What places in the world, or what people in the world, are you curious about? What do you think civilized men can learn by investigating the habits, living conditions, and behavior of primitive people?

6. If you are curious about what happened to the Lambs, be sure to read their book Quest for the Lost City. They found a remnant of the lost civilization, and had many adventures.

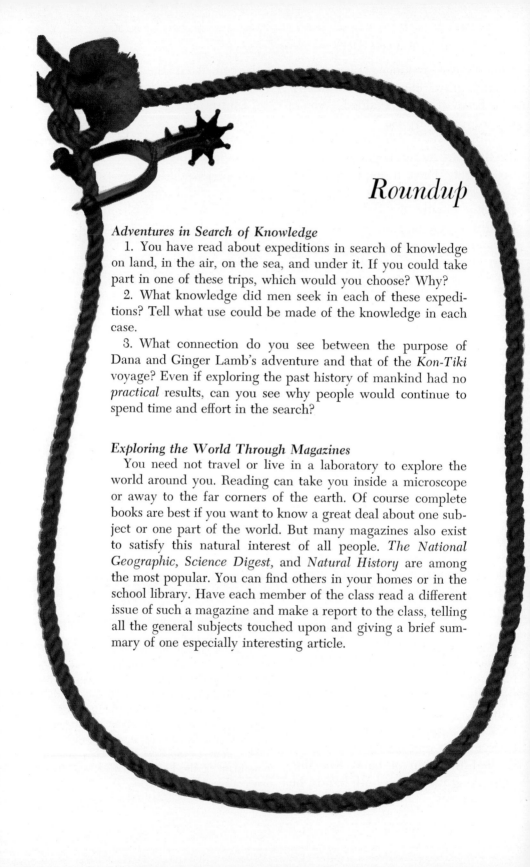

Roundup

Adventures in Search of Knowledge

1. You have read about expeditions in search of knowledge on land, in the air, on the sea, and under it. If you could take part in one of these trips, which would you choose? Why?

2. What knowledge did men seek in each of these expeditions? Tell what use could be made of the knowledge in each case.

3. What connection do you see between the purpose of Dana and Ginger Lamb's adventure and that of the *Kon-Tiki* voyage? Even if exploring the past history of mankind had no *practical* results, can you see why people would continue to spend time and effort in the search?

Exploring the World Through Magazines

You need not travel or live in a laboratory to explore the world around you. Reading can take you inside a microscope or away to the far corners of the earth. Of course complete books are best if you want to know a great deal about one subject or one part of the world. But many magazines also exist to satisfy this natural interest of all people. *The National Geographic, Science Digest,* and *Natural History* are among the most popular. You can find others in your homes or in the school library. Have each member of the class read a different issue of such a magazine and make a report to the class, telling all the general subjects touched upon and giving a brief summary of one especially interesting article.

The Boy's Book of Rockets, by Raymond F. Yates (Harper, 1947)
Easy reading and much information.

The Bright Design, by Katherine B. Shippen (Viking, 1949)
Electricity and the men who have harnessed it. In *A Bridle for Pegasus* (1951) this author tells the story of aviation from man's first dreams of wings.

The Conquest of Space, pictures by Chester Bonestell and text by Willy Ley (Viking, 1949)
Wonderful pictures, some in color, of the surface of the planets with explanations of how men expect to reach them. Ley tells more about this subject in *Rockets, Missiles, and Space Travel* (1951).

Construction Ahead, by Henry Billings (Viking, 1951)
Romance and drama in the building of our highways.

A Dipper Full of Stars: a Beginner's Guide to the Heavens, by Lou Williams (Follett, 1944)
Charts to help you locate constellations, and interesting old legends and modern theories.

Electronics for Young People, by Jeanne Bendick (Whittlesey House, 1947)
The science behind wonders like television and radio.

Everyday Weather and How It Works, by Herman Schneider (Whittlesey, 1951)
Easy reading about something that affects our daily lives.

First Electrical Book for Boys and *First Chemistry Book for Boys and Girls,* Alfred Morgan (Scribner, 1951, 1950)
Easy introductions to two popular sciences.

High, Wide, and Deep, by John J. Floherty (Lippincott, 1952)
Exploring the ocean's depths and its changing coastlines.

Modern Medical Discoveries, by Irmengarde Eberle (Crowell, 1948)
Dramatic steps in man's battle for health and long life.

Modern Wonders and How They Work, by Captain Burr Leyson (Dutton, 1949)
Satisfaction for the reader who is interested in the *how.*

The Stars in Our Heaven, by Peter Lum (Pantheon, 1948)
Facts and legends to help you explore the night sky.

The Story of Mountains, by Ferdinand C. Lane (Doubleday, 1950)
How they came into being and some of man's adventures on them.

The Talking Wire: the Story of Alexander Graham Bell, by O. J. Stevenson (Messner, 1947)
Biography of the inventor of the telephone.

Television Works Like This, by Jeanne and Robert Bendick (Whittlesey, 1949)
How programs are worked up and how they get to your screen.

Today's Science and You, by Lynn Poole (Whittlesey, 1952)
Explanations and narratives by the director of the Johns-Hopkins TV Science Review.

Trailblazer to Television: The Story of Arthur Korn, by Terry and Elizabeth P. Korn (Scribner, 1950)
Interesting information about the beginnings of television plus an interesting life story.

You and Space Travel, by John Lewellen (Children's Press, 1951)
Present plans and problems still to be solved. In *You and Atomic Energy* (1949), the same author explains how this new marvel of atomic energy works and how it can be used for good instead of destruction.

Section of Grant Wood's "The Midnight Ride of Paul Revere." Courtesy of Metropolitan Museum of Art

Exploring America's Past

Paul Revere's Ride

HENRY WADSWORTH LONGFELLOW

At the start of the American Revolution the British were much stronger than the colonists in arms and trained soldiers. They set out secretly to capture a precious store of gunpowder that the colonists had hoarded. Why didn't they succeed? You will find the answer in this famous poem.

> Listen, my children, and you shall hear
> Of the midnight ride of Paul Revere,
> On the eighteenth of April, in seventy-five;
> Hardly a man is now alive
> Who remembers that famous day and year.   5
>
> He said to his friend, " If the British march
> By land or sea from the town tonight,
> Hang a lantern aloft in the belfry arch
> Of the North Church tower, as a signal light —
> One, if by land, and two, if by sea;   10
> And I on the opposite shore will be,
> Ready to ride and spread the alarm
> Through every Middlesex village and farm,
> For the country folk to be up and to arm."

193

Then he said " Good night! " and with muffled oar   15
Silently rowed to the Charlestown shore,
Just as the moon rose over the bay,
Where, swinging wide at her moorings, lay
The *Somerset*, British man-of-war:
A phantom° ship, with each mast and spar   20
Across the moon, like a prison bar,
And a huge black hulk, that was magnified
By its own reflection in the tide.

Meanwhile, his friend, through alley and street,
Wanders and watches with eager ears,   25
Till in the silence around him he hears
The muster of men at the barrack door,
The sound of arms, and the tramp of feet,
And the measured tread of the grenadiers
Marching down to their boats on the shore.   30

Then he climbed the tower of the Old North Church,
By the wooden stairs, with stealthy tread,°
To the belfry chamber overhead,
And startled the pigeons from their perch
On the somber rafters, that round him made   35
Masses and moving shapes of shade —

20. **phantom** (făn′tŭm): ghost. 32. **with stealthy** (stĕl′thĭ) **tread:** stealing along quietly to escape
notice.

By the trembling ladder, steep and tall,
To the highest window in the wall,
Where he paused to listen and look down
A moment on the roofs of the town,   40
And the moonlight flowing over all.

Beneath, in the churchyard, lay the dead,
In their night encampment on the hill,
Wrapped in silence so deep and still
That he could hear, like a sentinel's tread,   45
The watchful night wind, as it went
Creeping along from tent to tent,
And seeming to whisper, " All is well! "
A moment only he feels the spell
Of the place and the hour, the secret dread   50
Of the lonely belfry and the dead;
For suddenly all his thoughts are bent
On a shadowy something far away,
Where the river widens to meet the bay —
A line of black, that bends and floats   55
On the rising tide, like a bridge of boats.

Meanwhile, impatient to mount and ride,
Booted and spurred, with a heavy stride
On the opposite shore walked Paul Revere.
Now he patted his horse's side,   60
Now gazed at the landscape far and near,
Then, impetuous, stamped the earth,
And turned and tightened his saddle girth;
But mostly he watched with eager search
The belfry tower of the Old North Church,   65
As it rose above the graves on the hill,
Lonely and spectral° and somber and still.
And lo! as he looks, on the belfry's height
A glimmer, and then a gleam of light.
He springs to the saddle, the bridle he turns,   70
But lingers and gazes, till full on his sight
A second lamp in the belfry burns!

A hurry of hoofs in a village street,
A shape in the moonlight, a bulk in the dark,
And beneath, from the pebbles, in passing, a spark   75

67. spectral: like a specter, or ghost.

Struck out by a steed flying fearless and fleet:
That was all! And yet, through the gloom and the light,
The fate of a nation was riding that night;
And the spark struck out by that steed, in his flight,
Kindled the land into flame with its heat.   80

He has left the village and mounted the steep,
And beneath him, tranquil and broad and deep,
Is the Mystic, meeting the ocean tides;
And under the alders that skirt its edge,
Now soft on the sand, now loud on the ledge,   85
Is heard the tramp of his steed as he rides.

It was twelve by the village clock,
When he crossed the bridge into Medford town.
He heard the crowing of the cock,
And the barking of the farmer's dog,   90
And felt the damp of the river fog
That rises after the sun goes down.

It was one by the village clock,
When he galloped into Lexington.
He saw the gilded weathercock   95
Swim in the moonlight as he passed,
And the meetinghouse windows, blank and bare,
Gaze at him with a spectral glare,
As if they already stood aghast
At the bloody work they would look upon.   100

It was two by the village clock,
When he came to the bridge in Concord town.
He heard the bleating of the flock,
And the twitter of birds among the trees,
And felt the breath of the morning breeze   105
Blowing over the meadows brown.

And one was safe and asleep in his bed,
Who at the bridge would be first to fall,
Who that day would be lying dead,
Pierced by a British musket ball.   110

You know the rest. In the books you have read
How the British Regulars fired and fled —
How the farmers gave them ball for ball,
From behind each fence and farmyard wall,
Chasing the Redcoats down the lane,   115
Then crossing the fields to emerge again
Under the trees at the turn of the road,
And only pausing to fire and load.

So through the night rode Paul Revere;
And so through the night went his cry of alarm   120
To every Middlesex village and farm —
A cry of defiance and not of fear —
A voice in the darkness, a knock at the door,
And a word that shall echo forevermore!
For, borne on the night wind of the Past,   125
Through all our history, to the last,
In the hour of darkness and peril and need,
The people will waken and listen to hear
The hurrying hoofbeats of that steed,
And the midnight message of Paul Revere.   130

Spreading the Alarm

1. What signal had Paul Revere planned with his friend? Where was Revere waiting for the signal?

2. How could the watcher in the belfry tell what signal to give? What did he actually see? What did he hear?

3. Compare lines 70–110 with the preceding ones. Which seem to move faster? Now try to discover how the poet got this effect. Find other passages in the poem that have a marked tempo. Why are they effective?

4. Paul Revere is known to many Americans only because of this popular poem, yet his " ride " was not the main reason he was famous in his own day. See how much you can find out about him from checking your library. Try to get pictures of his work as a silversmith and engraver.

Words Create Moods

All words carry meaning, but some words also stir up feelings. These double-duty words give extra spirit to any sort of writing, and they are the very life of poetry. Longfellow wanted you to feel the suspense of the dark night when Paul Revere and his friend waited for the British to reveal their plans. He used a number of words that built up that mood of mystery and danger. Just say over to yourself *phantom, stealthy, somber, shadowy, spectral.* How do they put you into the right mood for this dramatic event in America's past?

You might try using words to create a

mood. Tell how the wind seems on a gay spring morning. Now create a different mood by telling how it seems when it is dangerous and destructive. You can use simple verbs that will carry feeling as well as meaning.

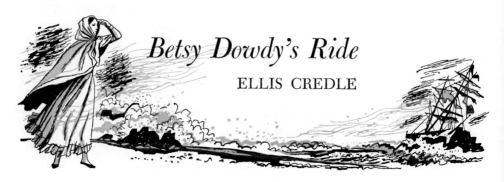

Betsy Dowdy's Ride

ELLIS CREDLE

BE A GOOD TRAVELER. Paul Revere's famous ride has been told many times in story and song. But did you ever hear of the young Revolutionary heroine who made a longer, more perilous ride to warn the militia that the enemy was marching toward their homes to burn and destroy them?

This story will take you along the wild Carolina coast and through dark swamps — country that is probably new and strange to you. What sort of traveler will you be? Some people on an automobile tour drive at top speed all day with their eyes glued to the highway. At night they can hardly tell what sort of country they have passed through. Some readers race through a story the same way. All they want to know is what will happen next. Like the high-speed tourist, they miss some interesting scenery.

The time and place of a story is called the *setting*. Sometimes an author spends only a few words describing the setting, especially if it has no important bearing on the people or events in the story. But often the setting *is* important. It may even be the clue to what happens in the story. For example, as Betsy Dowdy hears the news of the advancing British, keep in mind the time of the story (there were few roads in 1776, and no automobiles!) as well as the place. What would she face if she attempted the ride? Be an alert traveler on the printed page as well as on the highway.

Along the highway which leads into Manteo,[1] North Carolina, where the first English settlement in the New World was attempted, are several historical markers. One tells briefly of a sixteen-year-old girl, Betsy Dowdy, who, in the winter of 1776, swam her pony across Currituck Sound [2] and rode fifty miles through the wilderness to warn General Skinner of the coming of the British.

Thousands of people have passed

[1] **Manteo** (măn'tē·ō).
[2] **Sound:** a long passage of water between the mainland and an island.

"Betsy Dowdy's Ride" by Ellis Credle. Reprinted by permission of the author and *The American Girl*, a magazine for all girls published by the Girl Scouts.

that sign and wondered at the bravery of the young girl who took a ride vastly more difficult and dangerous than that of the better-known Paul Revere. No doubt they have wished to know more of Betsy Dowdy and how she came to make her perilous journey.

The story begins in the year 1774 when Betsy Dowdy was only fourteen years old. In that year most of our vast land was uncharted wilderness. Only thirteen colonies, the ones along the eastern coast of North America, were populated, and those only thinly. The few roads which traversed this new country were hardly more than trails through the wilderness.

Betsy Dowdy lived in a wild and lonely spot. The roar of the ocean was always in her ears, for her father's small cottage huddled in the shelter of a great dune [1] on a desolate sand bar called Currituck Beach. It was one of a chain of long, narrow islands. In front of her door the Atlantic tossed endlessly, and in every other direction a waste of sandy hillocks reared and tumbled and sprawled out over the landscape.

The sand banks of North Carolina, on which Betsy lived, have been the dread of all mariners since the first settlement of the land. Here long fingers of sand stretch out into treacherous currents to pull down any ship which comes within reach. In the early days, when all commerce was by water, hundreds of vessels went down in that death grip, and the white sand of Currituck Beach was strewn with the bleaching skeletons of wrecked ships.

Joe Dowdy, Betsy's father, made his living from these wrecks. As their valuable merchandise was washed ashore he recovered it, stored it as best he could, and later shipped it away to be sold for whatever it would bring. This was a legitimate business in those days, and Joe Dowdy was an upright and God-fearing man. Every night before going to bed, he prayed devoutly for the souls of all sailors at sea, asking God to take care of them and preserve them from shipwreck. But he always closed with a silent petition that if there should be a wreck, it might be on Currituck Beach.

Perhaps Joe Dowdy's prayers were answered, for many a time had young Betsy Dowdy stood upon the beach, braced against the gale, and watched some proud vessel founder [2] in the thunderous surf. Joe Dowdy always did his utmost to save the unfortunate passengers and crew, and often Betsy peered through blinding rain and salt spray to watch her father and their only neighbor, Sammy Jarvis, struggling to get a lifeline to some doomed ship.

After a wreck, Joe Dowdy's humble cottage was often crowded with exhausted, water-soaked survivors. Some of them lingered for weeks recovering from exposure and shock. Joe gave them every care his small home afforded, and Betsy was glad to do her part in nursing them back to health.

From these castaways came her

[1] **dune**: a hill of sand piled up by the wind.

[2] **founder**: fill with water and sink.

only word of the great world beyond the sand banks. A fine gentleman, who sat sipping daintily at a bowl of clam chowder which she had prepared for him, told young Betsy about England and the magnificent affairs at the court of King George III, but these grand doings across three thousand miles of ocean seemed remote and unreal to the little girl of the sand banks. The stories of places nearer home interested her more.

She listened, entranced, when a shipwrecked planter told her of Edenton. This important town of the growing colony was less than fifty miles from her own home — not too far away to dream of going there some day. She was all ears as the planter described the grand houses there, the high paneled rooms and tall carved mantels, the beautiful ladies dressed in silks and brocades who played so sweetly on the harpsichord.[1] He pictured for her the white plantation houses along Albemarle Sound, their green lawns sloping down to the waterfront and blowing with flowers planted from English seeds and cuttings.

Around his leaping driftwood fire, Joe Dowdy often discussed the questions of the day with his shipwrecked guests. Sometimes their neighbor, Sammy Jarvis, took part. Betsy, sitting on the edge of the group, gathered from the talk that the colonies were not always on the best of terms with the mother country. The words "taxation without representation"

meant little to her, but she disliked it when the conversation drifted around to them, for these words always brought the men to the pitch of shouting and brandishing [2] fists. It was only after a castaway had told of the Edenton tea party that Betsy began to understand their meaning.

Fifty-one Edenton ladies, related the shipwrecked citizen, had gathered one afternoon at the home of Mrs. Elizabeth King. They had drunk a beverage made of the leaves of dried raspberries, and had drawn up a resolution declaring that they would drink no more tea until England removed the hateful tax on tea.

It was quite understandable to young Betsy that the ladies should be annoyed at having to pay more for their tea, but why her father should work himself into a fury over it she could not understand. The only tea that was ever served in the Dowdy home was made of yaupon,[3] the kind which the Indians had taught them to use. There was no tax on that, no cost of any kind, for the leaves were gathered from low, glistening green bushes which grew wild in the lee of the dunes.

"I'd be mad if they put a tax on sand crabs!" cried Joe Dowdy when his daughter asked him to explain. "It's takin' away our freedom! England ain't got no right to lay taxes on us unless we consent to it. And she ain't even asked our consent. We ain't got nobody over there to represent us in the Parliament, and it's the right

---

[1] **harpsichord** (härp′sĭ·kôrd): a musical instrument from which the piano was developed.

[2] **brandishing:** waving threateningly.

[3] **yaupon** (yô′pŏn): shrub of the holly family.

of every Englishman to have a say-so in the government. They shan't take that right away from us! Englishmen always will be free — that they will! "

" Yes! That they will! " shouted his recuperating [1] guests in agreement.

Betsy came to understand that freedom was a very precious thing, something for which men were willing to fight and, if need be, to die.

The little girl of the sand dunes had no companions of her own age, but she was never lonely. There was much to be done around the house, and she spent many a happy hour galloping over the dunes on her small mare, Nellie. Nellie belonged to a breed of horse peculiar to the sand banks. For this reason they were called " banker " ponies. Larger than ponies, yet smaller than proper horses, hundreds of them grazed wild among the marshes and low myrtle bushes. When a banker pony was thirsty, he pawed a hole in the sand and waited for the brackish water to seep into it.

No one knows how these wild ponies came to be upon the sandy ridge across the Carolina coast. It is one of the many mysteries of the region, but it is known that early settlers found them there. And up to this day they may still be seen, cropping [2] the rushes along the sand banks.

In those colonial days, Joe Dowdy herded hundreds of the wild ponies, broke them to the saddle, and sold them to the settlers along the Albemarle. His daughter Betsy had taken one for her own. The young girl galloped many a mile over the dunes, and through the tall pines and live oak trees, to fill great baskets with wild grapes or bright wild flowers. With flying hoofs, Nellie took her young mistress wherever she wished to go and brought her safely back again.

On these long rides, Betsy turned over in her mind the things which she had heard at her father's hearth fire. She began to understand why the men always grew angry at the thought of taxes laid by England. What right had those Englishmen, far across the sea, to lay taxes on this

[1] **recuperating** (rḗ·kū′pēr·āt·ĭng): recovering health or strength.

[2] **cropping**: biting the tops off.

new land? *They* had not built the houses, nor chopped down the trees, nor plowed the ground, nor fought off the Indians. Betsy's young and independent mind told her that this land should belong to those who settled it. They should be the ones to govern it. They should decide the taxes.

In 1775 the violent gales of the spring equinox [1] sent a Massachusetts schooner aground upon Currituck Beach. Those saved from the wreck were full of a battle fought at Lexington. The words fairly tumbled over each other, so eager were they to tell of the happenings of that early morning of April nineteenth, 1775.

The British Regulars had set out secretly, they related, under cover of night, to arrest the great Massachusetts leaders, Samuel Adams and John Hancock. But their secret had been found out. Paul Revere, artist and silversmith of Boston, had ridden madly through the countryside, ahead of the advancing army, and had given the alarm. On the village green of Lexington, the British had found fifty stern-faced farmers, muskets in hand, determinedly blocking their way.

"Disperse,[2] ye villains!" the British leader, Pitcairn, had shouted. But the minutemen had not dispersed.

The British had opened fire, and eighteen embattled farmers had fallen, eight dead, ten wounded.

[1] **equinox** (ē′kwĭ·nŏks): the time when the sun's center crosses the equator and day and night are everywhere the same length, usually a time of stormy weather.
[2] **Disperse**: scatter.

"Then it's war!" said Joe Dowdy, shaking his head.

Yes, war with England had come at last. Young Betsy's mind was prepared for it, but still it seemed unreal, like another tale told around her father's fireside. All summer, while the ocean lay rolling lazily and blinking at the sun, the opening battles of the Revolutionary War were fought. Betsy Dowdy swam happily in Currituck Sound, and the war seemed far away and unconnected with the pleasant summer days along the sand banks.

It was not until the winter, when the tail end of tropical hurricanes set the clouds flying and the ocean churning, that the war came near to Betsy. A fishing schooner from Norfolk, Virginia, having fared badly in one of these gales, anchored off the Currituck coast to repair her shredded sails and cracked masts. Joe Dowdy, with young Betsy, rowed out to inquire the news of the day.

"Hey-oh, up there!" shouted Joe Dowdy through cupped hands. "What news on the mainland?"

"News a-plenty!" shouted back a gnarled old seaman.

A swaying rope ladder was let over the side, and father and daughter climbed on board. The word was that Lord Dunmore, the Royal Governor of Virginia, had been driven from his palace in Williamsburg by the indignant settlers. Taking his army with him, he had marched upon Norfolk, the most important city in the state.

When they heard this, Betsy and her father pricked up their ears, for

Norfolk was scarcely more than fifty miles from their home.

The fishermen interrupted each other to tell of the outrages of Dunmore. He had destroyed the hard-won crops of the settlers round about Norfolk, they related indignantly. He had burned houses, and slaughtered the cattle, hogs, and poultry. Planters had seen their life work destroyed in the space of an hour. And it was rumored, declared they, that Dunmore was planning to march upon North Carolina and destroy the settlement along the Albemarle.

That night, sitting around the drift-wood fire, Joe Dowdy retold the news to his neighbor, Sammy Jarvis. "There's a report that he's plannin' to march into the Albemarle settlement, a-burnin' and a-killin' and a-plunderin'."

Across the hearth Betsy sat quietly, but her eyes were wide and her small face pale.

"I'm a-goin' crost the sound to the mainland tomorrow and find out all about it!" declared Sammy Jarvis, and the next morning his neighbors watched him set off in a small boat, his back bending valiantly to the oars.

It was late afternoon when he returned. Betsy was making preparations for supper when there came a loud knocking on the door.

"Come in!" bawled Joe Dowdy, and Sammy Jarvis burst into the room. Betsy started up at sight of his staring eyes and perspiring face.

"It's a fact!" shouted Sammy at the top of his lungs, without waiting for a word of greeting.

"What in tarnation! What's a fact, Sammy? You mean Dunmore's marchin' into Carolina?"

"He's on his way!" panted Sammy Jarvis. "Got as far as Great Bridge, this side o' Norfolk!"

Betsy Dowdy said nothing, but she put aside the bluefish she was about to fry.

"Ain't there nobody tryin' to stop him?" asked Joe Dowdy, half out of his chair.

"Well, they say some Virginia troops are marchin' toward Great Bridge — John Marshall is with 'em. But there's only a handful of 'em, and them as green as grass!" Sammy Jarvis ran his hand through his hair until it stood up wildly. "Why, it's just like opposin' a lion with a swarm o' gnats!"

"Why don't they get word to General Skinner up on Yeopim[1] Creek?" asked Joe Dowdy. "He's got the militia up there, a whole passel[2] of 'em. He'd stop old Dunmore, if anybody could."

"There was talk o' that," said Sammy Jarvis, "but hit's so tarnation far to Yeopim Creek, they didn't figger they could make it before dark — and 'twould be too late to wait till tomorrow to set off to Yeopim. If he didn't get the word by daybreak tomorrow, he couldn't get to Great Bridge in time."

"If a man rode all night, seems to me like he'd be able to make it to Yeopim Creek by daybreak," said Betsy's father.

---

[1] Yeopim (yō'pĭm).

[2] passel: a large number.

"Take that ride at night!" cried Sammy Jarvis. "Man alive, are you crazy? There's fifty mile o' swamp and woods and water atween here and Yeopim Creek. It's as much as a man can do to get through in the daytime. There ain't a chance in a hundred he could do it at night. And there's Currituck Sound atween here and the mainland — how'd you get your horse acrost that? It's safe enough to swim him acrost in the daylight — but in the night, with the tide runnin' strong, well — I'd ruther commit suicide some other way!"

Joe Dowdy looked down at the floor. "Reckon you're right, Sammy," he agreed slowly. "Reckon there ain't nothin' we can do about gettin' word to General Skinner."

Sixteen-year-old Betsy Dowdy still stood by the table. Already she could see the British putting torches to the fine homes along the Albemarle. She could hear the lowing of cattle led to the slaughter, the whinnying of horses driven off with the British army. Like a sword thrust came the thought that her own home might be one of those laid waste, her own beloved Nellie taken away for some British soldier to ride.

A wave of devotion for her own wild home-place surged upon Betsy and half choked her. She loved the tumbling hills, the lonely stretches of marshland, and the gnarled live oaks. Her eyes caressed the humble and familiar things in her father's home. The fish nets hanging from the rafters — during long hours her father had worked at them, twisting the threads

and knotting them by hand — and in the corner her own little bed with its patchwork quilt — what labor had gone into the making of that! Pots and kettles simmering over the blazing fire; upon the window sill a row of treasures gathered along the beach — a conch shell lined with pink, a starfish, and a branch of rose coral washed up from who knows what tropical shore. This was home!

Betsy's young face set into firm lines. The British should not lay waste the plantations along the Albemarle, not if she could help it! They should not put the torch to her own small home! Silently she brought out a small pouch and filled it with coins;

into another pouch she put some slices of meat and a piece of corn bread. The two men, engrossed in the impending [1] disaster, spread their hands to the fire and croaked on and on. They did not even look up as the girl, a heavy cape across her shoulders, opened the cottage door and slipped outside.

The sun was sinking and chill mists were winding about the dunes as she stepped from the cottage door and made her way to the herding pen.

[1] **impending:** threatening to happen any moment.

"Nellie! Nellie!" she called softly. The banker pony came whickering out of the fog. Dear, faithful Nellie, companion of many a happy gallop across the dunes! She was to have a longer, grimmer ride tonight, and, before it was over, she was to prove her worth. With sure hands Betsy cinched [1] the saddle upon the pony's back and flung herself into it. Her long cape flew out with the wind as they set off at a gallop across the sands.

The pony's hoofs fell with muffled

tuck Sound lapping gently at the other.

Betsy knew that in order to reach the mainland she must cross the Sound, which seemed to stretch so

beat as they sped on and on. Well-known mounds and hillocks seemed strange and unfamiliar in their misty winding sheets. The wind was cold and, before five miles had been passed, Betsy began to think wistfully of her father and his old friend sitting cosily in front of the fire. But she did not consider turning back. Along the sand bank she flew, the ocean beating upon one side, Curri-

shorelessly to the right of her. Its narrowest stretch was at a point opposite Church Island and she rode her pony slowly now, peering anxiously across the water for a sight of the island. At last, far across the water, she saw a dark smudge which might be the pines and live oaks on Church Island.

[1] cinched (sĭnch'd): fastened the straps that held the saddle in place.

The moon was up now, but shining so faintly through the mist that she could not be sure, though she knew that she must chance it.

Tucking up her skirts, she urged her pony into the murky water. The sturdy animal waded until her feet could no longer touch bottom, then she swam. The tide was running strong as the brave animal struck out through the deep water for the distant shore line. Three long miles she swam through chill dark water and, when at last her hoofs touched solid ground, the young girl on her back breathed a prayer of thankfulness. They had reached the shore of Church Island.

Nellie shook herself and threaded her way among the somber pines and fragrant myrtles toward the opposite shore. The whole of Currituck Sound was not yet crossed; a still longer stretch lay between the island and the mainland. Betsy did not pause as she reached the far beach.

"Come, Nellie! One more stretch to cross! On! On!" The little mare dashed again into the cold waters of the Currituck. Wide silver ripples streamed out behind the two in the water as the pony swam strongly against the tide. Betsy clung to the saddle and kept her eyes wishfully upon the dark line which was the mainland. It grew steadily larger as Nellie swam confidently onward.

Dripping with cold water, the pony climbed at last upon the marshy shore of the mainland. With a thankful heart Betsy turned and looked back at the water just passed. Her cottage home with its hearth fire seemed far away in some other, secure existence. There could be no turning back now, and she set her mind resolutely ahead.

This territory was new and strange to the girl. She had heard her father describe the trails that ran through this country, but things did not look as she had pictured them. The marsh stretched out for miles and there did not seem to be a path anywhere. Perhaps the pony's eyes were keener than her own. Betsy gave her free rein, and Nellie stepped out confidently. Sometimes she sank into the mire and floundered almost to her belly in mud. The dry rushes swirled around her rider's legs. They struggled on and on, and at last the ground grew firmer under foot.

A dark wall of forest stood up in front of them now, grimly forbidding. Betsy tried not to think of the stories she had heard of the Currituck wilderness: the lurking Indians always ready with their tomahawks, the bears, the poisonous moccasins,[1] the panther-cats ready to leap from overhead branches upon the unwary traveler. At the edge of the forest, the banker pony snorted and pranced unwillingly. Betsy trembled, but she urged Nellie into the blackness.

Trying to close her mind to the terror of the forest, Betsy kept her thoughts steadfastly upon the fine house on Yeopim Creek, the militia, and General Skinner, but she could not help shivering at each rustling in the underbrush, each unexpected

[1] moccasins: water snakes.

snapping of a twig. Perhaps the beasts and the reptiles and the savages declared a truce that night, for Betsy Dowdy passed through the forest unharmed. The rude trail led her at last to the shores of the Pasquotank [1] River. She knew that a ferry was run here by an old man called Gid Lamb, and she thudded up to his cabin and knocked upon the door.

"Hello!" called Betsy. "Hello! Hello!"

There was no answer, and the girl leaned over and pounded loudly upon the door.

Gid Lamb at last put his head out of the door. "Eh — eh — what's up? Who's disturbin' the peace so late at night?" he inquired crossly.

"It's me — me, Betsy Dowdy," a young voice piped out of the dark. "Please hurry up! Take me across the river — I'm riding to warn General Skinner that the British are coming!"

"Eh! What! The British are comin'?" Betsy could hear the old man stumbling hurriedly about inside. Soon he appeared, half dressed. Betsy guided her mount upon the ferryboat and Gid Lamb loosed it upon the current. As the old man poled the flat boat across the river, Betsy dismounted. The pony stood quietly, grateful for the short rest. The moon sailed high now and Betsy's spirits rose. Half the journey was behind her — she would get there in time, she was quite sure she would!

As the ferry bumped the shore, she took a coin and offered it to the ferryman, but he waved it aside.

"No charge for you tonight, child," he said, "and Godspeed to you!"

Betsy leaped into the saddle. "Thank you, sir!" she cried, and went pounding away into the darkness. On and on she rode, through the swamps of Pasquotank, threading a perilous way among cypress and juniper trees.

In the cold darkness just before the dawn, she clattered wearily into the town of Hertford. Her pony's hoofbeats echoed among the silent houses. That house with the grand double porches must be the Eagle Tavern. Betsy knew it by descriptions from castaway guests. She drew up, knocked upon the door and shouted for directions to General Skinner's place on Yeopim Creek. The innkeeper, roused from his bed, set her on the right road, and on she thudded.

A flush of pink, like the lining of her treasured conch shell, was spreading over the sky as Betsy rode up the highlands of Perquimans [2] County, through which ran Yeopim Creek. Soon she would be at the end of the journey. She thought, almost with unbelief, of the dark and dangerous miles spread out between her and her home.

The sun was rising as she rode in through the gate of General Skinner's home on Yeopim Creek. Life on the busy plantation was just beginning for the day. Slaves and indentured servants going about their tasks, and the General himself was at hand to see that all began smoothly. When he saw the mud-spattered girl on her

---

[1] **Pasquotank** (păs'kwŏ·tăngk).

[2] **Perquimans** (pĕr·kwĭm'ănz).

tired pony he came forward and greeted her with amazement. His eyes snapped as she poured out her story of Lord Dunmore and the impending battle at Great Bridge.

Hardly waiting for her to finish, the hardy soldier began shouting for his horse, his sword, his boots and spurs. Young Betsy was handed over to the care of his three daughters, Dolly, Penelope, and Lavinia, and the General rode swiftly away to assist the Virginians at Great Bridge.

Resting upon a huge bed in an upstairs room of the comfortable plantation house, Betsy could hardly believe that this was she. She glanced upward at the snowy valance [1] of the tall four-poster bed and aside at the three beautiful and daintily dressed young ladies fluttering about, one carrying washbasin and towels, another a tray with rolls, slices of venison and wild turkey, and still another, a pot of yaupon tea. They plied her with a hundred questions.

The little girl of the sand banks lingered in the plantation house on the Yeopim only until noon. Her father, she felt sure, would be anxious about her. She mounted her pony after the midday meal, and set off on the homeward journey.

Lord Dunmore and his British soldiers did not destroy the humble home on the sand banks. He did not lay waste the fine plantations on the Albemarle. He got no farther toward North Carolina than Great Bridge across the Virginia line. There he was met by the Virginia sharpshooters and

[1] **valance** (văl′ăns): decorative drapery.

the troops from North Carolina, and he was defeated utterly. The patriots sent him flying back to Norfolk where he took refuge on the *Liverpool,* a British battleship, which had just sailed into the harbor.

The humble cottage where Betsy Dowdy lived has long since fallen into ruin, and even the site of it has been forgotten. But the brave little girl and her banker pony are still remembered. Around the hearth fires which glow in the homes along the sand banks, and through the lush farm country which she once saved from the British, they still tell the story of Betsy Dowdy and her dangerous ride to save her homeland.

Noticing the Setting of the Story

1. Describe the place where Betsy and her father lived. Why did they get news from the other colonies sooner than their neighbors farther inland did?

2. What was the news that made Joe Dowdy and his friends grow indignant? How did it concern them, even though they lived on a remote island?

3. How did Betsy learn that the British were marching toward North Carolina? What facts about their location made the men decide no warning could be sent to the militia in time?

4. Describe the country Betsy passed through on her ride. Tell three different dangers that she faced. Which one would you be most afraid of?

5. How were you told early in the story that Betsy was a good rider? In what way was Nellie different from other horses?

6. Think back over the story and point out Betsy's change of feelings about the British as time went on. What did she think about the war talk concerning the Boston tea party? Later, why did she become excited by the war talk?

Exploring America's Past

The Old Soldier

DOROTHY CANFIELD

Patriotic Americans always honor the heroes who fight in their country's wars. The people of this little Vermont town had for many years paid proper tribute to their Revolutionary War veterans, but now there were no old soldiers left. What happened next showed that they could honor peace as well as war.

NO MATTER how I set this story down, you will take it, I fear, as a fable. But it is not. It is as literally true as a local news item in your this-morning's newspaper. It happened up the state a ways from our town, " over the mountain," as we call that middle upland valley of Vermont.

For a long time, after the Revolution, the little town of Sunmore had made a great day out of the Fourth of July. They seemed to hear, more clearly than some other towns, the very sound of the old Liberty Bell in Philadelphia as it rang out in joy over the signing of the Declaration of Independence. They had not at all forgotten what the Fourth meant. As the years went by, a set form grew up for the day's celebration. At dawn, the big boys fired off again and again the old cannon which stood on the village common. There was a meeting, about eleven in the morning, at the Town Hall, where people made speeches, and sang patriotic songs. After that, a picnic lunch was eaten out on the green. If it rained, the lunch was eaten inside the Town Hall. Then, rain or shine, the procession formed to escort the old soldiers out to the Burying Ground, a mile from town, where they put flags on the graves of their comrades among the Sunmore men, who, like them, had been soldiers in the Revolution.

Nearly everybody in town marched in this procession, carrying flags and flowers and keeping step with the music of the town drum-and-fife corps. " Whee-dee-deedle-dee " went the high thin voices of the fifes; and " boom-boom-boom " went the deep voices of the drums. Tramp! tramp! tramp! went the feet of the Sunmore men and women and children — especially boys.

The boys looked forward to this celebrating from one year to the next, chiefly of course because to share in the firing of the cannon marked a long step forward in growing up. The cannon was generally said to have been in the Battle of Bennington in 1777. Ordinary people said yes of course it was. But more careful folks said this was not sure. As the years went by after that battle, twenty, forty, fifty, and finally by the time of this story, in 1848, seventy years, fewer and fewer people could remember it. And of course there were fewer and fewer old Sunmore men who had been Revolutionary soldiers.

Until they were past eighty, they had walked in the procession like everybody else. After that, Dr. White, who of course took care of them all when they were sick, said their joints were too stiff. He took them out in his own chaise, behind his slow, ancient roan horse. Dick was rather stiff in his joints too, and was glad to walk with ceremonial slowness.

Dr. White knew more about medicine than anyone else in town. This was to be expected because nobody else knew anything at all about it. But on the subject — local history — of which many people knew a great deal, he was also the local specialist. On the shelves of his library, mixed up with his medical books, stood more histories of Vermont than the rest of Sunmore people had, all put together. When anyone wanted to find out something about what had happened in the past, Dr. White was asked. He always knew the answer.

When May and June came in, people began to plan for the Fourth of July celebration. But there were no old soldiers left. For four or five years

there had been only two. Both of them were very old of course, for the year 1848 was seventy-one years after the Battle of Bennington. One had been ninety, and the other eighty-six. Now both were gone. The older one had died in the winter, and the family of the other one had moved away out west into York State and taken the old man with them.

It was too bad. Everybody was saying that the celebration wouldn't be much without old soldiers in it, to connect the town with the Revolution. Without one, how would people remember what the Fourth of July was really about? The ancients had always sat on the platform of the Town Hall, while the singing and speech-making went on, their long firearms across their knees, their soldier's leather belts strapped on over their Sunday coats. Of course what uniforms they had had, had gone all to pieces, if they'd ever had any, which was unlikely, buckskin being the wear in those early days. They had ridden in Dr. White's chaise, just behind the fife-and-drum corps, and the little girls in white dresses carrying the bouquets, ahead of the marching men and women, four abreast in the road. When the procession reached the cemetery, the little girls handed the flowers to the big boys, and they passed them out to the hobbling old soldiers, who laid them on the graves of their comrades in the Revolution. The smaller boys had the honor of planting fresh American flags on the graves, waving above the flowers.

One of the boys in town, one of the Bostwick family, heard his folks lamenting that the celebration would not seem right with no old soldiers at all. He was the third child, Andrew was his name; he was about ten years old when this happened. He went to the nearby district school and read in the fourth reader, but long before he knew his alphabet, he knew about the Battle of Bennington and the Revolutionary War.

He was just getting to be old enough to help fire off the cannon, and to hand the flowers to the old soldiers in the cemetery. And now they were all gone.

One day in June, when he was sent out to look for a cow which, the night before, hadn't come back to the barn from the mountain pasture, he met a schoolmate up there, Will Hunter. Will's mother had sent him out to pick wild strawberries on that sloping clearing. After the two boys met, the cow and the strawberries were forgotten. They sat down on a ledge to have a talk. Before long Andrew said

something about the Fourth of July celebration with no old soldier left, not a single one.

The other boy said, " There's an old fellow lives with the Hawleys, 'way up Hawley Hollow from our house. He's their great-grandfather, I think. Maybe he was a soldier in the Revolution. He's old enough. They say he's ninety. More."

Andrew's ten-year-old mind was already firmly lodged behind the tight narrow wall of the idea of the Town. " They don't live in Sunmore," he said. " We have to have a Sunmore old soldier for our Fourth."

" Yes, they do, too, live in Sunmore," said the other boy. " They don't trade at the Sunmore stores much, because from that end of the Hollow where their house is, it's easier to go out the far end to Canbury. But they vote in our Town Meeting."

The two boys looked at each other. Thinking no more of the cow and the strawberries they set out for Hawley Hollow.

So there *was* to be a Revolutionary soldier after all for the Fourth of July celebration! Everybody was talking about the old man, eighty-nine years, or maybe ninety, maybe more, back up on the far side of Westward Mountain, who had been remembered just in time. When the two boys told their fathers about him, two of the selectmen of the town had gone over the

mountain to see him. They said his back was bent with rheumatism, he was almost stone deaf, and he hobbled along with two canes to steady him. But he still had his old rifle, and even his cracked leather soldier's belt, just as the others had. And they reported that when, shouting loudly in his ear, they had asked him if he had fought in the Revolutionary War, he had nodded his head. Then they asked had it been in the Battle of Bennington? When he finally heard what they were asking he nodded his head and told them, "Yes, yes, *sir*, it certainly was."

They said the Hawleys up there, for all he was so old, thought a great deal of him. It was his great-grandson's family he was with — young people they were, had been married only five or six years. When the last of his grandchildren had died of old age, these young people had left their little cottage in Canbury and gone up to take care of him. An arrangement often made, in our country — he was to leave them his house and farm and they were to provide for his old age. They had never heard, naturally, what he had been doing seventy years ago — neither of them was over twenty-five — but they had always seen the old long gun, laid on the pegs over the fireplace, and the old belt hung with it.

Wasn't it remarkable, Sunmore people said, that just that very year when the last of the old heroes had gone, this other old Revolutionary soldier had been found. And who had found him? Why Andrew Bostwick

and William Hunter, two little boys. They were bright little boys to have known enough history to understand about the Fourth of July. Patriotic too. The program committee arranged that they were to stand on the platform during the meeting on each side of the old soldier, and to march in the procession just in front of Dr. White's chaise, each one carrying an American flag. They were to be called the "Young Guard of Honor." You don't need anyone to tell you that those boys could hardly wait for the Fourth of July to come.

On the morning of the Fourth, Andrew's father got up early, took the boys, and drove his farm wagon all the way around the mountain and up into the Hollow to bring the old man back. It was ten o'clock when they came back into Sunmore Street. A crowd was waiting in front of the Town Hall. They began to clap their hands and cheer when Mr. Bostwick helped lift the bent old man out of the wagon and led him into the Hall. Andrew and Will, the Young Guard of Honor, carried his ancient gun in and put it across his knees. He had his rusty belt strapped on over his coat.

When they took his gun to carry, he gave them such a pleasant smile of thanks that they understood why his great-grandchildren thought so much of him. He was a very nice-looking old man, everybody thought, clean and neat, with quiet gentle eyes; and although he hadn't a tooth left, his mouth still looked as though he liked jokes.

The people came into the Town Hall, took their seats, and began fanning themselves. It was a hot day, as the Fourth often is. The speaker was there, a lawyer from Canbury. The chorus of local singers stood below the platform, facing the audience. Their leader rapped his stick. They stood at attention. But they did not begin to sing. For at this point Dr. White, who always sat on the platform with the selectmen and the speaker, called out to Andrew, "Here! Let me look at that gun! Pass it over to me."

Andrew was surprised. He put his hand on the gun, and leaning down to the old man's ear said to him as loudly as he could, "Dr. White wants to see your gun."

He shouted with all his might but he could not make himself heard. The old soldier was almost stone deaf. But he was willing to do anything that was wanted. His cheerful old face was bright. He felt the friendliness all around him. He smiled and nodded and passed his gun to Andrew.

The doctor took one sharp look at it and motioned to the singers in the chorus. "Wait a minute!" he told them.

Then he put on his glasses (he was the first person in Sunmore to have spectacles), and looked very carefully at a certain place near the trigger. Everybody kept still, wondering what was in his mind.

When he looked up, his face was all astonishment. He spoke so loudly that everybody in the whole Town Hall could hear him. "This is a Hessian gun! The old man must have been one of the Hessians who fought against the Americans."

There was such a silence in the Town Hall you could hear a wasp buzzing at one of the windows.

He was a Hessian! He had fought on the other side. People's mouths dropped open, they were so taken back.

The old man hadn't heard any of this because he was so deaf. He sat quietly there, between the two little boys, his gentle old eyes looking around at the people in the hall.

For a minute nobody said a word. Nobody could think what to say. Or what to do.

Then Andrew ran out to the front of the platform and began to talk very fast. "Listen," he said. "That was a hundred years ago. Well, more than seventy years anyhow. No matter how mad you are at somebody, you don't keep it up forever. The Bible says not to. He's lived close to us all that time, and farmed it like anybody, and had his family, and paid his taxes. He's old, so old — it would be *mean* of us to — "

Andrew had never even spoken a piece in school. He had forgotten where he was. When he realized what he was doing, he stopped talking and hung down his head. He went back and put one hand on the old man's shoulder. The wrinkled face lifted to smile at him. Andrew smiled back. But his lips were trembling.

People began to rustle and move their feet. But when Dr. White stood up as if to say something, they were still again, to listen.

He said, " I remember now, when I came to Sunmore to practice medicine and first began to be interested in Vermont history, I did hear some very old people talk about a young Hessian soldier who had been wounded in the Battle of Bennington, and was picked up unconscious, in the woods, the day after. One of the old history books in my Vermont collection says that he was carried to a farmhouse and taken care of there. By the time he was well enough to get around, many months afterwards, there were no more soldiers or armies around. He was only nineteen by that time, and he had come to love the way of life he saw around him. He wanted to be an American and live here.

" That history book didn't say anything more about him. But I heard something else from old Mr. Hale." The doctor looked down into the audience at a middle-aged man in the second row. " He was your grandfather, Jim Hale. He was sort of connected, -in-laws somehow, with the Bennington family that took in the Hessian boy. He told me they always liked him, the young soldier, I mean. When he learned enough English, he told them his story. He had always had it hard in the Old Country, he said. He was an orphan, very poor, seventeen years old, when a recruiting gang picked him up off the street and carried him off to the barracks in Brunswick. He never liked soldiering, he said. He never understood what the fighting was about, because he never knew any English till he learned it from the Vermont family who took care of him."

The doctor still held the old rifle in his hands. He turned around now and laid it back on the old man's knees. Then he said to the audience, " I rather think Andrew Bostwick was right. Seventy years is too long to go on being mad. I think our celebration would better go on. Maybe the Reverend Hardwick might have something to say to us about this."

The old man from Hawley Hollow had evidently thought the program was going on, and that the doctor had been making one of the planned-for speeches. Now, seeing the minister stand up and step forward, he thought that the prayer was to be said. He composed his face, leaned forward in his chair in the respectful position you take when somebody is praying in public, and dropped his eyes to the ground.

As a matter of fact, the Reverend Hardwick did pray. He stood silent a long time. Then he said, " May war pass and peace be with us. Amen."

He sat down. The moderator of the town stood up. He was a burly, powerful, middle-aged man, with a serious, responsible face. He said, soberly, " I think this is something we ought to take a vote on. Don't you think so, Mr. Hardwick? "

The minister nodded. " Yes. It is something for each one of us to decide. But before we vote, I think we ought to sit quiet for a moment. And think."

The moderator reached for the clergyman's cane, and with it struck a gavel-like blow on the table. In his moderator's voice, he said, "The question before this House is whether we can live in peace when war has long gone by."

They all sat still.

The deaf ears of the old soldier had, of course, not heard any of this. It looked all right to him. He was very much bent with rheumatism. His hands lay thin and knotted on the arms of his chair. His clean old face was calm. In the silence he looked from one person to another in the audience. He smiled a little. After a moment, he turned his white head to look back at his little-boy guard of honor. There they were, one on each side of his chair. He nodded, and leaned back as if to say, "It's all right, if you are there."

The water came into Andrew's eyes.

The people in the rows of chairs on the floor were all looking up at the old soldier and the little boys.

A man stood up and said, "Mr. Moderator, I move that our celebration proceed."

Several voices said, "I second the motion."

Then the vote was taken. Everybody voted "aye."

So that afternoon, after the usual speaking and singing had been done, and the picnic lunch eaten out on the Common, the procession formed as usual, to march out to the cemetery.

The old soldier looked very tired by this time, but still cheerful. He came out of the Town Hall on Dr. White's arm, and was helped up into the chaise. The Young Guard of Honor held their flags high, so that they stirred in the breeze. The little girls in white dresses were pushed by their mothers into line, two by two. They carried the flowers, lilies, roses, carnation pinks.

The men and women formed, four by four. The doctor slapped the reins over the old horse's back. The leader of the band lifted his hand and said, commandingly, "A-a-all ready!"

The marchers held their flags straight.

"Forward, *march!*" cried the bandmaster.

The fifes sang out, "Whee-dee-deedle-dee" in thin high voices.

In a deep roar, the drums said, "Boom! boom! boom!"

And away they all went.

A New Thought for the Fourth

1. Why were the boys especially eager to find an old soldier to take part in the ceremony? Why had people not known of this one before?

2. How did the doctor discover that the old soldier had fought on the other side? What did he recall about the Hessian's history?

3. Do you think the old man had become a good American? Why was the old soldier not upset by all the discussion?

4. Skim back through the story and find the sentence that is the heart of Andrew's argument for going on with the ceremony. Then find what the minister had to say. Are their thoughts alike or different? How do you feel about their ideas? Discuss this question in class.

Daniel Boone

ARTHUR GUITERMAN

Daniel Boone at twenty-one
Came with his tomahawk, knife, and gun
Home from the French and Indian War
To North Carolina and the Yadkin° shore.

He married his maid with a golden band,   5
Builded his house and cleared his land;
But the deep woods claimed their son again
And he turned his face from the homes of men.
Over the Blue Ridge, dark and lone,
The Mountains of Iron, the Hills of Stone,   10
Braving the Shawnee's jealous wrath,
He made his way on the Warrior's Path.
Alone he trod the shadowed trails;
But he was the lord of a thousand vales
And he roved Kentucky, far and near,   15
Hunting the buffalo, elk, and deer.

What joy to see, what joy to win
So fair a land for his kith and kin,
Of streams unstained and woods unhewn!
"Elbowroom!" laughed Daniel Boone.   20

On the Wilderness Road that his axmen made
The settlers flocked to the first stockade;
The deerskin shirts and the coonskin caps
Filed through the glens and the mountain gaps;
And hearts were high in the fateful spring   25
When the land said "Nay!" to the stubborn king.
While the men of the East of farm and town

4. **Yadkin**: a river running through North Carolina.

"Daniel Boone" from *I Sing a Pioneer* by Arthur Guiterman.

Strove with the troops of the British Crown,
Daniel Boone from a surge of hate
Guarded a nation's westward gate.   30
Down on the fort in a wave of flame
The Shawnee horde and the Mingo° came,
And the stout logs shook in a storm of lead;
But Boone stood firm and the savage fled.
Peace! And the settlers flocked anew,   35
The farm lands spread, the town lands grew;
But Daniel Boone was ill at ease
When he saw the smoke in his forest trees.
"There'll be no game in the country soon.
Elbowroom!" cried Daniel Boone.   40

Straight as a pine at sixty-five —
Time enough for a man to thrive —
He launched his bateau° on Ohio's breast
And his heart was glad as he oared it west;
There were kindly folk and his own true blood   45
Where great Missouri rolls his flood;
New woods, new streams, and room to spare,
And Daniel Boone found comfort there.
Yet far he ranged toward the sunset still,
Where the Kansas runs and the Smoky Hill,   50
And the prairies toss, by the south wind blown;
And he killed his bear on the Yellowstone.
But ever he dreamed of new domains
With vaster woods and wider plains;
Ever he dreamed of a world-to-be   55
Where there are no bounds and the soul is free.
At four-score-five, still stout and hale,
He heard a call to a farther trail;
So he turned his face where the stars are strewn;
"Elbowroom!" sighed Daniel Boone.   60

Down the Milky Way in its banks of blue
Far he has paddled his white canoe
To the splendid quest of the tameless soul —
He has reached the goal where there is no goal.

---

32. **Mingo:** a name for the Iroquois Indians. 43. **bateau** (bă·tō′): a flat-bottomed boat.

Now he rides and rides an endless trail   65
On the Hippogriff° of the flaming tail
Or the Horse of the Stars with the golden mane,
As he rode the first of the bluegrass strain.
The joy that lies in the Search he seeks
On breathless hills with crystal peaks;   70
He makes his camp on heights untrod,
The steps of the Shrine, along with God.
Through the woods of the vast, on the plains of Space
He hunts the pride of the Mammoth race
And the Dinosaur of the triple horn,   75
The Manticore° and the Unicorn,
As once by the broad Missouri's flow
He followed the elk and the buffalo.
East of the Sun and west of the Moon,
" Elbowroom! " laughs Daniel Boone.   80

66. **Hippogriff**: a fabulous monster, part horse and part griffin. A griffin is part lion and part eagle. 76. **Manticore**: another monster in fables, part man, part lion, and part dragon.

Old Ironsides

OLIVER WENDELL HOLMES

One of the causes of the War of 1812 was the kidnaping of American sailors by English ships. The tiny American navy seemed powerless to prevent it. But when war broke out, American ships inflicted surprising defeats on the British, and won respect for their country. The frigate *Constitution* made a glorious record of victory after victory. Yet a few years later Congress ordered the ship scrapped. Then a poet wrote some lines that roused all America to cry out in defense of the old ship. Here is the poem that saved it from destruction.

Aye, tear her tattered ensign° down!
  Long has it waved on high,
And many an eye has danced to see
  That banner in the sky;
Beneath it rung the battle shout,   5
  And burst the cannon's roar —
The meteor of the ocean air
  Shall sweep the clouds no more.

Her decks, once red with heroes'
    blood,
  Where knelt the vanquished foe,
When winds were hurrying o'er the
    flood,   11
  And waves were white below,
No more shall feel the victor's tread,
  Or know the conquered knee —
The harpies° of the shore shall pluck
  The eagle of the sea!   16

1. **ensign:** a flag flown on a ship. 15. In old myths, **harpies** were evil creatures, half bird, half woman, who snatched away the souls of the dead.

Oh, better that her shattered hulk
  Should sink beneath the wave;
Her thunders shook the mighty deep,
  And there should be her grave;   20
Nail to the mast her holy flag,
  Set every threadbare sail,
And give her to the god of storms,
  The lightning and the gale!

The Poet Saved the Ship

1. What stirring events in the past history of the *Constitution* did the poet review?

2. Why did he think it would be better to sink the ship at sea than to let it be torn up for the materials that could be saved?

3. Some members of the class may have visited the *Constitution* at the Charlestown Navy Yard near Boston, where it is still kept as a proud symbol of American victories. Have them describe the ship to you, or if no one has seen it personally, try to obtain pictures of it.

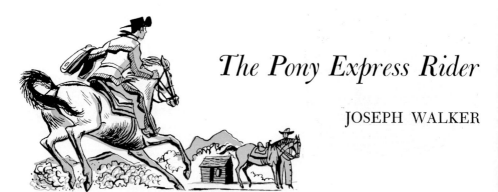

The Pony Express Rider

JOSEPH WALKER

Speed, danger, thrills — and valuable service! Today that means airplanes. In 1860 it meant the pony express. The skill, the speed, and the courage of the pony express riders and their horses were as amazing for their time as those of the fastest planes and bravest pilots are for today.

"The Pony Express Rider," from *How They Carried the Mail*, by Joseph Walker. Reprinted by permission of Dodd, Mead and Company, Inc.

IT's A pity you're not a few years older, Billy. I would give you a job as pony express rider. There's good pay in it."

Thus spoke George Chrisman, a Western express agent for a company that was on the point of launching a venture which many people called ridiculous, but which nevertheless appealed to the imagination of everybody between the Mississippi River and the Coast. It was nothing more nor less than to maintain a chain of fast riders reaching clear to California, nearly two thousand miles, for the regular carrying of the mail.

Though Chrisman spoke jestingly, the boy at his side looked up quickly.

"Oh, I say, Mr. Chrisman, give me a chance at it! I can ride as well as any man — you know I can!"

"Sure you can ride," replied his friend good-naturedly; "but it takes more than riding — it takes *sand!*"[1]

Before them on a table lay a St. Louis paper containing the notice which had set the whole West buzzing, and Chrisman picked it up for the boy, William Cody, to read for himself. This is what he read:

To San Francisco in 8 days by the Central Overland California and Pike's Peak Express Company. The first courier of the Pony Express will leave the Missouri River on Tuesday, April 3rd, at 5 o'clock P.M., and will run regularly weekly thereafter, carrying a letter mail only. The point of departure on the Missouri River will be in telegraphic communication with the East, and will be announced in due time.

"Aw, shucks, Mr. Chrisman, give me a chance at it, won't you?" pleaded the boy, his eyes shining. "Where is it to start from?"

"From St. Joe. Want to go over and watch 'em get away?"

"Sure I do. But I want more than that: I want to carry that mail myself!"

"Well, we'll think about it," said Chrisman laughingly.

To understand the setting of this story, we must remember that California, up to the year 1860, was as remote from the rest of the United States as Madagascar.[2] The usual route for mails was by water, either around Cape Horn, requiring weeks, or carried across the Isthmus of Panama from one ship to another and thence up the coast, a journey nearly as tedious. Between the Mississippi River on the east and the Pacific on the west lay hundreds of miles of trackless wilderness, barren desert, and frowning mountain. No railroad had yet pierced it, and the telegraph had yet to stretch its wires across. A war might break out in the East — as, in fact, actually threatened at the time this story opens and soon became reality — and the Californians would be blithely ignorant of it for weeks.

A quicker and steadier means of communication was a necessity. Thus thought three men whose names became famous in the old West for their freighting and express business carried on by coach and horsemen. Their

---

[1] *sand:* courage and endurance.

[2] **Madagascar** (măd'á·găs'kẽr): an island off the southeast coast of Africa.

names were Russell, Majors, and Waddell, and with fine imagination they began quietly to lay plans for this fleet of fast riders, called the pony express. So quietly did they work that they had all their plans made and most of their equipment ready before putting the notice in the St. Louis *Dispatch,* announcing the opening date.

" Say — you'll have a whale of a bunch of horses and riders for that outfit! " said young Cody.

" You're right. That's one of my jobs out here — getting good horses for 'em. No horse is too good for the service. Why, we are paying as high as two hundred dollars apiece for 'em. And riders will draw down from fifty to a hundred and fifty dollars a month — but they must be the best little old riders in the world and afraid of nothing! "

" How many will you need? " persisted the boy, his voice vibrating with eagerness.

" Well, we're planning to put on eighty riders to start, and four hundred and twenty horses, for we are putting in relay stations about fifteen miles apart clear across the Plains. There'll be no monkey business about this. Our boys will ride at top speed all the time — just like Indians were after 'em — as may be the case, like as not! "

Chrisman then proceeded to paint the difficulties and dangers of this route, which were evident enough, for the West of those days was a very Wild West indeed. But the more he talked, the more eager became his lis-

tener to try express riding for himself. Finally the older man compromised.

" You're a bit under age, Will," he said; " but I'll tell you what I'll do. I'll take you on as a substitute for a rider named Trotter out here on my division. He has only a short run — forty-five miles — and a change of three horses for it. That ought to be a cinch for you. You were born on horseback, I reckon! "

" That's great, Mr. Chrisman! " said the boy, who was, indeed, already famous for his feats of horsemanship.

The opening day at St. Joseph, Missouri, was a gala occasion. A great crowd had assembled in the streets, and the excitement was at fever heat. Flags were flying everywhere, and a brass band added to the hubbub. A short-line railroad, the Hannibal and St. Joseph, had arranged to run an excursion as well as bring in the mail from the East. It was due in the afternoon, and at last the waiting throng heard a faint whistle down the track. " Here she comes! " they shouted, and up puffed the train, on time.

Scarcely had it stopped, when busy hands were transferring the mail pouches to a wagon, which rattled down the streets to the post office. A few minutes more and the Pacific mail was sorted out and ready for the express rider. His name was Johnnie Frey, and he was a wiry little fellow, scarcely twenty years old, and weighing only one hundred and twenty-five pounds.

Mr. Russell himself, one of the three members of the firm, adjusted the letter pouch on the saddle. It was limited to twenty pounds and contained, besides letters and a New York newspaper printed on tissue paper, a message of congratulations from President Buchanan to Governor Downey of California. As the last buckle was adjusted, Johnnie sprang into the saddle; a few of the nearest of the excited crowd pulled hairs from his horse's tail for souvenirs, then the throng scattered to make way for him, and down the main street of St. Joe he went at a mad gallop, the people shouting themselves hoarse.

At the foot of the street at the Missouri River landing, a ferryboat was waiting for him, and on it he dashed. Hardly had his steed's hoofs struck the planking when the bells clanged and the craft pushed off into midstream. The first trip of the pony express was begun.

On the Kansas side of the river the swift scene was re-enacted. As the ferry touched the wharf and before it was made fast, Johnnie spurred his impatient horse forward, the margin of water was cleared at a bound, and horse and rider disappeared in a cloud of dust out toward the western sun. Strangers gripped each other's hands at the sight, clapped one another on the back, shouted themselves hoarse — and in more than one man's eyes tears could be seen. Yes, it meant a lot to the West!

What lay ahead? At the end of Johnnie's run, another man and yet another would spring into saddle and ride night and day to deliver that precious parcel at its destination, two thousand miles away. The route lay through northeastern Kansas and into Nebraska, up the valley of the Platte River, across the great plateau into the foothills and over the summit of the Rockies, into the arid Great Basin, over the Wasatch Range, into the valley of Great Salt Lake, through the terrible alkali deserts of Nevada and the parched sink of Carson River, over the lofty Sierras with their snow-encumbered passes, and finally into the valley of the Sacramento, where a waiting steamer would take the mail for the last lap of its journey to San Francisco.

What a prospect! To the terrors of an untraveled country were added prowling savages, wild beasts, winds, rains, blizzards, intense cold, parching heat, the blazing sun of noonday, the intense darkness of midnight — but through it all the riders must press forward night and day — the mail pouch *must* go through!

The wildest and most unexplored parts of America lay ahead. Along the entire route there were only four military posts, two or three hundred miles apart. The small relay stations established by the company were the only human habitations for other hundreds of miles. Exposed as they were to the attacks of Indians, they were liable to be wiped out, and more than one station suffered this dire fate, as the tired express riders found to their own distress after completing a toilsome run. There was no relief horse or rider waiting.

But despite these almost insurmountable difficulties, the pony express was established and maintained.

At the same day on which Johnnie Frey rode out of St. Joe, another rider, Harry Roff, started on the eastern trip from Sacramento. Each rider covered from seventy-five to one hundred and twenty-five miles, depending upon the nature of the country, and changed horses every ten, fifteen, or twenty miles. The horse tender at the lonely relay station would see him coming, a mile or two away, and would have his fresh mount saddled, bridled, and waiting. Up would come the rider at full gallop, pull his tired beast short up on its haunches, leap to the ground, transfer and buckle on his saddlebags, and go on his way, often hardly stopping to take a gulp of water. Two minutes was the time allowance for a stop, but half that time often sufficed. The men made a speed of about eighteen miles an hour. Harry Roff on his first eastbound trip covered the first twenty miles in fifty-nine minutes.

Meanwhile the succession of riders who relieved Johnnie Frey on his westward trip kept up the same good speed that he had set for them. The original mailbag with the President's message was delivered in Sacramento in nine days and twenty-three hours. The same great scenes of wild excitement marked the end of this famous run as did its beginning. Bells were rung, whistles were blown, men shouted, and business was at a standstill. When the panting horse and rider dashed into the streets of Sacramento, they were almost mobbed. Stopping only a few moments to toss off the local mail, the rider hurried aboard a waiting steamer for the last lap of the journey down the river to San Francisco. That city was reached in the dead of night; but as soon as the whistle of the steamer heralded its approach, the city came awake as by magic. People hastily dressed came running down to the wharf. Whistles screeched their welcome, and a fire engine dashed madly out to escort the express rider to the post office.

But during all this fever heat of the inauguration of the service, what of the boy, William Cody? Within a few days, to his great joy, his friend sent word for him to present himself for riding. He was to be put on the forty-five-mile run that Chrisman had mentioned. After he had filled out the application blank and answered questions as to his parents and habits, he was required to swear to an oath which was required of every rider entering the express service. This was the oath repeated by Cody with uplifted hand:

I, William F. Cody, do hereby swear, before the Great and Living God, that during my engagement, and while I am an employee of Russell, Majors, and Waddell, I will, under no circumstances, use profane language; that I will drink no intoxicating liquors; that I will not quarrel or fight with any other employee of the firm, and that in every respect I will conduct myself honestly, be faithful to my duties, and so direct all my acts as to win the confidence of my employers. So help me God!

This oath told eloquently of the high character of the riders employed, as well as of the company employing them. It could well be tacked up on the lintel [1] of every office today. Within a few weeks after its establishment, in fact, the pony express had won the confidence of the entire nation, and later it performed inestimable service at the outbreak of the War Between the States.

Cody, like the other riders, wore no special uniform. The men dressed to suit their tastes. But their usual garb was a buckskin hunting shirt, cloth trousers, high boots, and a slouch hat. Often a large handkerchief protected their necks from the sun or flies. As for weapons, they carried a sheath knife and a pair of Colt pistols. At first they slung a carbine [2] around their shoulders, but soon discarded this. Nearly all the riders were quite young, few exceeding twenty-five, and were light of frame and wiry.

The saddlebag used by the rider for carrying the mail was called a *mochila*.[3] It had openings in the center to allow it to fit snugly over the horn and tree of the saddle and yet be removable without delay. The *mochila* had four pockets called *cantinas*,[4] one in each of its corners — so that there were two in front and two behind the rider's legs. In these *cantinas* the mail was carried under lock and key. Three had keys which permitted them to be opened at the military posts along the way, while the fourth was reserved for local or way mail

stations. In this *cantina* was a time-card for noting time of arrival and departure of the rider.

The letters were wrapped in oiled silk to protect them from moisture, either from rain, or from water in fording streams, or perspiration of the horse. While the weight of the mail was limited to twenty pounds, it rarely exceeded fifteen. The postal charges at first were five dollars for each letter weighing half an ounce, which seems cheap enough when the trip is considered, but as the service got better established, the Post Office Department reduced this charge to one dollar for each half ounce. As a result, persons writing letters to their friends in San Francisco usually used a very thin tissue paper. A few newspapers were so printed, but were not sent regularly.

As for William Cody, he entered into his new duties with a light heart. His first run was not dangerous nor long. Accustomed as he was to the saddle all his life, he treated his forty-five-mile dash, using three horses, as a great lark. He had no difficulty in riding on schedule, often cutting down the time. But he was only a substitute and after a few weeks the regular man, Trotter, returned and Will was out of a job.

Riding east as far as Fort Leavenworth, he obtained a letter of recommendation from Mr. Russell, the head of the firm, and presented this to Jack Slade, the superintendent of another route. Slade — a noted and notorious [5]

---

[1] **lintel:** the wooden crosspiece over a door.
[2] **carbine** (kär′bīn): a short, light rifle.
[3] *mochila* (mō·kē′lȧ).
[4] *cantinas* (kän·tē′nȧs).

[5] **notorious** (nō·tō′rĭ·ŭs): widely but unfavorably known.

character of the frontier — was just then hunting for an experienced rider to cover one of the hardest of his routes, and glanced askance [1] at the youthful applicant. But when he read Russell's letter and learned that Cody had ridden another route satisfactorily, he decided to give him the job, despite his youth. The new route was seventy-six miles long, running from Red Buttes to Three Crossings — a place on the Sweetwater River so called because the stream, as it followed the bed of a canyon, had to be crossed three times in a distance of sixty yards. The water, being a mountain stream, was icy cold, and there were pitfalls and deep pools lurking for the unwary.

Another fording hardly less hazardous was across the North Platte, which had dangerous quicksands, the river being half a mile wide at the ford, and twelve feet deep in places. And as if this were not enough, his route lay through hostile Indian country, and was also infested by desperados.

Despite these dangers, young Cody rode his route successfully for two or three weeks. He was almost on the point of thinking that it would prove as monotonous as his former one, when a series of adventures brought him up sharply. One day, after riding in his usual mad galloping way, he reached the end of his journey, Three Crossings, well within the allotted time. What was his horror to find that the relief rider, who was to have tak-

[1] glanced askance: looked at him sideways, showing distrust.

en the mail farther, had been murdered, either by redskins or by bandits. It was clearly up to him, tired as he was, to carry on. Fortunately there were fresh horses, and within a few moments he had remounted and started out on a new and strange route which led him to Rocky Ridge, eighty-five miles away. Buoyed up by the perils of his trip he continued on to this terminal and then started back with the eastbound mail, ending by going again over his own division and into Red Buttes. When the tired youth almost fell off his last mount, they found that he had covered the amazing distance of 322 miles — but he had carried the mail!

On more than one occasion Cody sighted redskins, but the speed of his mount carried him out of danger. It is said that the Indians frequently stared open-mouthed at the mad riding of these reckless horsemen. Nothing like it had been seen in their tribes. One day a band of Sioux decided they would like to add that fast pony to their string, to say nothing of an extra scalp for some warrior's belt. But young Cody had different ideas; he needed both himself. As the Sioux swooped down upon him, firing as they came, he lay flat upon his pony's back and urged the faithful little animal to still better speed. For agoniz-

ing minutes the race with death held on, the bullets and arrows whizzing all about him but luckily missing. Then the training and endurance of his mount told. He slowly drew away from the red pursuers and thundered into Sweetwater, his next stop, minutes ahead of time. However, not yet was he out of danger. The Indians had been there ahead of him, killed the keeper, and driven off all the reserve stock. There was nothing for him to do but to continue on with his tired horse for twelve miles more, where the relay station was fortunately intact.

On another occasion he was entrusted with a large sum of money in currency, and had reason to believe that bandits knew of its passage. These "road agents," as they were called, did not hesitate at murder as well as robbery, and Cody felt he must outwit them. He obtained an extra *mochila* which he stuffed with papers and placed in the regular posi-

tion on the horn of his saddle. The other one with the bills was then hidden under his saddle. He had not ridden many miles when, in a lonely spot, his fears were confirmed by seeing two masked men who stood directly in his path with loaded pistols.

"Halt, young fellow!" they challenged sharply. And as he perforce reined in, they continued, "Throw up your hands!"

Slowly young Cody's hands went up, while he never took his eyes off

his assailants.

"We don't want to hurt you, young fellow," one of them continued, "but we do want that package of letters powerful bad."

"Don't you know they will hang you for fooling with the United States Mail?" Cody asked, to gain time.

"They'll have to catch us first. Now you unfasten that sack and be quick about it. If you start any monkey business we'll drill you full of holes."

Will reached around for the dummy sack, which he made a great pretense of having trouble in unfastening. Suddenly he straightened up. "Here it is!" he shouted, and hurled it directly into the face of one of the road agents. The fellow was bowled over by the blow. Quick as a flash the young express rider dug his spurs into the side of his horse and headed full at the other man. He dodged, but got a vicious kick from one of the animal's hoofs. Away galloped Cody, not looking back. He reasoned that the surprise the bandits had gotten would prevent them from shooting, and besides they had the mail sack they thought they wanted. He rode on unmolested to the next station and delivered his package of money safely. But he said afterward that he would have given a good deal to see the look on the faces of the highwaymen when they opened their sack and found nothing but waste paper.

Many were the thrills and adventures of Cody's associates also on these long, lonely rides across the plains. In a few instances they ended tragically for some brave young fellow, who never came back, and whose bones were left to whiten alongside the trail. As for Cody, when he left the service unharmed, it was to engage in other forms of scouting quite as exciting. He has come down to fame as one of the greatest of our scouts — "Buffalo Bill."

But the supreme or "acid" test of the pony express service came with the election of Abraham Lincoln to the Presidency. It was a hair-trigger time when the North and South were squaring off at each other and threatening to fight. When Lincoln was elected in November, 1860, it was highly important that the news should be sent to the Coast as speedily as possible, in order to hold this faraway part of the country safe for the Union.

Away from St. Joseph dashed the first rider, amid excitement rivaling that day when the first letter had started west. At every relay station extraordinary plans had been made to make their usual good time even better. Picked horses were led out, at some points, two or three miles in advance of the station to furnish an extra relay and added speed. On and on the reckless fellows dashed, scarcely slackening speed even when riding in the dark — truly a test for any horseman's nerve! Relay after relay was clicked off in record-breaking time. The last rider dashed into Sacramento and was whisked on a waiting boat and thus taken to San Francisco, followed by yells of "Lincoln is elected! Lincoln is elected!" The total journey of exactly 1,966 miles had been made in eight days.

It would seem as if human endurance had reached its limit — but the pony express was not through with records yet. In March of the next year, Lincoln made his first inaugural address, while the East was palpitating [1] on the verge of war. What would the West think and do? It was of supreme importance that the government should find out.

The message was sent by the fastest trains to St. Joe, and again the gallant riders were told to better their best.

"Take this message to the Coast faster than any word has ever yet gone through!" ordered Mr. Russell.

The boys, one after another along the line, repeated the words with grim earnestness. And they did. How they rode! "Pony Bob" Haslam, one of the best men that ever pressed stirrup leather, galloped at breakneck speed for one hundred and twenty miles, pausing only to change mounts every ten miles, and covered his route in eight hours and ten minutes — or at a rate of nearly fifteen miles an hour. Another man rode ten miles in thirty minutes. The total journey from St. Joseph to Sacramento required just seven days and seventeen hours!

The pony express did not die of old age; it passed away in its prime. The fall of that same year, 1861, saw the first telegraph poles pushing their way across the plains, and before the end of the year a line had been opened through the Sierras. The click of the telegraph instrument was much more prosaic [2] than the clatter of pony's hoofs, but it did in minutes what had required the brave horse and rider days and days to perform. So within a year and a half after its beginning, the pony express was no more.

In that brief time, however, what a valiant service it had performed, and what romance had gathered about its deeds! It is part and parcel with the old West. Mark Twain, who knew the frontier in his boyhood, says in one of his early books: [3]

The pony rider was usually a little bit of a man, brimful of spirit and endurance. No matter what time of the day or night his watch came on, and no matter whether it was winter or summer, raining, snowing, hailing, or sleeting, or whether his "beat" was a level, straight road, or a crazy trail over mountain crags and precipices, or whether it led through peaceful regions, or regions that swarmed with hostile Indians, he must always be ready to leap into the saddle and be off like the wind. There was no idling time for a pony rider on duty. He rode fifty miles without stopping, by daylight, moonlight, starlight, or through the blackness of darkness just as it happened. He rode a splendid horse that was born for a racer and fed and lodged like a gentleman; kept him at his utmost speed for ten miles and then, as he came crashing up to the station where stood two men holding fast a fresh, impatient steed, the transfer of rider and mail was made in the twinkling of an eye, and

---

[1] **palpitating** (păl'pĭ·tāt·ĭng): trembling, wavering.

[2] prosaic (prô·zā'ĭk): dull, commonplace.

[3] *Roughing It,* a book about his first trip to the West.

away flew the eager pair and were out of sight before the spectator could get a ghost of a look.

We had had a consuming desire to see a pony rider [continues Mark Twain, who was riding in an overland stage] but somehow or other all that passed us and all that met us managed to streak by in the night, and so we heard only a whiz and a hail, and the swift phantom of the desert was gone before we could get our heads out of the windows. But now we were expecting one along every moment and would see him in broad daylight. Presently the driver exclaims: " Here he comes! " Every neck is stretched further and every eye is strained wider.

Away across the endless dead level of the prairie a black speck appears against the sky, and it is plain that it moves. Well, I should think so! In a second or two it becomes a rider, rising and falling — sweeping toward us nearer and nearer — growing more and more distinct, more and more sharply defined — nearer and still nearer, and the flutter of the hoofs comes faintly to the ear — another instant a whoop and a hurrah from our upper deck, a wave of the rider's hand, but no reply, and man and beast burst past our excited faces and go winging away like a belated fragment of a storm.

So sudden is it all, and so like a flash of unreal fancy, that but for a flake of white foam left quivering and perishing on a mail sack after the vision had flashed by and disappeared, we might have doubted whether we had seen any actual horse and man at all, maybe.

Fast Mail in 1860

1. Check your ability to remember details by seeing how many of these points you can recall *without looking back at the story:*

a. the route for mail to California before the pony express was started

b. the cross-country system on which the pony express operated

c. the equipment of the riders

d. the postage rates

e. different perils the riders faced

f. the record time made on a trip

g. the reason the pony express ended so soon

2. How was William Cody able to get a job riding for the pony express even though he was too young? How do you know that requirements for the job were strict?

3. What jobs in our modern world call for as much endurance and courage as the pony express did?

Same Sound, Different Meaning

Some English words lay traps for careless spellers. While two words can sound exactly alike, they may have different spellings and different meanings. Such pairs of words are called *homonyms* (hŏm′ō·nĭmz). In reading you can tell the difference between homonyms by noticing their spelling. When you hear them spoken, however, you must depend on the general sense of the passage to tell you the right meaning.

Fill in the blank in each of these sentences with a word that sounds like the italicized word but is spelled differently:

a. A boy who can perform that *feat* of horsemanship can ride anything with four . . . .

b. When he stopped to *wait* for the next rider, he checked the . . . . of the pouch.

c. Even when the *rain* poured down, the rider did not . . . . in his horse.

There are many more words in this story that have homonyms — *mail, waist, scene, eight, week, break, hole,* to mention a few. Put three of them, along with their homonyms, into sentences like those above, being careful to use the spelling that fits the meaning intended.

The Boy Who Voted for Abe Lincoln

MILTON RICHARDS

FACT AND FICTION. Did you know that more books have been written about Lincoln than any other American? There are thousands of books that tell of young Abe and of Abraham Lincoln, the President of the United States. Most of the books and stories about him are " true," in the sense that they stick to facts and tell of actual happenings. But some of the stories are fiction; they are made up or imagined by the author. Here is a fiction story that presents Lincoln the citizen, the friendly neighbor.

In reading a fiction story about a real person, you can add to your enjoyment by following this hint: keep in mind the things you *already* know about the person. The story may tell about imaginary happenings, but if it is a good story it will give an accurate and believable picture of the man himself. In reading this story, for example, ask yourself whether the author's picture of Lincoln seems to fit the stories about him you have read. Are the actions described ones that Lincoln could actually have performed in real life? If you ask such questions — and answer them — in your own mind, you will be in a position to judge how well the story is written. And you will enjoy reading it all the more.

S AM Adams climbed to the wagon seat and spoke to the yoke of oxen. His father was out of sight now, over the hill, heading for the wheat field. Jolting on the hard plank, Sam looked back and waved to his mother. She was standing in the middle of the farmyard, her yellow hair and gray calico skirt blowing in the brisk wind.

She waved anxiously. " Hurry now, Sam! " she called. " You know how much that wheat means to your pa. If those cattle get in before he gets the fence up — ! " She left the sentence unfinished.

" I'll get there, Ma," he called back reassuringly. " Don't worry."

But he couldn't help worrying himself. A herd of cattle roving over the hills had already destroyed the Hillis's cornfield and the Moores' oats. It was Mr. Moore who had ridden over to warn Sam's father that the cattle were headed that way.

Sam gritted his teeth. That wheat field meant everything to his father, to the whole family. If anything happened to it, next winter would be a barren one. Food scarce. Money

"The Boy Who Voted for Abe Lincoln" by Milton Richards. Reprinted by permission of *The Catholic Boy*.

scarcer. Sam could remember two years ago, when he had been only ten. All winter long there had been an empty ache where his stomach should have been. No. He didn't want another winter like that.

He tried to get the oxen to move faster. But the road was narrow and full of deep ruts. It was muddy, too, from yesterday's rain.

Bumping and sliding, the wagon, with its burden of fence rails, came finally within sight of the field.

Sam gave a glad shout. He was almost there, and the wheat was rippling in the wind, still untrampled. He could see his father riding along the far edge.

But Sam's shout had stopped the oxen. To them it had sounded like a call to halt. Too late, Sam tried to urge them forward. The right wheels were sunk deep, up to the hubs, in the sticky mud.

"Giddap," cried Sam desperately. It was no use. The wagon was stuck, glued to the slimy ruts. He lifted his head, opened his mouth to call for his father to come and help. The shout died in his throat. Thronging the hill beyond the wheat field were moving cattle, a hundred head or more. They were coming steadily on toward the precious wheat field.

No use now to call his father. They would never get the wagon out in time, nor the fence up. Could his father head the cattle off alone? If he did, it would be a miracle.

Sam choked. He had tried to be brave, but now tears came to his eyes. It was no use. The cattle would ruin the wheat. Eyes blinded, he slid from the wagon seat.

As he did so, he heard the familiar beat of a horse's hoofs behind. Someone was coming down the road!

Shouting hoarsely, Sam waved his arms and pointed to the wheat field. Tears and excitement blurred his vision so that he could not tell if the man approaching was friend or stranger.

He backed against the wagon as the horse galloped forward, spurting mud toward him.

"Don't worry, son! Block up your wheels and put rails under them. I'll help head off the cattle."

He hadn't had time to see what the man looked like. Now, brushing the tears from his eyes, he stared after him in relief. Help for his father. The wheat field had a chance now, maybe.

The man on the horse was long and lanky, Sam saw. But in heading off cattle, he was clever and successful. Soon he and Sam's father had managed to herd the steers away from the wheat. They thundered off, bellowing, in the direction they had come.

His heart hammering gratefully, Sam watched the stranger dismount and talk with his father. Then he remembered the horseman's instructions for getting the wagon out of the mud.

Busily Sam started to work.

The cattle had been headed off for the time being, but no telling how soon they might come back again. The sooner he got the fence rails to the field, the better.

When he looked up again, the

stranger had climbed on his horse again and was riding off down the road at a canter, his lean form swaying awkwardly.

Mr. Adams crossed the field toward his son. He was mopping his brow with a large handkerchief.

"That was sure a close shave, son," he said, coming up to the wagon. "If it hadn't been for Abe, we'd have lost the wheat, sure. I never coulda headed them steers off alone."

"Abe who?" asked Sam. "A friend of yours, Pa?"

"Why, that was Abe Lincoln, son. He was on his way back to Springfield after making a speech some place. As for being a friend of mine, I guess Abe's just about everybody's friend."

"He sure was our friend, all right," said Sam gratefully. "What does this Abe Lincoln do, Pa? Is he a-farming, like us?"

"He's a lawyer, son; in politics, too. In fact, he's just been nominated for the presidency of the United States. On the new Republican Party ticket. Don't know as he's got much of a chance, though."

"Why not?" asked Sam loyally. "I guess we'd be lucky, wouldn't we, Pa, to get a man as good as him?"

"You bet we would. But, you see, he's up against some pretty smart fellows. Men that makes a business of being smart. Educated folk. Stephen Douglas, for instance."

"But you're going to vote for Mr. Lincoln, aren't you, Pa? You'd like for him to be President, wouldn't you?"

"You bet I'll vote for him, Sam.

Nothing can stop me from polling my vote for Abraham Lincoln, come November."

But something did stop Hank Adams from voting for Abraham Lincoln. In early July he was thrown from a horse and seriously injured. Judith, his young wife, and his son, Sam, were beside him when he died.

"Don't — forget — the — wheat, Sam. Take — it — into — Springfield." He sighed, closed his eyes. "I — meant — to — take — it — in — election day. When — I — voted — for Abe. Too bad."

Two weeks later Sam answered a knock at the door. Two men stood outside.

"This the Adams farm?" asked one.

"Yes, sir. Will you come in?" Sam answered.

"Who is it, Sam?" called his mother. She came in, wiping her red, roughened hands on her apron.

"I'm Joe Winship, mum," said the taller of the two strangers. "And this is my pardner, Jerry Hogan. We've brought you a letter from Mr. Abe Lincoln."

"From Abe Lincoln?" She took it wonderingly. "Why, it's addressed to both of us, Sammy."

"To me, too?" asked Sam eagerly. "Open it, Ma. What does it say?"

She looked up at the two men whom, in the excitement of the letter, she had almost forgotten. "Oh, I'm sorry. I — I guess I've clean forgot my manners, gentlemen. Sammy, push up some chairs for Mr. Winship and Mr. Hogan."

"Oh, don't mind us, mum. We're just — just part of the letter, you might say," flushed Mr. Hogan.

But Sam ran for some chairs. When he came back, his mother had the letter open. She looked up from it, her face glowing.

"God bless Abe Lincoln," she said softly. "It's a beautiful letter."

"He's a kind man, mum," said Mr. Winship fervently. "There ain't many lawyers would let Jerry and me work out a debt like this, instead of paying straight cash."

"What does it say, Ma?" asked Sam eagerly.

"It says," replied his mother gently, "that Mr. Lincoln is deeply sorry to learn of your pa's going. And he hopes we'll be kind enough to let these two friends of his, Mr. Winship and Mr. Hogan, work out their debt to him for legal work by helping us with the farm work for a spell."

"Glory, Ma!" breathed Sam. "That means we'll have help threshing the wheat."

"You sure will," said Mr. Hogan, grinning widely. "All the help you need."

"I — I don't know what to say," said Mrs. Adams, choking. "It — it just seems like help from heaven. Of course, Sam's been doing fine, but he's a long way from being a man grown. How can I thank Mr. Lincoln?"

"We'll just tell him about the look on your face when you read the letter, Miz Adams. That'll be thanks enough for Abe."

"Is that all the letter, Ma?" asked Sam. "Didn't he say anything about me? You said the letter was addressed to me, too."

"Why, yes, Sam. There is a note for you."

The boy took the page eagerly. It read: "Sam, I used to hear your father talk about what a fine, good boy you were. He was very proud of you. I know he's glad you're there to take care of your mother. Don't ever give up if you should get stuck in the mud again. There's always a way out. Something or someone will come along to help if you just keep trusting the Almighty."

Sam put the letter down. "Glory, Ma! Abe Lincoln's just got to be elected President. Why, I reckon he must be the best man in the whole world."

In November, Sam Adams took the wheat into Springfield to sell. It was fine wheat, he thought proudly, and he ought to get a fine price for it. Before they had left to go back to town, Joe Winship and Jerry Hogan had told him where to take it in order to get the best price.

It was good to know that his mother wouldn't have to worry about money all winter long. They'd have enough to eat now. He wished he could keep her from missing Pa too much. Maybe if he brought her something . . . something with the money she'd said he could have for his very own.

It was still early morning when he rolled into Springfield. There were a lot of people going to town — more than he'd ever seen before. The streets of the little town hummed with excitement. There was something in the air, something in the way women laughed and whispered, in the way men gathered in groups on street corners, that set young Sam Adams's pulses throbbing. Unusual happenings today, sure enough. He reckoned maybe it was a parade or a fair.

Then a group of men marched down the street bearing banners. A band played blaring music. The banners said: " Elect Stephen Douglas President."

Sam sat bolt upright, shocked. Elect Mr. Douglas? Why, it was Abe Lincoln they should be electing. His own pa had been going to vote for Lincoln.

He knew then why there were so many people here in Springfield today. It was election day — the day the people voted for President of the United States. He wondered why his mother hadn't told him. But they'd been working so hard lately that she must have clean forgot.

Well, he was here now, luckily. He'd go sell the wheat first, then come back. He got an even better price for it than he'd expected. The man who bought it, Mr. Salford, said he'd been expecting him. Joe Winship had told him about Sam.

" Too bad your mother couldn't come in to town, too," said Mr. Salford, helping Sam unload the bags of wheat.

" I reckon she'll be mighty sorry, too, when she hears it's election day," said Sam. " But someone had to stay and take care of the farm. There's only us two now."

" Well, you're a fine, strong lad," complimented Mr. Salford. " I'm sure your mother depends on you a good deal."

Sam asked the way to the nearest polling place. The town hall was closest, Mr. Salford said, waving good-by.

The street outside the town hall was crowded. The sidewalks were clotted with gesticulating groups of men, all talking in loud voices or speaking in low confidential asides.

Sam nudged a man with a very red nose and a fierce, black beard.

" Where do folks go to vote? " he asked timidly.

" Just follow the crowd," answered the man, waving a hand. " Just follow the crowd." Then, getting a good look at Sam for the first time, he stared. " Are you figuring to vote, son? " He burst into loud laughter. " Well, if you do, don't vote for that scarecrow, Abe Lincoln! " A group of men nearby also laughed uproariously.

Sam felt his ears get hot. He hurried past them. There were little booths in the room where people voted. As soon as one man left one of the booths, another man went in. Sam waited patiently for his chance. At the first opportunity he went into a booth.

" Hey! " said a voice. " A kid went in that booth! Yank him out."

They did yank him out. " But — but I want to vote," pleaded Sam. " I want to vote for Mr. Lincoln."

A man laughed. " But you're not old enough to vote, kid. You have to be twenty-one in order to vote." He gave him a shove. " On your way, son! "

" But please, mister — I'm voting for my pa. He aimed to cast his ballot for Lincoln."

" Well, he'll have to come himself," said the man impatiently. " Now go on — get out of here. You're just taking up floor space needed by legal voters."

" But my pa can't come himself," pleaded Sam. " Honest, mister, why ain't it all right for me to — "

The man beckoned two burly-looking men. " The youngster's stubborn, boys. I reckon you'd better show him the way out."

The two men took hold of Sam and lifted him squirming from the floor.

Two minutes later he picked himself up from the street outside. His best pants were torn. His hat had fallen into the gutter. His knees and one elbow were skinned. But worst of all was the way he felt inside. He'd failed. Failed both his pa and Mr. Lincoln.

He got up and picked his hat out of the gutter. It was crumpled and muddy. His eyes filled with tears. He tried to choke back sobs.

A heavy hand fell on his shoulder. Sam looked up, startled.

" Please, mister. I ain't doing anything. I'm going now."

" What's the trouble, son? "

Sam looked up into the face of a man so homely that, despite the kindness of his tone, the boy's fright returned. Maybe they'd sent this man to come and put Sam in jail. Maybe they put folks in jail for trying to vote when they oughtn't to.

" Please, mister," he sobbed. " I didn't know it was wrong. I was just trying to help make Mr. Lincoln President."

" Were you now? And what makes you think he ought to be President? "

" Because he's so good," said Sam tearfully. " That's why I wanted to vote for him."

The long arm went around his shoulder, tightened. " You mean — you tried to cast a vote for him, son? "

Sam nodded. " I was going to vote for my pa, mister. He can't vote for Mr. Lincoln like he said he wanted to, because — because — he's dead, mister." He shook the tears from his eyes and looked up proudly. " You see, my pa, he knew Mr. Lincoln."

The eyes that looked down at him were warm and pitying. All at once the man's face didn't look homely to Sam any more. Instead, it was the kindest face he had ever seen.

" What was your father's name, son? "

" Henry Adams, mister. We live out by Apple Creek. There's just my ma and me now, though. But Mr. Lincoln sent some men out to help us thresh our wheat, and so we won't have to worry all winter about having enough," he said earnestly. " My pa said Mr. Lincoln was always doing nice things like that. He was everybody's friend, he said."

" I knew your father, son. He was a fine man. I'm glad you got the wheat crop threshed all right."

" I'm glad, too," said Sam. But his face clouded again. " But my pa's going to feel awful bad up there in heaven, on account of not casting his vote for Mr. Lincoln."

" Is he? " said the man softly. " I reckon we ought to do something about that. You know, I haven't voted yet myself. I was kind of debating about the matter. You see, I'm not completely convinced that Abe Lincoln is the man for President."

" But he is, mister. Honest he is. Pa said so."

" Well," the tall man drawled, rubbing his chin, " I don't know that I can sincerely cast my vote for Abe on my own account. But I'll tell you what I'll do. I'll go in and vote for Lincoln for your father's sake."

" Glory, mister! " Sam's face glowed. " That's sure fine of you. Me and my pa and ma'll be mighty grateful to you."

He watched the tall, thin figure mount the steps. He seemed to know a great many people, for he spoke to nearly everyone, nodding and smiling.

" I wonder who he is," thought Sam. " He's a mighty nice man, even if he wasn't quite sure about voting for Mr. Lincoln. I reckon that since he knew my pa, I should have found out his name to tell Ma."

It was getting late. He'd have to hurry if he wanted to get that present for Ma. He hastened along the street to the general store. The store was crowded. Sam had to wait a long time to get waited on. He came out, his arms full of packages, and went to find the team and wagon, still waiting patiently where he had left them.

He climbed to the seat and clucked to the horses. It was getting late. He'd have to hurry to get home before Ma began to worry about him.

As he started up, there was a commotion on the street. People were cheering and shouting. Towering above the crowd was the man Sam had persuaded to cast his father's vote.

Quickly he leaned down and called to a boy his own age, who was standing near the wagon.

" Say, can you tell me what that man's name is there? That tall one? "

The boy stared. " You must be from the country. Everybody in Springfield knows Abe Lincoln! "

Finding Truth in Fiction

1. How does this fiction story match with the true ones you know about Lincoln? Try to mention at least one true story that bears out the picture of Lincoln in each of these episodes:

a. Lincoln's ready neighborliness in helping young Sam after a chance encounter on a country road.

b. Lincoln's ability to ride a horse and perform a chore like chasing away cattle.

c. Lincoln's kindness in remembering Mrs. Adams's need after her husband died.

d. Lincoln's sense of humor in not telling Sam who he was when he quizzed him about Lincoln, the candidate.

e. Lincoln's humility in his doubts about voting for himself.

2. How did Sam carry out his father's intention to vote for Lincoln? What advice did Lincoln write to Sam?

3. Do you think that Lincoln was actually unsure about voting for himself? Often you hear that a candidate should, out of courtesy or modesty, vote for his opponent. You should be able to have a lively debate about this question with your classmates!

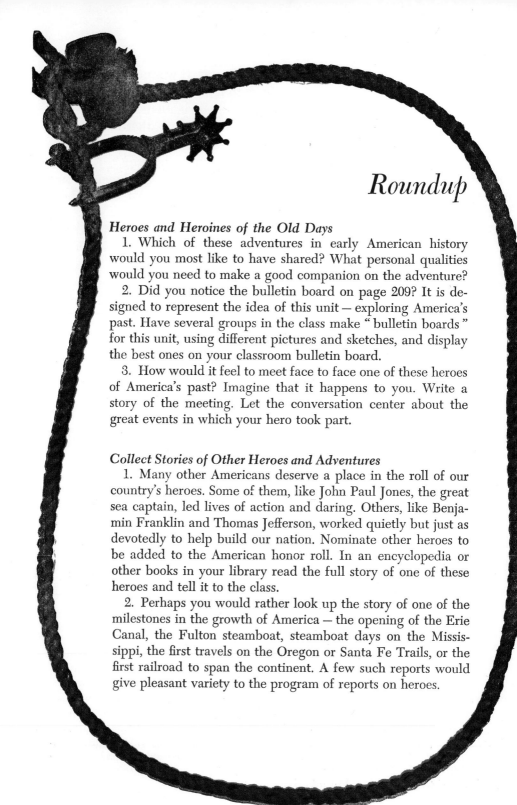

Roundup

Heroes and Heroines of the Old Days

1. Which of these adventures in early American history would you most like to have shared? What personal qualities would you need to make a good companion on the adventure?

2. Did you notice the bulletin board on page 209? It is designed to represent the idea of this unit — exploring America's past. Have several groups in the class make "bulletin boards" for this unit, using different pictures and sketches, and display the best ones on your classroom bulletin board.

3. How would it feel to meet face to face one of these heroes of America's past? Imagine that it happens to you. Write a story of the meeting. Let the conversation center about the great events in which your hero took part.

Collect Stories of Other Heroes and Adventures

1. Many other Americans deserve a place in the roll of our country's heroes. Some of them, like John Paul Jones, the great sea captain, led lives of action and daring. Others, like Benjamin Franklin and Thomas Jefferson, worked quietly but just as devotedly to help build our nation. Nominate other heroes to be added to the American honor roll. In an encyclopedia or other books in your library read the full story of one of these heroes and tell it to the class.

2. Perhaps you would rather look up the story of one of the milestones in the growth of America — the opening of the Erie Canal, the Fulton steamboat, steamboat days on the Mississippi, the first travels on the Oregon or Santa Fe Trails, or the first railroad to span the continent. A few such reports would give pleasant variety to the program of reports on heroes.

Your Bookshelf

Buckskin Brigade, by Jim Kjelgaard (Holiday, 1947)
Ten short stories about pioneers.

Door to the North, by Elizabeth Coatsworth (Winston, 1951)
Viking explorations of North America, long before Columbus.

Gentlemen, Hush! by Jere Wheelwright (Scribner, 1948)
The trials of Reconstruction with three likable young Rebel soldiers.

Island Girl, by Ada Clare Darby (Lippincott, 1951)
Like Betsy Dowdy, she lived on a Carolina island in Revolutionary times.

Leif Eriksson, First Voyager to America, by Katherine B. Shippen (Harper, 1952)
Thrilling adventures of the Norse hero.

Mary Montgomery, Rebel, by Helen Fern Daringer (Harcourt, Brace, 1948)
Dramatic happenings fill this girl's part in the War Between the States.

My American Heritage, a Collection of Songs, Poems, Speeches, Sayings, and Other Writings Dear to Our Hearts, collected by Ralph Henry and Lucille Pannell (Rand McNally, 1949)

Of Courage Undaunted: Across the Continent with Lewis and Clark, by James Daugherty (Viking, 1950)

Patsy Jefferson of Monticello, by Marguerite Vance (Dutton, 1948)
Colonial and Revolutionary times with Thomas Jefferson's daughter.

River of Wolves, by Stephen W. Meader (Harcourt, Brace, 1948)
A pioneer boy in Maine spends a winter as a prisoner of the Indians.

Robert E. Lee, Knight of the South, by Isabel McLennan McMeekin (Dodd, Mead, 1951)
The leader who remained a hero in defeat and won honor from the whole nation.

Rusty: A Cowboy of the Old West, by Ross Santee (Scribner, 1950)

The Spirit of the Eagle, by Merritt Parmelee Allen (Longmans, 1947)
Exploring the Western frontier.

Storm Canvas, by Armstrong Sperry (Winston, 1944)
The frigate *Thunderbolt* fights for freedom of the seas in the War of 1812.

Ten Brave Men, by Sonia Daugherty (Lippincott, 1951)
Leaders whose ideals guided America, from William Bradford to Lincoln.

That Lively Man, Ben Franklin, by Jeanette Eaton (Morrow, 1948)
The amazingly varied career of a great early American.

The Two Arrows, by Cornelia Meigs (Macmillan, 1949)
A rousing story of two English boys who were indentured servants in colonial America.

Wilderness Clearing, by Walter D. Edmonds (Dodd, Mead, 1944)
Young patriots fight Indian raids in the Mohawk Valley.

Yankee Doodle, Stories of the Brave and the Free, selected by Phyllis R. Fenner (Knopf, 1951)

Book Series: Landmark Books (Random House, 1950–52)
You will want to read many books in this series. They are all written by authors who specialize in writing for boys and girls, and they tell of great achievements and adventures in American history. For a start, try *The Landing of the Pilgrims,* by James Daugherty, *The California Gold Rush,* by May McNeer, *The Building of the First Transcontinental Railroad,* by Adele Nathan, *The Santa Fe Trail,* by Samuel Hopkins Adams, *The Panama Canal,* by Robert Considine, or the *Pirate Lafitte and the Battle of New Orleans,* by Robert Tallant.

Devaney

Tall Tales and Fantasy

The Whistling River

GLEN ROUNDS

TALKING TALL. Paul Bunyan was the American logger's tall-tale hero. In every lumber camp, men gathered around the stove on cold nights and added new tales about Ol' Paul and stretched the old ones. This one is about the struggle he had with a mean river.

One of the loggers tells the story, and from the start you know that he is talking in a tall style. The river, he says, " let loose a whistle that could be heard for a distance of six hundred and three miles in any direction." That single statement is a good example of exaggeration for the sake of humor. What do you find amusing in the exact measurement of the distance the whistle could be heard?

Of course a river that whistles or a logger who combs his beard with a pine tree must be imaginary, but part of the fun in reading tall tales is watching how they " explain " real places and events. In this story, notice how such things as Indian trail habits, the great Galveston flood, and present-day dust storms are explained by Paul Bunyan's doings. Through it all, the storyteller keeps a straight face, but you won't be able to!

IT SEEMS that some years before the winter of the Blue Snow (which every old logger remembers because of a heavy fall of bright blue snow which melted to ink, giving folks the idea of writing stories like these, so they tell) Ol' Paul was logging on what was then known as the Whistling River. It got its name from the fact that every morning, right on the

"The Whistling River" from *Ol' Paul, the Mighty Logger,* by Glen Rounds. Reprinted by permission of Holiday House, Inc.

dot, at nineteen minutes after five, and every night at ten minutes past six, it r'ared up to a height of two hundred and seventy-three feet and let loose a whistle that could be heard for a distance of six hundred and three miles in any direction.

Of course, if one man listening by himself can hear that far, it seems reasonable to suppose that two men listening together can hear it just twice as far. They tell me that even as far away as Alaska, most every camp had from two to four whistle-listeners (as many as were needed to hear the whistle without straining) who got two bits a listen and did nothing but listen for the right time, especially quitting time.

However, it seems that the river was famous for more than its whistling, for it was known as the orneriest river that ever ran between two banks. It seemed to take a fiendish delight in tying whole rafts of good saw logs into more plain and fancy knots than forty-three old sailors even knew the names of. It was an old " sidewinder " [1] for fair. Even so, it is unlikely that Ol' Paul would ever have bothered with it, if it had left his beard alone.

• It happened this way. It seems that Ol' Paul is sitting on a low hill one afternoon, combing his great curly beard with a pine tree, while he plans his winter operations. All of a sudden like, and without a word of warning, the river h'ists itself up on its hind legs and squirts about four thousand five hundred and nineteen gallons of

river water straight in the center of Ol' Paul's whiskers.

Naturally Paul's considerably startled, but says nothing, figuring that if he pays it no mind, it'll go 'way and leave him be. But no sooner does he get settled back with his thinking and combing again, than the durn river squirts some more! This time, along with the water, it throws in for good measure a batch of mud turtles, thirteen large carp, a couple of drowned muskrats, and half a raft of last year's saw logs. By this time Ol' Paul is pretty mad, and he jumps up and lets loose a yell that causes a landslide out near Pike's Peak, and startles a barber in Missouri so he cuts half the hair off the minister's toupee,[2] causing somewhat of a stir thereabouts. Paul stomps around waving his arms for a spell, and allows:

" By the Gee-Jumpin' John Henry and the Great Horn Spoon, I'll tame that river or bust a gallus [3] tryin'."

He goes over to another hill and sits down to think out a way to tame a river, forgetting his winter operations entirely. He sits there for three days and forty-seven hours without moving, thinking at top speed all the while, and finally comes to the conclusion that the best thing to do is to take out the kinks. But he knows that taking the kinks out of a river as tricky as this one is apt to be quite a chore, so he keeps on sitting there while he figures out ways and means. Of course, he could dig a new channel

---

[1] "sidewinder": a heavy-slugging fighter.

[2] toupee (tōō·pā'): a small wig to cover a man's bald spot.

[3] gallus (găl'ŭs): suspender.

and run the river through that, but that was never Paul's way. He liked to figure out new ways of doing things, even if they were harder.

Meanwhile he's gotten a mite hungry, so he hollers down to camp for Sourdough Sam to bring him up a little popcorn, of which he is very fond. So Sam hitches up a four-horse team while his helpers are popping the corn, and soon arrives at Paul's feet with a wagonload.

Paul eats popcorn and thinks. The faster he thinks the faster he eats, and the faster he eats the faster he thinks, until finally his hands are moving so fast that nothing shows but a blur, and they make a wind that is uprooting trees all around him. His chewing sounds like a couple hundred coffee grinders all going at once. In practically no time at all the ground for three miles and a quarter in every direction is covered to a depth of eighteen inches with popcorn scraps, and several thousand small birds and animals, seeing the ground all white and the air filled with what looks like snowflakes, conclude that a blizzard is upon them and immediately freeze to death, furnishing the men with pot pies for some days.

But to get back to Ol' Paul's problem. Just before the popcorn is all gone, he decides that the only practical solution is to hitch Babe, the Mighty Blue Ox, to the river and let him yank it straight.

Babe was so strong that he could pull mighty near anything that he could be hitched to. His exact size, as I said before, is not known, for although it is said that he stood ninety-three hands high, it's not known whether that meant ordinary logger's hands, or hands the size of Paul's, which, of course, would be something else again.

However, they tell of an eagle that had been in the habit of roosting on the tip of Babe's right horn suddenly deciding to fly to the other. Columbus Day, it was, when he started. He flew steadily, so they say, night and day, fair weather and foul, until his wing feathers were worn down to pinfeathers and a new set grew to replace them. In all, he seems to have worn out seventeen sets of feathers on the trip, and from reaching up to brush the sweat out of his eyes so much, had worn all the feathers off the top of his head, becoming completely bald, as are all of his descendants to this day. Finally the courageous bird won through, reaching the brass ball on the tip of the left horn on the seventeenth of March. He waved a wing weakly at the cheering lumberjacks and 'lowed as how he'd of made it sooner but for the head winds.

But the problem is how to hitch Babe to the river, as it's a well-known fact that an ordinary log chain and skid hook [1] will not hold water. So after a light lunch of three sides of barbecued beef, half a wagonload of potatoes, carrots, and a few other odds and ends, Ol' Paul goes down to the blacksmith shop and gets Ole, the Big Swede, to help him look through the big instruction book that came with

[1] **skid hook:** a steel-capped stick for dragging logs.

the woods and tells how to do most everything under the sun. But though Paul reads the book through from front to back twice while Ole reads it from back to front, and they both read it once from bottom to top, they find nary a word about how to hook onto a river. However, they do find an old almanac stuck between the pages and get so busy reading up on the weather for the coming year, and a lot of fancy ailments of one kind and another, that it's suppertime before they know it, and the problem's still unsolved. So Paul decides that the only practical thing to do is to invent a rigging of some kind himself.

At any rate he has to do something, as every time he hears the river whistle, it makes him so mad he's fit to be tied, which interferes with his work more than something. No one can do their best under such conditions.

Being as how this was sort of a special problem, he thought it out in a special way. Paul was like that. As he always thought best when he walked, he had the men survey a **circle** about thirty miles in diameter **to** walk around. This was so that if **he** was quite a while thinking it out he wouldn't be finding himself way down in Australia when he'd finished.

When everything is ready, he sets his old fur cap tight on his head, clasps his hands behind him, and starts walking and thinking. He thinks and walks. The faster he walks the faster he thinks. He makes a complete circle every half hour. By morning he's worn a path that is knee-deep even on him, and he has to call the men to herd the stock away and keep them from falling in and getting crippled. Three days later he thinks it out, but he's worn himself down so deep that it takes a day and a half to get a ladder built that will reach down that far. When he does get out, he doesn't even wait for breakfast, but whistles for Babe and tears right out across the hills to the north.

The men have no idea what he intends to do, but they know from ex-

perience that it'll be good, so they cheer till their throats are so sore they have to stay around the mess hall drinking Paul's private barrel of cough sirup till suppertime. And after that they go to bed and sleep very soundly.

Paul and the Ox travel plenty fast, covering twenty-four townships at a stride, and the wind from their passing raises a dust that doesn't even begin to settle for some months. There are those who claim that the present dust storms are nothing more or less than that same dust just beginning to get back to earth — but that's a matter of opinion. About noon, as they near the North Pole, they begin to see blizzard tracks, and in a short time are in the very heart of their summer feeding grounds. Taking a sack from his shoulder, Paul digs out materials for a box trap, which he sets near a well-traveled blizzard trail and baits with fresh icicles from the top of the North Pole. Then he goes away to eat his lunch, but not until he's carefully brushed out his tracks — a trick he later taught the Indians.

After lunch he amuses himself for a while by throwing huge chunks of ice into the water for Babe to retrieve, but he soon has to whistle the great beast out, as every time he jumps into the water he causes such a splash that a tidal wave threatens Galveston, Texas, which at that time was inhabited by nobody in particular. Some of the ice he threw in is still floating around the ocean, causing plenty of excitement for the iceberg patrol.

About two o'clock he goes back to his blizzard trap and discovers that he has caught seven half-grown blizzards and one grizzled old nor'wester, which is raising considerable fuss and bids fair to trample the young ones before he can get them out. But he finally manages to get a pair of half-grown ones in his sack and turns the others loose.

About midnight he gets back to camp, and hollers at Ole, the Big Swede, "Build me the biggest log chain that's ever been built, while I stake out these dadblasted blizzards! We're goin' to warp it to 'er proper, come mornin'."

Then he goes down to the foot of the river and pickets one of the blizzards to a tree on the bank, then crosses and ties the other directly op-

posite. Right away the river begins to freeze. In ten minutes the slush ice reaches nearly from bank to bank, and the blizzards are not yet really warmed to their work, either. Paul watches for a few minutes, and then goes back to camp to warm up, feeling mighty well satisfied with the way things are working out.

In the morning the river has a tough time r'aring up for what it may-be knows to be its last whistle, for its foot is frozen solid for more than seventeen miles. The blizzards have really done the business.

By the time breakfast is over, the great chain's ready and Babe all harnessed. Paul quick-like wraps one end of the chain seventy-two times around the foot of the river, and hitches Babe to the other. Warning the men to stand clear, he shouts at the Ox to pull. But though the great beast strains till his tongue hangs out, pulling the chain out into a solid bar some seven and a half miles long, and sinks knee-deep in the solid rock, the river stubbornly refuses to budge, hanging onto its kinks like a snake in a gopher hole. Seeing this, Ol' Paul grabs the chain and, letting loose a holler that blows the tarpaper off the shacks in the Nebraska sandhills, he and the Ox together give a mighty yank that jerks the river loose from end to end, and start hauling it out across the prairie so fast that it smokes.

After a time Paul comes back and sights along the river, which now is as straight as a gun barrel. But he doesn't have long to admire his work,

for he soon finds he has another problem on his hands. You see, it's this way. A straight river is naturally much shorter than a crooked one, and now all the miles and miles of extra river that used to be in the kinks are running wild out on the prairie. This galls the farmers in those parts more than a little. So it looks like Paul had better figure something out, and mighty soon at that, for already he can see clouds of dust the prairie folks are raising as they come at top speed to claim damages.

After three minutes of extra deep thought he sends a crew to camp to bring his big crosscut saw and a lot of baling wire. He saws the river into nine-mile lengths and the men roll it up like linoleum and tie it with the wire. Some say he used these later when he logged off the desert, rolling out as many lengths as he needed to float his logs. But that's another story.

But his troubles with the Whistling River were not all over. It seems that being straightened sort of took the gimp [1] out of the river, and from that day on it refused to whistle even a bird call. And as Paul had gotten into the habit of depending on the whistle to wake up the men in the morning, things were a mite upset.

First he hired an official getter-upper who rode through the camp on a horse, and beat a triangle. But the camp was so big that it took three hours and seventy-odd minutes to make the trip. Naturally some of the men were called too early and some too late. It's hard to say what might

[1] **gimp**: spirit.

have happened if Squeaky Swanson hadn't showed up about that time. His speaking voice was a thin squeak, but when he hollered he could be heard clear out to Kansas on a still day. So every morning he stood outside the cookshack and hollered the blankets off every bunk in camp. Naturally the men didn't stay in bed long after the blankets were off them, what with the cold wind and all, so Squeaky was a great success and for years did nothing but holler in the mornings.

Enjoying the Humor in Exaggerations

1. Were you more amused by the exaggerations of usual things, like the amounts Paul ate, or by the completely fantastic ideas, like catching a blizzard in a trap? Give some more examples from the story of these two kinds of tall-tale humor.

2. What explanation does the storyteller give for the dust storms? for the eagle's baldness? for the tidal wave at Galveston?

3. Why didn't Paul dig a new channel for the river? How did he finally straighten it out? What later use did he make of it?

4. How did taming the river upset life at the lumber camp? In what exaggerated way was that problem solved?

The Cremation of Sam McGee

ROBERT W. SERVICE

Television dramas and "comic" books have no monopoly on tales that give you the shivers. Here the favorite poet of the far North sets out to entertain you with a ridiculous, bloodchilling yarn.

His tall tale is complete with sound effects (read it aloud to hear them) and an amazing twist at the end. Could he hold his own in a contest with other unbelievable shockers?

There are strange things done in the midnight sun°
By the men who moil° for gold;
The Arctic trails have their secret tales
That would make your blood run cold;

1. **midnight sun** takes you at once to the polar regions where the sun never sinks in the summer, and the **northern lights** (l. 5) dance in the sky. 2. **moil:** to work hard, especially at wet, slushy work like panning for gold.

> *The northern lights have seen queer sights,*   5
>   *But the queerest they ever did see*
> *Was that night on the marge of Lake Lebarge*
>   *I cremated Sam McGee.*

Now Sam McGee was from Tennessee, where the cotton blooms and blows.
Why he left his home in the South to roam round the pole, God only knows.
He was always cold, but the land of gold seemed to hold him like a spell;   11
Though he'd often say in his homely way that " he'd sooner live in hell."

On Christmas Day we were mushing° our way over the Dawson Trail.
Talk of your cold! Through the parka's fold it stabbed like a driven nail.
If our eyes we'd close, then the lashes froze till sometimes we couldn't see;
It wasn't much fun, but the only one to whimper was Sam McGee.   16

And that very night, as we lay packed tight in our robes beneath the snow,
And the dogs were fed, and the stars o'erhead were dancing heel and toe,
He turned to me, and " Cap," says he, " I'll cash in this trip, I guess;
And if I do, I'm asking that you won't refuse my last request."   20

Well, he seemed so low that I couldn't say no; then he says with a sort of
    moan:
" It's the cursèd cold, and it's got right hold till I'm chilled clean through to
    the bone.
Yet 'tain't being dead — it's my awful dread of the icy grave that pains;
So I want you to swear that, foul or fair, you'll cremate my last remains."

A pal's last need is a thing to heed, so I swore I would not fail;   25
And we started on at the streak of dawn; but God! he looked ghastly pale.
He crouched on the sleigh, and he raved all day of his home in Tennessee;
And before nightfall a corpse was all that was left of Sam McGee.

There wasn't a breath in that land of death, and I hurried, horror-driven,
With a corpse half hid that I couldn't get rid, because of a promise I'd given;
It was lashed to the sleigh, and it seemed to say: " You may tax your brawn
    and brains,   31
But you promised true, and it's up to you to cremate those last remains."

Now a promise made is a debt unpaid, and the trail has its own stern code,
In the days to come, though my lips were dumb, in my heart how I cursed
    that load.

13. **mushing:** traveling on foot with dogsleds to carry supplies.

In the long, long night, by the lone firelight, while the Huskies, round in a
    ring,   35
Howled out their woes to the homeless snows — O God! how I loathed the
    thing.

And every day that quiet clay seemed to heavy and heavier grow;
And on I went, though the dogs were spent and the grub was getting low;
The trail was bad, and I felt half mad, but I swore I would not give in;
And I'd often sing to the hateful thing, and it harkened with a grin.   40

Till I came to the marge of Lake Lebarge, and a derelict° there lay;
It was jammed in the ice, but I saw in a trice it was called the *Alice May*.
And I looked at it, and I thought a bit, and I looked at my frozen chum;
Then " Here," said I, with a sudden cry, " is my cre-ma-tor-i-um."

Some planks I tore from the cabin floor, and I lit the boiler fire;   45
Some coal I found that was lying around, and I heaped the fuel higher;
The flames just soared, and the furnace roared — such a blaze you seldom
    see;
And I burrowed a hole in the glowing coal, and I stuffed in Sam McGee.

Then I made a hike, for I didn't like to hear him sizzle so;
And the heavens scowled, and the Huskies howled, and the wind began to
    blow.   50
It was icy cold, but the hot sweat rolled down my cheeks, and I don't know
    why;
And the greasy smoke in an inky cloak went streaking down the sky.

I do not know how long in the snow I wrestled with grisly fear;
But the stars came out and they danced about ere again I ventured near;
I was sick with dread, but I bravely said: " I'll just take a peep inside.   55
I guess he's cooked, and it's time I looked " . . . then the door I opened
    wide.

And there sat Sam, looking cold and calm, in the heart of the furnace roar;
And he wore a smile you could see a mile, and he said: " Please close that
    door.
It's fine in here, but I greatly fear you'll let in the cold and storm —   59
Since I left Plumtree, down in Tennessee, it's the first time I've been warm."

---

41. derelict (dĕr′ĕ·lĭkt): a deserted ship.

There are strange things done in the midnight sun
  By the men who moil for gold;
The Arctic trails have their secret tales
  That would make your blood run cold;
The northern lights have seen queer sights,   65
  But the queerest they ever did see
Was that night on the marge of Lake Lebarge
  I cremated Sam McGee.

Warm at Last!

1. What details in the refrain (the first and last stanzas) make you see the arctic setting of this tale?

2. When did you first suspect that the poet was playing a trick on his readers instead of telling a horror story?

3. What bearing does Sam's being from Plumtree, Tennessee, have on the story?

4. Pick out phrases or whole passages that you especially liked and read them to the class. This poem can easily be arranged for choral reading. Elect three class members to study the poems on pages 19, 429, and 439, as models for dividing this poem into parts for group and solo voices, and decide on a pattern to use. (Boys and girls may read separately, or together.)

Stuart Little's Sailboat Race

E. B. WHITE

FANTASY FOR FUN. You have as many different tastes in reading as you have in eating. A live mind can be as hungry for good solid information as a growing boy is for steak and potatoes. But your mind also relishes pure entertainment, just as you relish dessert or a candy bar between meals. A favorite kind of entertainment in stories is fantasy — an imaginative situation that you know cannot be true but is fun to think about, anyhow. That is what you'll get in the story of Stuart Little.

Reading a fantasy is more fun if you notice how neatly the writer gets you to accept some impossible things. At the start of this story you are told that Stuart is a mouse, and what is more, a mouse who speaks and wears a gray hat and carries a cane! But the author seems

proposed legislation falling within the compe-
standing committees.

members and an equal number of alternates are
ginning of each Riksdag session by the plenary
party caucuses deciding on the nominees. Mem-
uted among the various parties (with the excep-
Party-Communists) on the basis of proportional
s in the case of the parliamentary speakers, indi-
re usually reelected as long as they are willing to
arty's strength in the Riksdag entitles them to a
ittee choses its own chairman and vice-chairman.
too, the positions are proportioned among the
s.

e Riksdag is empowered with a comprehensive
king, control, and supervisory functions. To the
ong both exclusive and shared legislative jurisdic-
ag alone has the legal power of taxation[11] and
It shares with the cabinet the right of constitu-
nt,[13] the right to legislate civil and criminal
ity to schedule advisory referenda "on questions
ance."[15]

time the Riksdag is enjoined from interfering in
powers of other political structures. Article 90 of
Government reads:

erations of the Riksdag or its committees no ques-
considered other than in instances or ways expressly
he constitution concerning the appointment or dis-
il servants, decisions of the government or courts,
een individuals and corporations, or the execution
tatute, or enactment.

this provision, which dates from the nineteenth
restrict legislative competence in the manner of
main of the laws" in the French Fifth Republic,
e the functional separation of legislative and ex-
Conversely, the king may not attend Riksdag and
rations.[16]

A product of modernizing processes in the nineteenth and
early twentieth centuries, parliamentarism in Sweden has undergone continual change in both form and substance. The most
recent step in structural rationalization was the constitutional reform of 1967–1969 establishing unicameralism. Substantively, the
realignment of political forces caused by the rise of the Social
Democrats to "permanent" majority status in the early 1930s
meant the demise of minority parliamentarism. Subsequent Socialist preeminence has been the decisive factor determining the
course of executive-legislative relations into the 1970s.

THE RIKSDAG: ORGANIZATIONS AND FUNCTIONS

The constitutional boundaries of Swedish government are prescribed by two documents: the Instrument of Government (*Reger-
ingsformen*), defining the fundamental basis of parliamentary and
executive competence, and the Act of Parliament (*Riksdagsord-
ningen*), governing the organization of the Riksdag and general
legislative procedures. Of equal constitutional status but not directly pertaining to structured political relations are the Law on
the Freedom of the Press (*Tryckfrihetsförordningen*) and the Act
of Succession (*Successionsordningen*). Each of these four documents, which together comprise the Swedish constitution, can be
amended only by a majority vote in two successive sessions of the
Riksdag with an intervening general election.[2]

As modified by custom and the political realities of majority-
minority relations, the rules contained in the Instrument of Government and the Act of Parliament (in conjunction with the Riksdag's own standing orders) provide a comprehensive outline of
parliamentary organization and functions. The nation's highest
representative structure, the Riksdag "has jurisdiction over the
rights and obligations that law accords citizens of the realm."[3] Its
formal role in Swedish political processes approximates that of the
British parliament, but like the House of Commons the Riksdag is
largely subordinate to cabinet domination.

[2] The constitutional texts are printed in Robert Malmgren, *Sveriges grundlagar och tillhörande författningar*, 8th ed. (Stockholm: P. A. Norstedts &
Söners Förlag, 1964). Data in this chapter on the constitutional amendments
of 1967–1969 are derived from *Statens offentliga utredningar 1967:26, Partiell
författningsreform* (Stockholm: Justitiedepartementet, 1967). For the sake of
brevity in the notes, the Instrument of Government will be referred to by its
Swedish abbreviation, RF, while the Act of Parliament is abbreviated as RO.

[3] *RF*, art. 49.

Until the constitutional reform of 1967–1969 took effect on January 1, 1971, the Swedish parliament consisted of two houses of disparate size that shared equal legislative competence. The lower chamber (*andra kammaren*) was popularly elected at four-year intervals, and consisted of 233 members chosen from 28 county and city constituencies. Members of Sweden's 31 provincial and city assemblies, who were similarly elected for terms of four years, selected the 151 representatives in the upper house (*första kammaren*) for staggered individual terms of eight years.[4]

With the introduction of unicameralism the former total membership of 384 deputies has been reduced to 350. Of this number 310 are chosen according to the modified Sainte Lagüe system of proportional representation in 28 individual constituencies. The remaining 40 delegates are elected on a national basis. As previously noted, a party must obtain either 4 percent or 12 percent of the national vote or votes cast in a single constituency, respectively, to win representation in the Riksdag. Terms of office are now three years instead of four. As agreed in the party compromise of 1967, national elections are held simultaneously with communal elections—always in September unless a dissolution election intervenes.

Riksdag candidates must be at least 23 years old. Once they are elected, parliamentary deputies are constitutionally guaranteed immunity from arrest and prosecution. Such immunity may be suspended only upon the affirmative vote of five sevenths of the Riksdag membership.[5]

Legislative officers include the Speaker and three Vice-Speakers. Appointed by the king until 1921, the speakers are now elected by majority vote.[6] Incumbents are usually reelected as long as they wish to remain in office. Custom decrees that the speakers, whose primary function is to preside over plenary sessions of the Riksdag, are chosen among the four major parties. Whenever a vacancy occurs, leaders of the four major parties meet informally to nominate a successor.

To guarantee the impartiality of the legislative officers, the Instrument of Government originally prohibited the presiding speaker from participating in discussions or voting on a particular

[4] When the bicameral system was adopted in 1865–1866, the number of lower house deputies was 230. An additional seat was added in 1956, and in 1964 the total was increased to 233. The size of the upper house, originally consisting of 150 members, was increased to 151 in 1956.

[5] *RF*, art. 110.

[6] Standing Orders, art. 6, in Malmgren, pp. 168–169.

parliamentary measure
in the lower house in
1961 to allow the speak

In addition to th
speakers serve with fou
chairmen of the standi
(*talmanskonferensen*).
once a month to coor
business, primarily on
committees.

Effective legislativ
executive proposals is
combined committees.
bicameral parliament,
that virtually all comm
number of representati
important functional ch
dag. The only exceptic
ternal Affairs that wer
only one of the chamb
issued simultaneously t
assured of speedy disp
ished, the committees re

The most importa
tees on foreign affairs,
banking, agriculture,
on the laws. Another s
Foreign Affairs (*utrik*
composed of seven me
committee on foreign
[cabinet] on matters c
eign powers . . ."[10] be
foreign policy decision
tees ranges from 17 m
on 1. The second type
pointed to consider m
standing committees.

[7] *RO*, art. 51. See Malm
[8] The deadlock occur
Chapter Eight.
[9] Malmgren, p. 175.
[10] *RF*, art. 54, and *RO*,

which deals wi
tence of two of t

Committee
elected at the b
body, with prio
bership is distri
tion of the Left
representation.
vidual members
serve and their
seat. Each com
In this instance
four major parti

Formally t
range of rule-m
first category be
tion. The Riks
appropriation.[12]
tional amendm
law,[14] and auth
of special impor

At the sam
the autonomous
the Instrument o

During deli
tions may b
provided in
missal of ci
relations be
of any law,

The purpose of
century, is not
the "skrunken o
but to undersc
ecutive powers.
committee delib

[11] *RF*, art. 57.
[12] *RF*, art. 60.
[13] *RF*, art. 81.
[14] *RF*, art. 87.
[15] *RF*, art. 49.
[16] *RF*, art. 55.

Control functions of the Riksdag include a variety of means to enforce executive accountability. One traditional source of parliamentary pressure on the national executive is the right of the committee on the constitution to review the annual minutes of cabinet meetings.[17] If the committee finds in examining the protocol

> that a cabinet minister has apparently acted against the nation's constitution or general laws, . . . [it] shall order an action to be brought against [that] person . . . before the Court of Impeachment. . . . If a cabinet member is found guilty of the charges against him, the Court of Impeachment shall sentence him in accordance with the general laws and the constitution.[18]

In addition to its authority to bring formal legal charges against cabinet members, the committee on the constitution is empowered by Article 107 of the Instrument of Government to move a vote of censure against an executive official who has "failed to take into account the nation's proper interests or to exercise with impartiality, zeal, competence, and energy the duties of the office entrusted to him."

The power of impeachment is more important as a theoretical possibility than as an established procedure. In practice, the committee on the constitution has not acted on its authority to instigate formal charges against a member of the cabinet since 1854. Instances of informal votes of censure have been relatively more common, and led as late as 1929 to the resignation of a cabinet official.

The constitutional revision of 1967–1969 introduced an important new parliamentary control device in the form of explicit provisions for a vote of "no confidence." Until 1971 Swedish cabinets were not legally subject to a no confidence motion, although several governments had resigned during the 1920s, after they had suffered parliamentary defeats on major legislative proposals. Judging the prerogatives of the committee on the constitution insufficient to ensure the "political accountability of the government," the constitutional reform committee therefore proposed that provisions regulating "relations of confidence between the government and the Riksdag" be expressly incorporated in the

---

[17] *RF*, art. 105.

[18] *RF*, art. 106. Duties of the Court of Impeachment are enumerated in *RF*, art. 102. The court would consist of higher-level judges, military officers, and civil servants.

Swedish constitution.[19] The amended Instrument of Government now provides that one tenth of the Riksdag deputies may move a motion of no confidence against an individual minister. If the motion is endorsed by an absolute majority of members, the minister (or, if the vote was directed against the prime minister, the entire cabinet) must resign.[20] Such a motion would become void if the cabinet decides within a week to dissolve parliament and call a new election.

In case of a dissolution election, members of the new Riksdag only serve out the remainder of their predecessors' term. Largely for this reason dissolution elections arising out of political controversies have been extremely rare in Sweden. The lower house was dissolved in 1887 at the height of the protectionist-free trade controversy and in 1914 during a conflict between king and parliament. Since the introduction of parliamentarism the lower chamber has been dissolved only once (1958).

Additional means at the disposal of the Riksdag to exert pressure on the executive are the right of interpellation and simple questions. In the case of interpellations, members of parliament may submit written queries to a cabinet minister, after receiving permission to do so from the house. Simple questions, in contrast, are posed without prior approval. Both forms are used to obtain information and ventilate criticisms of government policy, and lead on occasion to general debates on matters of principle. Since 1950 the frequency of simple questions has increased significantly. The number of interpellations more than doubled through 1969 in the upper house, declined temporarily in the lower house after a Question Hour modelled after the British precedent was introduced in 1964, but resumed an upward trend in 1966. During the same period approximately 80 percent of the interpellations and simple questions were introduced by the opposition parties.[21] Given the majority status of the Social Democrats, the political effect of such questions on executive behavior was limited.

The Riksdag's supervisory powers pertain to indirect controls over administrative agencies. The most important is the authority of parliament to elect Sweden's ombudsmen, officials with independent investigatory powers who oversee the nation's administrative and court systems.[22] Three ombudsmen and two deputy

---

19 *SOU 1967:26*, p. 238.

20 *RF*, art. 107.

21 Nils Andrén, "Interpellationer och enkla frågor," in Arthur Thomson (ed.), *Samhälle och riksdag*, II (Stockholm: Almqvist & Wiksell, 1966), p. 239.

22 *RF*, art. 96, and *RO*, art. 68.

Table 14   Questions in Parliament[a]

Year	Interpellations		Simple Questions	
	Upper Chamber	Lower Chamber	Upper Chamber	Lower Chamber
1950	26	59	5	26
1955	33	68	8	65
1960	44	146	7	20
1965	40	126	40	201
1967	105	187	92	260

[a]*Statistisk årsbok 1970*, p. 394.

ombudsmen are chosen for four-year terms by the entire membership of the Riksdag.[23] The ombudsmen submit an annual report to the Riksdag on their activities, which allows deputies an opportunity to view their record and, if it should prove unsatisfactory, to dismiss an incumbent on the motion of one or more of the legal committees.[24]

In addition the Riksdag appoints a council of 48 persons to determine whether members of the Supreme Court and the Supreme Administrative Court "deserve to remain in their important positions";[25] elects the commissioners of the Bank of Sweden and the National Debt Office;[26] and designates 12 parliamentary auditors to examine the records and performance of the national administration, the Riksbank, and the National Debt Office.[27]

PARLIAMENTARY PROCEDURE

The Swedish parliament meets in two annual sessions, the first (the spring session) beginning on January 10 with a ceremonial flourish in the royal palace in the presence of the king. After a summer break, which must commence at the latest on June 15, the Riksdag resumes deliberations at the fall session in early October.

[23] Until 1971 the ombudsman was elected by a special parliamentary committee composed of 48 deputies.

[24] *RF*, art. 97.

[25] *RO*, art. 69. Ben Arneson notes: "This procedure has never been used, and at present it has no significant place in a realistic picture of modern Swedish government." Arneson, *The Democratic Monarchies of Scandinavia* (New York: D. Van Nostrand Company, Inc., 1949), p. 168.

[26] *RO*, art. 70.

[27] See Nils Andrén, *Modern Swedish Government* (Stockholm: Almqvist & Wiksell, 1961), pp. 140–141.

Unless the cabinet decides there is a pressing need to extend parliamentary meetings, the Riksdag officially concludes its work by December 31.[28]

The start of each session is marked by a government declaration of policy, including the presentation of the annual budget in January, in the form of cabinet propositions (*propositioner*) for legislative enactment. For the first several days opposition leaders engage cabinet officials in a sometimes lively general debate on policy issues, outlining their own catalogue of alternative measures. Within 15 days individual deputies may respond to the government policy statement and budgetary requests with private members' motions, which must be submitted in writing. As Andrén notes, such motions are rarely draft bills. Instead, they may call for a committee of investigation, seek to amend propositions, or propose "new expenditures for various purposes, such as pensions and other compensation for individuals, or support for some matter which is thought to have been disregarded by the Government."[29] Private members' motions may also be introduced later in the session, within nine days after a government proposition (unless the Riksdag extends the period to 15 days) or at any time concerning a question that has already been decided by the parliament.[30]

Propositions, accompanied by documents compiled during the prior circulatory process (for example, from Royal Commissions and *remiss* procedures), committee bills, and private members' motions, are submitted by the legislative officers to the appropriate standing committee or, if circumstances dictate, to a special or combined committee. It is at this stage that the Riksdag makes its most cogent contribution to formal decision processes. Because most committee members serve on a given committee for a number of years, they bring to committee deliberations considerable specialized knowledge and expertise. Moreover, committee meetings are closed to the public, which combined with close personal contacts among members encourages a high degree of informality usually free of partisan ideological controversy. Hence issues tend to be considered on their technical merits, with "divergent opinions which may exist resolved in most cases in a compromise solution."[31]

[28] *RO*, art. 2.
[29] Andrén, *Modern Swedish Government*, p. 80.
[30] *RO*, art. 55.
[31] Raymond Fusilier, *Les Monarchies Parlementaires* (Paris: Les Éditions Ouvrières, 1960), p. 173.

If a unanimous report nevertheless proves impossible, the committee submits a majority recommendation accompanied by one or more reservations or amendments appended by dissenting members. In case of a committee deadlock the fate of a report is decided by drawing lots. The "winning" viewpoint is then designated the official recommendation, while the second is attached as a reservation. Contrary to American practice, committees may not simply shelve controversial legislation. They are required by the constitution to report back to the Riksdag on all proposals submitted to them.[32]

When the committees complete their deliberations on propositions and private members' motions, the speakers, in consultation with other members of the Speakers Conference, arrange to place their reports on the agenda for Riksdag consideration. Although committee recommendations have the lowest priority in the required sequence of agenda items (preceded by government propositions and messages, committee announcements or proposals for parliamentary decisions, and reports from the Riksdag auditors and the ombudsmen), they in fact occupy most of the time the Riksdag spends in plenary sessions. The number of committee reports has increased steadily during the postwar period, and in 1969 totaled 720. The fewest number of reports was submitted to the committee on foreign affairs; the largest number, by the committee on supply.

Three readings are required for parliamentary ratification of a particular measure. Debate tends to be perfunctory, with party viewpoints having already been aired at length during committee meetings. In most cases, as a majority of committee reports are unanimous, the voting procedure is simple: the speaker merely calls for an affirmative vote on the proposal. Attached reservations or amendments, in contrast, involve a complicated process of successive elimination. In such instances a division of the house is called in which deputies vote "yes" or "no" on one motion—for example, to adopt an alternative bill—that is paired as a "proposition" against a second such motion, termed the "counterproposition." The motion that survives this elimination contest is then moved as a counterproposition against the "main proposition" of the majority committee report. Should an impasse result, a final decision may be reached by lottery. Once the Riksdag affirms a given bill, it is submitted to the king-in-council for royal approval and formal promulgation.

[32] *RO*, art. 58.

Table 15   Committee Reports 1950–1969[a]
(Absolute numbers)

Year	Foreign Affairs	Constitution	Supply	Ways & Means	Banking
1950	17	19	232	68	31
1955	6	22	195	59	40
1960	6	28	210	86	40
1965	10	48	195	58	67
1969	24	52	191	76	54

Year	Laws[b]			Agriculture	Miscellaneous Affairs
	1	2	3		
1950	32	50	29	62	
1955	41	40	33	43	17
1960	43	71	34	43	29
1965	41	80	36	30	56
1969	60	89	64	57	53

[a]*Statistisk årsbok 1970*, p. 394.
[b]Until 1971 there were only three committees of law.

Under the previous bicameral system it was possible for the two houses to disagree on a particular measure. If a conflict concerned appropriations or expenditures, the two chambers voted together on the bill, with a majority of the combined membership of 384 deputies determining its outcome. Other types of legislation were referred back to committee for reconsideration. If agreement was not reached in a successive attempt, the bill would be dropped from that session of the Riksdag unless the cabinet chose to dissolve one of the houses and schedule new elections.

The first procedure—called joint votes (*gemensam votering*) —was of decisive political importance. Unless a cabinet could be assured of majority support among members of the two houses collectively, it faced the prospect that important legislation might be defeated. On the other hand, a majority in one chamber might be sufficiently large to provide a majority in joint votes, thereby enabling a government to compensate for its minority status in the other house.

MEMBERS OF PARLIAMENT

Like legislative assemblies elsewhere, the Swedish Riksdag is not representative in its social composition of a cross-section of the population.[33] During the past three decades members of free professions (including journalists and professional politicians) and the civil service have persistently dominated parliamentary membership, while women and workers have constituted a clear minority. In aggregate terms Riksdag deputies have tended to be well-educated and middle-aged. By the early 1960s earlier differences in the composition of the lower and upper houses had virtually disappeared.

Between 1937 and 1961, as indicated in Table 16, the percentage of high-level civil servants and government officials fell in the upper house but rose slightly in the lower house so that the figures became approximately equal in both chambers. The combined total for the first three columns, which include civil servants or salaried employees of all ranks and free professionals, increased from 40.9 percent (1937) to 54.6 percent (1961) in the lower house and from 55.1 percent to 57.6 percent in the upper chamber. The entrance of a significantly higher number of professional politicians into parliament by 1961 accounted for most of the increase in free professionals. Their rank grew from 15 to 47 in the lower house and from 4 to 28 in the upper. Most of them were members of the Social Democratic party.

The most substantial decline in parliamentary representation was among deputies with farming backgrounds, which is a predictable consequence of the declining importance of agriculture in the Swedish economy. Workers, too, decreased in numbers—most noticeably in the lower house.

Women have always been underrepresented in the Riksdag. In 1937 they comprised only 3 percent of the lower house membership and were not represented at all in the upper chamber. By 1961 women deputies had increased marginally: to 14.2 percent in the lower house and 7 percent in the upper.[34]

Education levels underwent a comparable levelling process during the same period. Over 37 percent of the deputies in the

[33] The literature on legislative recruitment is voluminous, although little of it lends itself to systematic cross-national comparisons. Recent publications of special significance include Gerhard Loewenberg, *Parliament in the German Political System* (Ithaca, N.Y.: Cornell University Press, 1967), Duncan MacRae, Jr., *Parliament, Parties, and Society in France: 1946–1958* (New York: St. Martin's Press, 1967); and Frederick Frey, *The Turkish Political Elite* (Cambridge, Mass.: Massachusetts Institute of Technology Press, 1965). See also Dwaine Marvick (ed.), *Political Decision-Making: Recruitment and Performance* (New York: Free Press, 1961).

[34] Lars Sköld and Arne Halvarson, "Riksdagens sociala sammansättning under hundra år," in Arthur Thomson (ed.), *Samhälle och riksdag*, I (Stockholm: Almqvist & Wiksell, 1966), pp. 437 and 479.

Table 16   Occupational Background of Riksdag Deputies,
1937–1961[a]

Chamber	High Level Government Officials, Civil Servants	Lower Level Civil Servants	Free Professions
	1937		
Lower House	14.8	5.7	20.4
Upper House	31.3	8.0	15.3

Chamber	Agriculture	Industry, Commerce	Workers	No Profession[b]
	1937			
Lower House	36.5	6.5	13.0	3.0
Upper House	28.7	13.3	3.3	

Chamber	High Level Government Officials, Civil Servants	Lower Level Civil Servants	Free Professions
	1961		
Lower House	15.9	7.3	31.9
Upper House	15.2	6.0	36.4

Chamber	Agriculture	Industry, Commerce	Workers	No Profession[b]
	1961			
Lower House	21.1	13.4	3.2	6.0
Upper House	25.8	12.6	2.0	2.0

[a]Adapted from Lars Sköld and Arne Halvarson, "Riksdagens sociala sammansättning under hundra år," in Arthur Thomson (ed.), Samhälle och riksdag, I (Stockholm: Almqvist & Wiksell, 1966), pp. 440, 444, 463, and 465.
[b]Includes nonworking women.

upper house had a university education in 1937 compared to 18 percent in the lower chamber. Only a third of the members of the upper house but nearly half (47.4 percent) of those in the lower had received no more than an elementary education. By 1961 these disparities had been eliminated. Approximately a quarter of the deputies in both chambers had university degrees and nearly an equal number had only an elementary education. The remaining parliamentarians, in both 1937 and 1961, had either attended secondary school, qualified for entrance to a university, or completed vocational training. Thus by 1961 fully three quarters of all members of the Riksdag had advanced beyond elementary school.[35]

The average age of Riksdag deputies has consistently remained over 50, increasing from 50.1 years in 1937 in the lower house to 52.4 years by 1961. In the upper chamber the average declined slightly, from 56.9 years to 55.4. The oldest members have been the Liberals (59.6 years in 1961 in the upper house, 54.3 in the lower), followed in order by the Communists, the Social Democrats, the Conservatives, and the Center.[36]

Although official statistical data for subsequent periods are not strictly comparable to the categories for 1937 and 1961 cited above, they appear to confirm continuity in occupation, sex, and age distributions among Riksdag delegates through the mid-1960s. Fifty-seven percent of those elected in 1964 were civil servants, salaried employees, or members of the free professions; 18 percent were farmers; 12 percent were engaged in business or commerce; and 5 percent were workers. (The occupation of the remaining deputies was not identified.) A nearly equal percentage of deputies in both houses were women (12 percent in the lower chamber, 13 percent in the upper house). The average age of members had declined by 1965 only slightly, to 51.2 years in the lower house and 53.6 years in the upper.[37]

THE EXECUTIVE

The pivotal component in Swedish political processes is the national executive. Composed of an hereditary monarch as head of state and a cabinet led by the prime minister as head of government, the executive performs the central functions of policy initiation and coordination. As in other modern systems, the political significance of executive actors has progressively increased in proportion to the growing complexity of industrial-welfare society.

The Role of the Monarch

Constitutionally "the Swedish realm shall be ruled by a king,"[38] who nominally possesses "the sole authority to govern the realm in accordance with the rules established by the Instrument of

---

[35] Sköld and Halvarson, pp. 446 and 468.
[36] Sköld and Halvarson, pp. 449 and 470.
[37] Sweden, Statistiska centralbyrån, *Riksdagsmannavalen åren 1961–1964*, II (Stockholm: Statistiska centralbyrån, 1965), pp. 51, 117–119.
[38] *RF*, art. 1.

Government."[39] Such rules include the investment of autonomous and shared powers in the hands of the Riksdag and the requirement that the monarch shall be "informed and advised by a council [the cabinet] appointed by the king and composed of knowledgeable, experienced, honest, and respected native-born Swedish citizens."[40]

The Act of Succession stipulates that the Swedish crown shall pass in order of direct descent to male heirs of the House of Bernadotte. The king must be Lutheran. He and his descendants forfeit their right of rule or succession in the case of marriage to a commoner.[41] Should there be no male heir, the Riksdag was empowered until 1971 to elect a new monarch. The paragraphs governing the election procedure were deleted in the constitutional reform of 1967–1969, indicating that the Swedish monarchy will lapse (to be replaced by an elected head of state) if a future successor abdicates or the present royal family dies out.

Since Jean-Baptiste Bernadotte's selection as regent in 1810, six kings have occupied the Royal Palace in Stockholm: Bernadotte as Karl XIV Johan (1818–1844), Oscar I (1844–1859), Karl XV (1859–1872), Oscar II (1872–1907), Gustaf V (1907–1950), and Gustaf VI Adolf (1950–). While the early kings played an active role in policy formulation, modernizing processes gradually eroded the political importance of the monarchy. The advent of parliamentarism in 1917 formally signaled the transfer of actual executive authority to the cabinet.

Despite the wording of the constitution, the Swedish King functions today, therefore, largely as a ceremonial figure—opening the annual sessions of the Riksdag, conferring Nobel prizes on international recipients, and presiding over cabinet meetings but exercising no substantive executive powers. At most he embodies the "expressive symbolism" of Swedish politics, providing in his person and the trappings of his office a visible link between the past and the present.[42] In times of international crisis the mon-

---

39 *RF*, art. 4.

40 *RF*, art. 4.

41 Act of Succession, arts. 1, 3, and 5.

42 The term "expressive symbolism" is borrowed from Harry Eckstein, "The British Political System," in Samuel H. Beer and Adam B. Ulam (eds.), *Patterns of Government*, 2d ed., rev. (New York: Random House, 1962), p. 91. Eckstein observes: "Merely by existing, the ceremonial institutions keep the past concretely alive in the present, and thus obscure the radical changes that have certainly occurred in British government, in however piecemeal a fashion, since the Middle Ages."

arch may serve, as did the kings of occupied Denmark and Norway during World War II, as an important focus of national unity. But it would be an exaggeration to claim for the Swedish royal house, as one can for the British monarchy, that it comprises one aspect of a pervasive "set of intelligible symbols of government and authority that fully enlist the fancies and emotions of her people."[43] Even though most Swedes venerate the present king as a person, many (including the Social Democrats in their official pronouncements) advocate the abolition of the monarchy, as it is a political anachronism.

Cabinet Responsibility

According to prevailing norms of parliamentary government the primary responsibility for executive action rests instead with the cabinet. Since 1917 political alignments in the Riksdag have determined the composition of successive Swedish cabinets, although disparities in the membership of the two houses and the absence of cohesive parliamentary majorities have resulted on occasion in anomalous applications of parliamentarian principles. With the adoption of provisions for a vote of no confidence by the Riksdag in 1967–1969, parliamentarism is now legally sanctioned by the constitution.

The cabinet is composed of the prime minister, twelve department heads, and two to five ministers without portfolio. The departments, which correspond approximately to national ministries in other parliamentary systems, include foreign affairs, finance, justice, defense, interior, industry, agriculture, commerce, social welfare, communications, the civil service, and education. The Act of Parliament requires that at least two members of the cabinet must have prior civil service experience.[44]

General procedures for appointing the prime minister and other members of the cabinet are regulated by political practice rather than constitutional provisions. The king retains the right of investiture, but he inevitably designates a prime minister who is capable of commanding majority support (or majority suffrance) in the Riksdag. After a general election or in case of a government crisis the established pattern is for the monarch to confer with the parliamentary speakers and the chairman of the political parties, obtaining from each of them advice concerning the candidate most

[43] Eckstein, "The British Political System," p. 92.
[44] *RF*, art. 6.

likely to enjoy the confidence of parliament. Alternatively when an incumbent has died (Hansson in 1946) or resigned (Erlander in 1969) the king has simply ratified the election of a new chairman by the party in power by appointing that new chairman prime minister. Once a prime minister has been named, he presents a list of his choice of other ministers to the king for the latter's formal approval.

The revised Instrument of Government and the Act of Parliament incorporate detailed prescriptions for the dismissal of cabinet officials. The right of parliament to force a minister or the cabinet to resign through a vote of no confidence has already been mentioned. In addition the constitution now entitles the prime minister to discharge cabinet ministers on his own initiative.[45]

Deriving its executive authority from its constitutional status as adviser to the king, the Swedish cabinet is the principal agent in preparing government propositions, the annual review of government policy, and the budget for submission to the Riksdag. Cabinet members meet at least once a week in preliminary cabinet sessions (*statsrådsberedning*) to determine the government's attitude on pending issues.[46] As noted in the preceeding chapter, the cabinet is required by the Instrument of Government to obtain expert advice from relevant administrative agencies before a given measure can be finally decided. Compiled usually on the basis of Royal Commission reports and *remiss* consultations with representatives of interest associations as well as the national administration, supporting documents and opinions are assembled by the minister in charge of a particular policy area for consideration by the cabinet. In practice, most decisions have already been made at the department level before they reach the preliminary cabinet sessions, with the latter serving as a forum to discuss and confirm the sometimes hundreds of matters that come before the cabinet in any given week. Only major policy questions are actually debated and decided in the full cabinet.

Cabinet decisions are formally sanctioned at weekly king-in-council (*konselj*) meetings that are conducted in the presence of the monarch (or, in his absence, the crown prince). The king is informed of the cabinet's "advice" on each issue, and may ask

[45] *RF*, art. 35.

[46] The preliminary cabinet meetings are a product of political practice rather than constitutional requirements. Since Bernadotte (King Karl XIV Johan) knew no Swedish, ministers found it necessary to confer on government policy and the cabinet agenda before official sessions with the monarch. With time the preliminary meetings became the actual setting for cabinet decisions.

questions about specific agenda items, but he never reverses a cabinet recommendation. Hence the cabinet's propositions and government messages are officially decisions by the king-in-council, with each minister required to countersign the signature of the monarch on all important bills and subsequent legislative enactments.

A second major function of cabinet ministers is to formulate general guidelines for the administration of government policies, although some 50 administrative agencies, which are legally independent of the ministerial departments, actually implement the policies.[47] Now officially codified in the Instrument of Government is a third significant cabinet prerogative, namely, the right of the prime minister on his own initiative to order the dissolution of parliament and to call for new elections. Such a decision must be promulgated within a week following a vote of no confidence by parliament.[48]

In its relations with parliament the cabinet is assigned joint responsibility with the Riksdag, as discussed above, for legislation concerning national referenda, constitutional amendments, and criminal and civil law. Ministers who are simultaneously parliamentary deputies are free to participate in parliamentary debates and vote in legislative decisions, but are not allowed to attend committee meetings.[49] The one exception is the committee on foreign relations; there the prime minister, the foreign minister, or one of their deputies may appear personally to submit reports on government policy.

CABINET RECRUITMENT

Recruited largely among parliamentary representatives, the cabinet is a microcosm of the majority faction in the Riksdag. The occupational backgrounds, education levels, and average age of cabinet members have remained largely constant in recent years, reflecting a continuation of long-term trends dating from the early 1930s. During the postwar period one of the salient characteristics of cabinet membership has been the stability of tenure among individual ministers.

[47] The civil service is discussed in Chapter Eight.
[48] *RF*, art. 108. Until the constitutional amendments of 1967–1969, the prime minister had to petition the king to dissolve either of the parliamentary chambers. The last time such a request was refused, however, was in 1905.
[49] *RO*, arts. 36 and 53.

The introduction of parliamentarism opened cabinet office to the new forces of sociopolitical modernization, thereby bringing to an end the earlier dominance of high-level civil servants. A sustained broadening of the social basis of ministerial recruitment dates from the formation of Prime Minister Hansson's first stable Social Democratic cabinet in 1932. Since then, except for the wartime four-party coalition, most executive officials have been drawn from the middle and lower social strata.[50]

Trends in occupational patterns among cabinet members during the past four decades indicate a decline in the number of civil servants and a corresponding increase in the free professions (especially professional politicians). Whereas the 1932–1936 government of Hansson included seven civil servants and five members of the free professions, Erlander's cabinet of 1965 contained five civil servants and eight free professionals. Among the latter were four professional politicians, two teachers, one journalist, and one trade unionist. No workers were represented in the 1932 cabinet; two workers were members of the Erlander government. In contrast to the greater hetereogeneity of parliamentary representation, there were no persons with farming or business backgrounds in either cabinet.

A majority of ministers has consistently claimed advanced educational backgrounds. Eleven out of twelve ministers who served from 1932 to 1936 had progressed beyond elementary school compared to ten out of fifteen in 1965. In each case seven officials had received university degrees, four in social science and three in law, in both cabinets. The number of those with no apparent secondary or university training, however, had increased from one in 1932 to five in 1965.

The average age of Swedish ministers has remained slightly lower than that for parliament as a whole: 46.5 years in 1932 and 53 years in 1965. With all but one change of government since 1932, the average age level has fallen from one to four years— indicating a continuing rejuvenation of the nation's political leadership.[51] Since 1954 one cabinet position has been filled by a woman; in 1966 a second woman minister was appointed.

The most persistent criterion of cabinet recruitment has been parliamentary experience. Since 1932 over 80 percent of Swedish ministers have served in the Riksdag prior to and during their

---

50 See Table 5 in Chapter Three.

51 When the Socialist-Agrarian coalition was formed in 1936, the average age of ministers rose to 51.5 years. The average age of the members of the Agrarian caretaker government had been 47.8 years.

tenure in executive office. Most of those with no parliamentary background were ministers without portfolio, who were recruited from the public administration. Their number averaged five from 1932 through 1960, but declined to two in 1965.

Political stability in Sweden is strikingly revealed in the long periods that key ministerial figures have retained office. Except for a brief interruption in 1936, Hansson remained prime minister for 14 years (1932–1946); his successor, Erlander, was head of government for 23 years (1946–1969). By 1970 Foreign Minister Torsten Nilsson and Defense Minister Sven Andersson had been in the cabinet 25 and 22 years, respectively. Five other officials, including Herman King (minister of justice), Gunnar Lange (minister of commerce), Sigurd Lindholm (minister of civil service), Rune Edenman (minister of education and ecclesiastical affairs), and Rune Johansson (minister of the interior and health), served more than ten years in executive office. For the cabinet as a whole the average tenure of ministers from 1960 to the beginning of 1968 was five years. Out of 23 cabinet members 8 served the entire period and only three for one year or less.

EXECUTIVE-LEGISLATIVE RELATIONS

The first 15 years of parliamentary government in Sweden were characterized by recurrent ministerial crises, with only one cabinet (the Liberal-Socialist coalition of 1917–1920) enjoying a stable parliamentary majority. As a result the Riksdag occupied by default the central stage in political processes, with each of the nine minority cabinets seeking to maximize support for its policies through party compromises in parliamentary committees. Executive authority was thereby diluted as it was in other new democratic systems elsewhere in Europe during the same period. The Socialist electoral victory of 1932, however, significantly altered the basic conditions of Swedish parliamentarism. Virtually uninterrupted Social Democratic ascendancy has subsequently shaped working relations between the cabinet and parliament for the past four decades.

The Social Democrats have maintained their majority position through a combination of tactical and formal alliances with other parties and their own numerical strength in the Riksdag. Although they lacked an absolute majority in both houses following the 1932 election, tacit Center support from 1933 to 1936 accorded the Socialists a comfortable 216-seat majority in joint

Table 17 Social Democratic Seats in Parliament and
Combined Parliamentary Support, 1933–1969

Chamber	Year					
	1933	1937	1941	1945	1949	1953
Lower House	104	112	134	115	112	110
Upper House	58	66	75	83	84	79
Total	161	178	209	198	196	189
Combined Parliamentary Support	216[b]	236[c]	376[d]	198	196	240[c]
Required Majority in Joint Votes	190	190	190	190	190	190

Chamber	Year				
	1957	1958[a]	1961	1965	1969
Lower House	106	111	114	113	125
Upper House	79	79	77	78	79
Total	185	190	191	191	204
Combined Parliamentary Support	228[c]	190	191	191	204
Required Majority in Joint Votes	191[e]	191	191	192[f]	192

[a]Special dissolution election.
[b]Informal cooperation with the Agrarians (Center).
[c]Socialist-Agrarian coalition.
[d]Wartime coalition of the Socialists, Agrarians, Liberals, and Conservatives.
[e]The number of seats was increased by one in both houses.
[f]The number of seats was increased in the lower house to 233.

votes, which was well above the necessary minimum of 190. (See Table 17.) When the Socialists formalized their cooperation with the Center party in a coalition ministry in 1936, the government partners claimed a solid majority of 148 seats in the lower house and 88 in the upper for a combined total of 236.

In 1941 the Social Democrats amassed for the first time a majority in the upper house, thereby gaining an independent majority of 209 seats within parliament as a whole. They were unable to utilize their margin of support for partisan goal-attainment, however, because the national wartime coalition composed of the four major parties had been formed two years earlier. With the dissolution of the coalition in 1945 the Socialists formed Sweden's first stable single-party ministry.

The decline in Socialist electoral support in both the 1948 and 1952 general elections and a gradual loss of seats in the upper house from the early 1950s onward prompted Erlander and his associates once again to approach the Center with an offer of cabinet collaboration. The resulting coalition of 1951–1957 thus compensated the Socialists for their minority in the lower house by providing the cabinet an aggregate majority of 240 seats. Concomitantly the coalition prevented the three nonsocialist parties from exploiting their combined majority in the lower houses to form an alternative government. Even apart from the Center's agreement to join the Socialists in executive office, the nonsocialist minority in the upper house (67 seats in 1951 compared to 79 for the Social Democrats) militated against such a move by denying the three parties a majority in joint votes.

The only overt threat to continued Socialist leadership came in 1957 when the Agrarians withdrew from the cabinet. Reduced to minority status in both the lower house and joint votes, the Social Democrats managed to retain office only by virtue of indirect parliamentary support by the Communist party. Nine Communist deputies during the 1957 session, seven from 1957 through 1960, and nine from 1965 through 1968 consistently voted with the Socialists or abstained in joint votes to prevent a government defeat at the hands of the nonsocialist opposition. Between 1961 and 1965 and after January 1969 the Social Democrats regained their own absolute majority.

With the inauguration of majority parliamentarism the cabinet displaced the Riksdag as the central site of important political decisions. Accordingly parliament has increasingly assumed secondary significance in popular affective orientations toward the political system. In the popular image of the Riksdag, parliamentary elections serve less to endorse particular candidates, who are responsive to constituent interests, than as a means to determine the composition of the executive or influence its policies.

The decline in the stature of parliament does not mean that the Riksdag has abdicated its rule-making, control, and supervisory responsibilities. Nor are members of the opposition parties wholly excluded from a share of legislative influence. A tradition of orderly parliamentary procedures, the customary practice of distributing committee chairmanships and assistant speakerships among the four principal parties, and proportional representation on the committees assure nonsocialist spokesmen participation in all phases of Riksdag deliberations. Moreover, opposition leaders are accorded informal channels of consultation with cabinet members through the postwar practice of standing, regular, and special leadership conferences that are called by the prime minister to discuss pending legislative issues and major foreign policy questions.[52] But like parliamentary assemblies in comparable situations of stable one-party or coalition rule the exercise of legislative functions, particularly in cases of partisan conflict, is contingent on the priorities and choices established by leaders of the dominant political faction.

Cabinet supremacy in executive-legislative relations can be illustrated empirically by the outcome of Riksdag action on government propositions and private members' motions. During the postwar period the number of cabinet bills has continued to decline annually from a peak of 417 in 1939, while private motions have steadily increased in volume. The former figures by no means signify a lessening of government activity; instead the downward trend in propositions reveals only that the cabinet has increasingly combined formerly separate bills into larger, more comprehensive proposals. Nils Stjernquist has tabulated, for example, that the 217 propositions submitted to the Riksdag in 1933 encompassed 6108 pages, while 204 government bills and messages in 1964 contained 13,054 pages.[53] The rise in the number of private members' motions, on the other hand, does provide an accurate measure of intensified activity on the part of the parliament, with backbench members and opposition leaders utilizing such motions in an effort to amend executive policy or substitute alternative measures.

The realities of the Socialist majority have dictated continued parliamentary endorsement of executive initiatives and in most cases the defeat of private motions. A sampling of committee deliberations during the 1947 session of the Riksdag revealed that the Second Legal Committee and a joint Legal and Supply Com-

---

[52] Ingvar Amilon cites as examples of topics that have been discussed at the leadership conferences: the Nordic Pact consultations of 1948–1949, the supplementary pension issue in 1957–1959, and the budget in the spring and fall of 1959. He observes that "few [of the conferences] have led to any positive results." Amilon, "Partiledarkonferenserna—en studie i parlamentarisk praxis," *Statsvetenskaplig tidskrift*, 66 (1963), 278–286. An abridged English translation is reprinted in Herbert Hirsch and M. Donald Hancock (eds.), *Comparative Legislative Systems: A Reader in Theory and Research* (New York: Free Press, 1971).

[53] Nils Stjernquist, "Riksdagens arbete och arbetsformer," in Arthur Thomson (eds.), *Samhälle och riksdag*, IV (Stockholm: Almqvist & Wiksell, 1966), p. 20.

Table 18   Propositions and Motions in Parliament, 1950–1969[a]

Year	Government Propositions	Private Motions
1950	261	743
1955	217	773
1960	190	944
1965	180	1017
1969	171	1375

[a]*Statistisk årsbok 1970*, p. 394.

mittee endorsed all 11 government propositions that had been referred to them for consideration. During the same session the Committee of Ways and Means accepted 14 out of 15 cabinet bills, substituting its own proposal for the fifteenth measure. Concurrently the Second Legal and joint Legal and Supply committees dismissed 12 out of 14 private members' motions that had been introduced by nonsocialist delegates, while the Committee of Ways and Means rejected 16 out of 19 such motions. The committees also rejected 10 Communist motions.[54]

A complete tabulation of all propositions and motions in 1964 confirms the dominance of the Swedish executive. According to Stjernquist, the various committees ratified 223 out of 258 propositions in their original version, modified to a greater or lesser degree 34 propositions, and disallowed only one. In comparison 746 motions out of 1227 were rejected out of hand, 445 were accepted in revised form, and 36 were endorsed as they were submitted. During subsequent parliamentary deliberations the Riksdag accepted 226 out of 258 government bills (including 220 as they had been drafted by the cabinet) and 213 out of 481 motions in the form recommended by the committees. The Riksdag sustained the committees' decision to dismiss 1 cabinet proposition and 731 out of 746 private members' motions. Hence the combined review by committees and parliament resulted in changes in only 38 propositions and the rejection of two thirds (748 out of 1227) of the private members' motions.[55]

Confronted by an entrenched Socialist majority and restricted in their capacity to utilize parliamentary channels to modify executive policy, nonsocialist spokesmen have sought a variety

[54] My calculations from the various committee reports.

[55] Stjernquist, p. 31. The author notes that some propositions and motions are counted twice in these calculations "partly because a committee issued more than one report on the same subject (for example, the budget) and partly because [particular] measures were referred to more than one committee."

of formulas during the postwar period to enhance their own claim to cabinet office. One was the decision by the Center to abandon opposition ranks and join the Socialists in the coalition of 1951–1957. A theoretical alternative, which was widely debated in the 1940s and early 1950s, was the proposal that the four major parties form a permanent all-party cabinet modeled after the Swedish wartime ministry and the Swiss pluralist executive. Herbert Tingsten, former editor of *Dagens Nyheter*, was a particularly outspoken advocate of such a system of proportional executive rule. Arguing that the tenuous balance of political forces during the 1950s threatened a possible return to the ministerial instability of minority parliamentarism, Tingsten evoked a positive response to his views among many nonsocialists. But when the Social Democrats refused to countenance a grand coalition after the Center withdrew from the cabinet in 1957, opposition leaders embarked on a third course—nonsocialist cooperation in elections and parliament—that was envisioned as a potential means to dislodge the Socialists from executive office altogether.[56]

Although nonsocialist forces achieved only partial success in coordinating electoral strategy during the 1960s,[57] opposition cooperation in parliament led to a significant increase in the number of jointly sponsored measures in the Riksdag. A principal index of nonsocialist collaboration was the frequency of committee reservations that were endorsed by either two or all three of the parties. As indicated in Table 19, committee reservations submitted by the 3 opposition parties rose from 51 in 1962 to 111 in 1964. While Liberal-Conservative reservations declined from 49 to 19, those sponsored by the Liberal and Center parties increased from 27 to 68. In combination two- and three-party reservations expanded at a significantly higher rate (from 138 in 1962 to 215 in 1964) than the number of single party nonsocialist reservations (from 298 to 309).[58]

An additional indication of nonsocialist parliamentary cohesion was the frequency of common votes among the three parties in plenary sessions of the Riksdag. In 1964 nonsocialist forces

[56] A comprehensive discussion of the debate on alternative government models in Sweden is presented in Olof Ruin, *Mellan samlingsregering och tvåpartisystem. Den svenska regeringsfrågan 1945–1960* (Stockholm: Bonniers, 1968). Ruin summarizes his major findings and conclusions in "Patterns of Government Composition in Multi-party Systems: The Case of Sweden," *Scandinavian Political Studies*, 4 (New York: Columbia University Press, 1969), pp. 71–87.

[57] See Chapter Six.

[58] The decline in all reservations in 1965 can probably be attributed to the fact that it was not an election year.

Table 19   Committee Reservations in Parliament:
1962–1965[a]

Session	Social Democrats	Single Party Nonsocialist Reservations	Liberals-Center-Conservatives
1962	47	298	51
1963	39	229	63
1964	51	309	111
1965	44	150	62

Session	Liberals-Center	Liberals-Conservatives	Center-Conservatives
1962	27	49	11
1963	45	34	11
1964	68	29	7
1965	59	20	5

[a]My computations from the records of the Committees on the Constitution, Ways and Means, Appropriations, Banking, Agricultural, Miscellaneous Affairs; the First, Second, and Third Legal Committees; and various special committees.

jointly opposed the Social Democrats and Communists in 118 instances out of 366 in which a division of either house was called—the highest total among all alignments between three and two parties. The second highest number was 38 (Social Democrats, Communists, and Center). In contrast the nonsocialist parties voted in concert with the Social Democrats only 16 times, although one or more nonsocialist parties supported the majority faction in most other legislative votes. The four highest instances of various party combinations were the Social Democrats and Communists (286), the Liberals and the Center (261), the Liberals and the Conservatives (211), and the Center and the Conservatives (191).[59]

The majority status of the Social Democrats, sustained by the legislative discipline of their parliamentary deputies, sharply circumscribed the immediate effectiveness· of such displays of nonsocialist unity. Nevertheless the instances of nonsocialist unity constituted an important symbolic step in the continuing evolution of executive-legislative relations in Sweden. The incipient move toward greater nonsocialist cohesion, in combination with the abolition of the structural obstacles to an alternation of executive

[59] Stjernquist, pp. 424–425.

power inherent in the previous system of joint votes, suggest a potential era of more dynamic interaction between representatives of the parliamentary majority and minority.

EXTRAPARLIAMENTARY AGENTS

Continued Socialist domination of the cabinet and parliamentary processes does not imply a monopoly by a single group on all relevant political decisions. Within the formal political system, authority is diffused among a variety of independent actors, including members of the public administration and the courts and the ombudsmen.[60] On the executive level civil servants have traditionally played a central role in the formulation of executive policy. Since the mid-1950s their numbers on official investigatory commissions have increased by a third, indicating an increasing tendency for cabinet ministers to rely on the public administration for expert advice and detailed drafts of government propositions.

Economic interest associations, as discussed in the preceding chapter, exercise autonomous bargaining functions in the extraparliamentary sphere of Swedish politics. The membership of organizations representing the private sectors of the economy on Royal Commissions and their participation in *remiss* consultations have to a significant degree compensated nonsocialist forces for the "permanent" minority status of the Liberal, Center, and Moderate Unity parties in parliament. Except for the Communists the four parties, too, are represented on most Royal Commissions, thus providing opposition spokesmen an opportunity to influence policy decisions before particular measures are formally submitted to the Riksdag.

A strong bourgeois press provides an additional channel of informal access to decision makers. The Liberals claim the largest newspaper support: 43 papers with a daily circulation of 2,059, 700. Conservative-oriented newspapers number 48 and have a daily readership of 820,300, while 12 papers with a circulation of 136,100 endorse the Center party. In comparison the Social Democratic total (859,700) barely exceeds that of the Conservatives.

Hence the nonsocialist papers, with a combined publication of over three million copies a day, easily dominate Sweden's aggregate newspaper circulation.[61] Admittedly there is little causal

60 See Chapters Eight and Nine.

61 Communist and nonaffiliated newspapers comprise the remaining distribution total of 397,600.

link between bourgeois readership and voting behavior since the number of readers does not correspond to the relative strength of the nonsocialist parties in the Riksdag.[62] Nevertheless the press contributes important indirect policy inputs by disseminating minority views among public officials and subjecting the political-administrative apparatus to incessant scrutiny. The ombudsmen, for example, rely heavily on newspaper accounts in their day-to-day investigation of the court and administrative systems.

An extraparliamentary opposition has also sought to influence public policy through diluted manifestations of confrontation politics. The most dramatic instance occurred in May 1968 when students in Stockholm, following the examples of their counterparts in France and West Germany, occupied the offices of the student government in protest against perceived shortcomings in university administration and curriculum. But the existence of open lines of communication between established political leaders and youthful political activists, and the willingness of officials to collaborate with the students in university reform in the particular case of the Stockholm incident, have militated against the growth of an extraparliamentary opposition movement in Sweden comparable in scope to those on the European continent and in the United States.

Although numerous groups and political views thus impinge on decision makers, members of the Swedish cabinet retain ultimate authority for determining the official course of national policy. Their capacity to initiate and oversee authoritative decisions is defined by the majority status of partisan forces within the formal parliamentary structure. Future change in the content of such decisions will depend in the first instance on which party or parties control executive office.

[62] According to a survey of 1174 persons, who were interviewed by the public opinion section of Sveriges Radio, the percentage of those who read editorials on a regular basis ranged from 37 percent of male voters from 22 to 30 years of age to 55 percent of those between 31 and 40. Corresponding figures among eligible female voters were significantly lower, decreasing from 38 percent for those who were 22–30 years of age to 28 percent of women between 51 and 60. This relative disinterest in editorial (and hence overt political) content suggests that the nonsocialist newspapers, many of which were founded prior to the rise of organized labor in Sweden, probably attract their large following more because of their excellent news coverage and intellectual essays than their political viewpoints. Source: Sveriges Radio, Sektionen för publikundersökningar, *Sveriges Radios valundersökning hösten 1962*, R-TV 5/62, del I (Stockholm. Sveriges Radio, 1963), p. 4. (Mimeographed.) Rokkan and Torsvik have reached similar conclusions about the status of the bourgeois press in Norway. See Stein Rokkan and Per Torsvik, "Der Wähler, der Leser und die Parteipresse," *Kölner Zeitschrift für Soziologie und Sozialpsychologie*, 12 (1960), 278–301. Reprinted as Chapter 13 in Rokkan, *Citizens, Elections, Parties* (Oslo: Universitetsforlaget, 1970).

EIGHT
CONFLICT AND COMPROMISE
The policy-making process

In all systems political processes take place in a variety of sites, which include both formal and informal settings of policy consultations and decisions.[1] In highly centralized one-party states the decisive decision-making sites are restricted to party leaders and their encounters with semiautonomous groups such as the military and public administration. Modern pluralist systems, in contrast, characteristically manifest multiple sites in which policy decisions are made. These range from representative structures such as the legislative assembly, the national executive, and local government units to the public administration and "quasi-official bargaining among giant associations."[2]

Depending on structured patterns of government authority and the concentration of parties and interest groups, the relative importance of any single site or combination of them varies from one pluralist system to another. Thus in a presidential system with only two national parties competing for office, the executive and the legislature constitute—usually in that order—decisive sites for

[1] As used here "site" refers to encounters among all participants in the decision process, not only those (as in Dahl's more restricted context) between the government and the opposition. See Robert A. Dahl (ed.), *Political Oppositions in Western Democracies* (New Haven, Conn.: Yale University Press, 1966), pp. 338–341.

[2] Dahl, pp. 344–345.

policy decisions. In a parliamentary system characterized by the fragmentation of parties and interest groups, with each displaying low internal cohesion, the public administration is likely to assume greater importance as a central site of decisions than either the cabinet or the legislature. Such was the case in the Third and Fourth Republics of France.

Under conditions of majority parliamentarism in Sweden the cabinet, as discussed in the preceding chapter, has assumed increased importance within the formal government structure. Yet, as also noted, the cabinet is not the only site of political decisions. Like the British cabinet the Swedish government "cannot unilaterally determine and enforce its preferences; its officials recognize that they need the assent and cooperation of others in order to obtain a more or less mutually satisfactory outcome."[3] Hence the process of policy formation and implementation involves not only the cabinet, as the dominant political actor, but also members of the opposition parties, interest associations, and the public administration.

Prevailing values in Swedish political culture, such as a sense of fair play and a willingness to moderate partisan demands, encourage a bargaining relation among diverse groups that is manifest at all stages of the decision-making process. Therefore many substantive issues are resolved on the basis of consensus among principal political and economic forces. On two occasions during the postwar period, however, majority and opposition views have clashed in protracted conflict: in the planned economy debate of the mid-1940s and in the supplementary pension controversy during the mid-1950s. Because the course and resolution of both issues revealed salient features of political processes in Sweden, each is examined in detail below.

THE STYLE OF POLITICAL PROCESSES

In contrast to the strong personalities in politics in many other countries, such as Winston Churchill in wartime England and Charles de Gaulle in the Fifth Republic of France, individual personalities play a relatively subdued role in Sweden. Certainly names of prominent political figures stand out—De Geer and Branting in the nineteenth century and Hansson, Erlander, and

---

[3] Richard Rose, *Politics in England* (Boston: Little, Brown and Company, 1964), pp. 220–221.

Ohlin in the twentieth. But their contributions to particular epochs have been basically the product of group achievements. Indicative of the role of personality in Swedish politics is Palme's characterization of the prime ministership before he assumed the office himself. When asked what the important qualifications of the head of government should be, Palme replied that "[he should have] the confidence of his party and the team he gathers around him. In Anglo-Saxon countries a president or a prime minister is very much a leader, but here he is one of a team and the important thing is to be effectively a part of that team. Not to stand above it."[4]

The accuracy of Palme's assessment is indicated by the style of policy processes in Sweden. Participation in decisions is synonymous with group participation, with institutionalized provisions for pluralist representation in important sites—for example, Royal Commissions—dating from the nineteenth century. Accordingly group values determine both the rules and substance of cosultative procedures.

The most prominent norm among policy participants, which is derived from shared cultural values of moderation and conciliation, is a mutual inclination among party and interest association leaders to respect Sweden's pervasive "obstruction taboo."[5] Rather than perpetuate conflicting views, political parties have repeatedly abandoned policy positions when they have no longer proved tenable. During the four decades of Social Democratic executive leadership opposition spokesmen have often refrained from overt confrontations with the Socialists to keep from jeopardizing their capacity to influence policies in noncontroversial areas. Even when the nonsocialist parties seemed to have a legitimate grievance against the government, as when they sponsored a vote of censure in 1964 against former Foreign Minister Östen Undén because of his alleged failure to maintain sufficient security controls over the suspected espionage agent Stig Wennerström, they have displayed a singular reticence to exploit Socialist shortcomings in subsequent electoral campaigns.[6]

---

[4] "Frost vs Palme," *Sweden Now*, 3 (June 1969), p. 5.

[5] Dankwart A. Rustow, *The Politics of Compromise* (Princeton, N.J.: Princeton University Press, 1955), p. 195.

[6] Wennerström was a colonel in the Swedish Air Force, who had served as air attache in Moscow (1949–1952) and in Washington (1952–1957), as an officer in Sweden's Defense Command Office (1957–1961), and as disarmament consultant for Undén in the Foreign Ministry (1961–1963). He was arrested in 1963 as a Soviet agent and was subsequently sentenced to life imprisonment. The Socialist majority in parliament rebuffed opposition efforts to censure Undén on the

Reinforcing cultural patterns of self-restraint is a variety of political factors. One such factor is that many issues subject to debate in other systems are relegated to administrative channels in Sweden. The most important example is the independent investigatory role assigned the ombudsmen. Through their impartial watchdog functions, the ombudsmen effectively preempt numerous potential charges of administrative misconduct that might otherwise provoke acrimonious exchanges among party representatives.

An additional factor proscribing the range of partisan conflict in Sweden is the constitutional requirement that all government documents, except those dealing with national security and defense questions and individual records of the insane, must be made readily available for public scrutiny.[7] Because the executive scrupulously observes this rule by publishing voluminous documentation relevant to policy decisions and their implementation, opposition leaders find little cause to press the government for additional details.

Moreover, opposition leaders are inhibited by the expectation that they may share in cabinet patronage if they refrain from persistent partisan attacks on the majority faction. In the postwar period the Social Democrats have rewarded nearly as many members of the nonsocialist parties with coveted appointments as provincial governors as they have their own party faithful.[8] As a variant on the same theme, the government appointed Heckscher, who resigned as Conservative chairman in 1965, Swedish ambassador to India.

In negotiations on the labor market similar tendencies for the major partners to respect the claims of each other have been cited in Chapter Six. Both sides have threatened and even engaged in extreme measures such as lockouts and strikes, but the prevailing style of LO-SAF relations is their joint attempt to settle differences between labor and management amicably.

Although Sweden's major political-economic organizations share a commitment to a procedural style of political processes

---

grounds that the foreign minister had, in fact, undertaken adequate surveillance measures against Wennerström. A comprehensive summary of Wennerström's espionage activities is contained in the official commission report: Sweden, Justitiedepartementet, *Statens offentliga utredningar 1964:15, Utlåtande av Juristkommissionen i Wennerströmaffären* (Stockholm: Justitiedepartementet, 1964). A popular account is Irwin Ross, "The Master Spy Who Almost Got Away," *Harper's Magazine*, 229 (December 1964), 47–54.

[7] Chapter II of the Law on the Freedom of the Press.

[8] See Table 8 in Chapter Four.

based on a predisposition toward compromise and nonobstruction-
ist behavior, they have simultaneously differed in their attitudes
toward substantive facets of domestic policy. The basis of disagreement, as indicated in previous chapters, is revealed in the
dichotomy between collectivist and individualist assumptions concerning political action that distinguish Socialist and nonsocialist
forces, respectively. As in the party debates on the role of local
government and constitutional reform, these opposing group perspectives have provided the principal source of intermittent socioeconomic conflict during the postwar period.

THE POLICY-MAKING ROUTINE

The recognition of policy needs and the choice of specific procedures for resolving issues differs according to their international
and domestic context. In the former case differences in the perception of policy requirements are largely minimal among politically
relevant groups. The nation's tradition of military neutrality and
common recognition of Sweden's vulnerability to fluctuations in
the international economic sphere engender a high degree of consensus among decision makers on foreign policy, with political
leaders utilizing informal leadership conferences and the Advisory
Council on Foreign Affairs in the Riksdag to reach agreements on
most government policies. Thus during the postwar period the
four major parties unanimously affirmed Sweden's application for
membership in the United Nations in 1946, concurred in Sweden's
membership in the European Free Trade Association in 1959,
consult annually to determine military appropriations, and have
resolved to postpone the question of possible Swedish nuclear
armaments. Unanimity concerning the goals of foreign economic
policy has also contributed to the durability of Sweden's official
record of labor peace, with both the LO and the SAF agreeing
that sustained productivity is a necessary condition for expanding
trade and continuing national affluence.

More complex is the policy routine in deciding domestic issues. Most initiatives arise within the cabinet and public administration during the regular course of proposition and budgetary
formulation. Requests to appoint investigatory commissions to
consider new policies may come from administrative agencies,
interest associations, members of parliament, and private individ-

uals.[9] Even the substance of a private member's motion rejected in one session of the Riksdag may reappear a year or more later as the cabinet's own proposal. In some cases prior consultations among party leaders may yield the impetus for a policy initiative. One example was the appointment of the first Royal Commission in 1954 to consider the abolition of the upper house. Important policy innovations have also emerged from collaborative efforts of the Social Democrats and the LO. This proved the case in both of the conflicts discussed below.

If a minister decides that a particular proposal justifies consideration, he may assign it to members of his department staff for preliminary appraisal. In important questions the cabinet typically appoints a Royal Commission to compile data and make specific policy recommendations. The minister in charge prepares a formal set of directives and designates the commission chairman and members. Utilized by Swedish governments to attain broadly-based support for their policies or postpone controversial legislation, Royal Commissions have become increasingly dominated in recent years by members of the civil service. The number of one-man commissions has increased from a quarter of the total in 1945–1954 to a third in 1961–1967, and over 90 percent of all commission chairman have been recruited from the public administration during the postwar era.[10] Nevertheless Royal Commissions remain an important site for direct pluralist participation in Swedish political processes. Since the beginning of the century, representatives of political parties and interest associations have been allocated an average of more than 50 percent of commission membership, with their aggregate share declining to 40 percent in the decade from 1955 to 1967. Parliamentarians and interest groups each contributed approximately one half of this total. (See Table 20.) During the same period nonsocialist delegates were accorded a slight overrepresentation (compared with the Social Democrats), which ranged from 1 percent for the Conservatives to 2 percent for the Liberals and 7 percent for the Center, in relation to their numerical strength in the Riksdag.[11]

[9] Meijer estimates that "demands from the public authorities make up the largest group [of requests for policy investigation] while the wishes of the Riksdag, of the interest organizations and of private individuals each constitute about one fifth of the total." Hans Meijer, "Bureaucracy and Policy Formation in Sweden," *Scandinavian Political Studies*, 4 (New York: Columbia University Press, 1969), p. 104.

[10] Meijer, "Bureaucracy and Policy Formation in Sweden," pp. 107–108.

[11] All totals from Meijer, "Bureaucracy and Policy Formation in Sweden," pp. 107–111.

Table 20 Royal Commissions:
Total numbers and membership recruitment[a]

Years	Total	Number of Commissioners	Percentage Members of Parliament	Percentage Civil Servants	Percentage Interest Groups
1905–1914	403	1579	27	51	21
1915–1924	504	2083	27	47	26
1925–1934	452	1690	32	43	25
1935–1944	618	2560	23	47	30
1945–1954	752	3306	25	41	34
1955–1967	989	3651	19	60	20

[a]Adapted from Hans Meijer, "Bureaucracy and Policy Formation in Sweden," *Scandinavian Political Studies*, 4 (New York: Columbia University Press, 1969), p. 109.

As approximately three quarters of all commission reports are unanimous, thereby all but committing the cabinet to the recommended course of action, Royal Commissions provide nongovernment groups highly effective leverage in decision processes. Usually only in instances of divided majority and minority commission reports does the cabinet exercise an independent option to press for a partisan solution or continue deliberations by appointing a second Royal Commission.

A second distinctive Swedish procedural device in policy formation is the *remiss* procedure (described in Chapter Six) that accords interest associations and administrative agencies an opportunity to review Royal Commission reports and government proposals. The use of the elaborate Royal Commission and *remiss* deliberations during the circulatory stage of legislation means that political processes in Sweden often extend over several years. But once a decision is made, through subsequent consideration in the cabinet and ratification by the Riksdag, "the authorities are usually prepared to translate the new policy into practical measures without delay."[12]

On three occasions the cabinet and the Riksdag have utilized their constitutional prerogative to involve the electorate directly in political processes through use of a national referendum. Unlike De Gaulle, who scheduled referenda to obtain successive mandates for his highly personal style of leadership in France, political authorities in Sweden have employed referenda only to determine electoral attitudes on unresolved issues. A referendum serves

[12] Meijer, "Bureaucracy and Policy Formation in Sweden," p. 115.

strictly consultative purposes and does not limit the freedom of policy choice by either the government or parliament.

National referenda have included one in 1922 on prohibition, a second in 1955 on whether Sweden should change to right-hand traffic, and a third in 1957 on supplementary pensions. In two cases the results were inconclusive, and in the third political leaders decided on an opposite course of action. A narrow majority of 51 percent of voters defeated prohibition in the first referendum, while no absolute majority preference was expressed in 1957 among the competing pension plans submitted by the various parties. A majority of 82.9 percent rejected right-hand traffic in 1955, but cabinet and parliamentary spokesmen concluded from the low turnout—only 53.2 percent of the eligible electorate—that the vote was not necessarily representative of genuine popular sentiment. Hence the Riksdag affirmed a decision to change to right-hand traffic anyway. The measure was implemented in 1967.

THE PUBLIC ADMINISTRATION

Political responsibility for coordinating the role of the public administration in decision processes is vested in the ministers in charge of the 12 departments that comprise the Royal Chancery. Each minister is assisted by an under secretary, who manages departmental policy initiatives and legislative propositions, and a permanent secretary, whose duties involve more routine tasks such as ministerial appointments. While the under secretaries are considered political appointees, the permanent secretaries are inevitably recruited from the civil service. The staffs of the various departments are small, numbering approximately 100 persons.[13] Members are organized in a series of functional bureaus that correspond to the major activities of the department.

A distinctive feature of the Swedish system of public administration is that once decisions have been reached through executive-legislative channels the ministers and the departments exercise no direct authority over the actual implementation of policy. In contrast to the centralized national bureaucracies of England or France, a network of independent boards and agencies (*centrala ämbetsverk*) enacts policy directives. In theory the boards and

---

[13] Meijer, "Bureaucracy and Policy Formation in Sweden," p. 104. For a detailed discussion of the organization of the executive departments, see Nils Andrén, *Modern Swedish Government* (Stockholm: Almqvist & Wiksell, 1961), pp. 111–112.

agencies are accountable only to the king-in-council and legal codes rather than to the cabinet ministers. "The essence of this system," Brian Chapman has observed, "is that . . . [each] ministry is primarily a small policy-making body, the sun, the source of energy; while the boards are the satellites, providers of information and services."[14]

Evolving from collegial administrative councils that were established in the seventeenth century, the independent boards and agencies today number over 50. They include the national court system; state-owned enterprises such as the Swedish railway system and the postal service; the government wine and liquor monopoly; regulatory commissions such as the Customs Office; and welfare agencies such as the Social Welfare Board, the National Insurance Office, the National Pensions Board, and the Board of Health.[15]

The various administrative agencies enact policy directives issued by the king-in-council and enforce conformity with legal codes through their own offices on the national and local levels and provincial and municipal authorities. In addition to their functions as executors of public policy and sources of expert opinion during *remiss* deliberations, the agencies play an active role in the annual budgetary processes. The cabinet relies primarily on administrative estimates of future expenditures in calculating its appropriation requests for submission each January to the Riksdag.

Like administrative structures in other modern political systems, the boards are organized on principles of bureaucratic hierarchy with members dedicated to achieving scientific-rational goals of orderly procedures and efficiency in their day-to-day work. Each is headed by a director-general, who is appointed by the king-in-council for a term of six years. Except for representatives of interest associations on some of the administrative bodies, all are staffed by members of the professional civil service.

Entrance into the civil service is based on competitive examinations, with advanced academic, professional, and vocational training providing the basic criterion for admission. In 1967, for example, only 6 percent of 111,798 high-level officials had obtained no more than a primary education.[16] As a result most civil servants are recruited from the upper and middle classes—a pattern common to all Western countries. Public servants enjoy con-

---

[14] Brian Chapman, *British Government Observed* (London: George Allen & Unwin, Ltd., 1963), p. 35.

[15] Gunnar Heckscher, *Svensk statsförvaltning i arbete* (Stockholm: Studieförbundet Näringsliv och Samhälle, 1952), p. 48.

[16] *Statistisk årsbok 1968*, pp. 231–232.

siderable social prestige, and possess a reputation for efficient, dedicated service. Political corruption is virtually unknown.

A persistent characteristic of the Swedish civil service is its claim to political neutrality. Although individual officials may hold public office while retaining their civil service rank, relatively few are actively involved in partisan political affairs. So strong is the nation's tradition of an impartial public administration that even a majority of under secretaries in the Royal Chancery are politically nonpartisan. In the period from 1945 to 1965 only 22 of the 61 under secretaries who served in the various departments were members of a party (all of them were Social Democrats). The greatest concentration of party members was in the Departments of Social Affairs, Finance, and Interior. Some ministries, including the Departments of Trade, Defense, and Foreign Affairs, had none.[17]

Because of the high social status that has traditionally been accorded civil servants in Sweden, the public administration functions in an "environment that is not only more stable than [for instance] the American but one that actively encourages further bureaucratic aggrandizement in the direction of controlled social change."[18] In recent years the government has initiated rationalizing steps to transform the administrative apparatus into an even more efficient instrument of state policy, including the merger of some agencies and the creation of the new ministry of industry to consolidate the various public enterprises into a single department. Parallel with this process civil servants have displaced party and interest group representatives as the dominant source of membership recruitment for Royal Commissions. Although such centralizing tendencies have helped generate radical attacks against the bureaucratization of Swedish politics, political authorities have shown little indication that they will reduce their reliance on the public administration as a major support in policy formation.

GROUPS IN CONFLICT

Sweden's characteristic style of compromise politics and provisions for multiple sites of pluralist participation in decision processes have contributed significantly to national economic and political stability. With the attainment of affluence and broad con-

[17] My calculations from *Sveriges statskalender* and *Vem är det?* and interviews with informed observers.

[18] Sjoberg, *et al., Politics in the Post-Welfare State: A Comparison of the United States and Sweden* (Bloomington, Ind.: Carnegie Seminar on Political and Administrative Development, 1967), p. 9.

sensus on the principles of the welfare state, "better conditions for compromise and agreement have, on the whole, been created. The effect has been cumulative: every compromise probably tends to reduce existing cleavages."[19] Hence political leaders have been able to achieve common decisions on numerous socioeconomic issues—including periodic increases in general retirement benefits and other welfare services—and the initially divisive question of parliamentary reform.

Yet Swedish politics has not been immune from conflict. Although protracted controversies of principle are the exception rather than the rule in group relations in Sweden, controversies have occurred at important junctures in the postwar period. As a measure of a nation's capacity to sustain genuine political stability (as opposed to superficial indexes of government stability), patterns of conflict resolution provide instructive insights into the nature of political processes. They reveal group strengths, weaknesses, and differences in fundamental perceptions of the system itself. Equally significant, conflicts are indicative of constants and changes in the distribution of political resources.

The planned economy and supplementary pension disputes in postwar Sweden resulted in contrasting outcomes. A government retreat in the first instance was followed by the consolidation of Socialist electoral and political strength in the second.

THE PLANNED ECONOMY DEBATE: 1945–1948

Sweden's first major postwar controversy was precipitated when the Social Democrats proclaimed a 27 point "postwar program of the working-class government" in 1944.[20] The fundamental issue was whether the Socialists would proceed with the program's goals to extend nationalization and economic planning in an effort to mitigate the effects of an anticipated recession. Challenging the proclaimed Social Democratic policies were the three nonsocialist parties and important interest associations, all united in the belief that nationalization would prove detrimental to the Swedish econ-

[19] Nils Stjernquist, "Sweden: Stability or Deadlock?" in Robert A. Dahl (ed.), *Political Oppositions in Western Democracies* (New Haven, Conn.: Yale University Press, 1966), p. 139.

[20] Sveriges socialdemokratiska arbetareparti, *Program och stadgar, enligt beslut å partiets sjottonde kongress 1944* (Stockholm: Tiden, 1944). Hereafter referred to as *Program*. An English translation is available in Landsorganisationen, *The Postwar Programme of Swedish Labor* (Stockholm: Landsorganisationen, 1948).

omy and a democratic form of government. "Neither before nor since," Lief Lewin states, "have ideological antagonisms been expressed with such force."[21]

Tactical considerations, psychological factors, and a genuine concern that the end of wartime hostilities would result in mass unemployment prompted the Socialist initiative. Although nationalization of industry had long been considered a dead letter among Swedish Social Democrats, a Communist advance of 2.4 percent in the 1942 communal election provoked internal concern that the party would lose additional support to the left unless it radicalized its appeal. Second, Socialist leaders seized upon nationalization and economic planning as an activist program compensating psychologically for Sweden's isolation during the war. Finally, the Social Democrats were obsessed with historical memories of Sweden's economic depression following World War I and viewed socialization as a possible means to avoid similar dislocations after the second World War.

The 27-point program was drawn up by a committee made up of LO and Socialist delegates under the chairmanship of Ernst Wigforss, minister of finance since 1936 and one of the more outspoken Socialist intellectual radicals. It was formally adopted by the Social Democratic seventeenth party congress in 1944. As a restatement of traditional ideological tenets, the program reflected the revisionist tendencies inherent in the Socialist movement since the party's founding in 1889. But it also contained a sharp critique of capitalist society and advocated greater social influence over the means of production. The opening paragraph proclaimed:

> The goal of Social Democracy is to reformulate the economic organization of bourgeois society so that the right to determine production is placed in the hands of all citizens; that the majority is freed from its dependence on a minority of capitalists; and that a social order built on economic classes gives way to a community of free and equal citizens.[22]

Charging that an unequal distribution of property rights had resulted in a concentration of economic power "in the hands of a minority," unemployment "in the midst of abundance," and "insecurity for the masses," the Social Democrats called for the crea-

---

[21] Leif Lewin, *Planhushållningsdebatten* (Stockholm: Almqvist & Wiksell, 1967), p. 529.
[22] *Program*, pp. 5–7.

tion of "such forms for the organization of production that will give the workers greater influence, responsibility, independence, and security."[23] The program declared further:

> Whether constituted on the basis of individual property rights or collective ownership, the economy must be coordinated on a planned basis so that human and material resources are not dissipated by unemployment or insufficient production. Such coordination can be achieved only under the direction of society. Individual profits and special group interests must be subordinated to the goals toward which society is striving.[24]

In more specific terms the 27 points of the Socialist program declared that "it is necessary to . . . nationalize natural resources, industrial firms, credit institutions, and means of transportation and communication."[25]

While the program hardly advocated a complete transformation of society to accord with classical Marxist principles—as evident in the tacit recognition of individual property rights—the Socialist demand for nationalization of industry and credit institutions evoked immediate resistance among nonsocialist leaders participating in the national coalition government. Their suspicions of Socialist intentions were heightened when the majority party introduced a series of motions in the Riksdag in early 1945 calling for the appointment of Royal Commissions to investigate socialization measures.

After the dissolution of the wartime coalition and the formation of a single-party Social Democratic cabinet on July 31, 1945, nonsocialist opposition to the 27 points erupted in open ideological conflict. While an underlying motive for the controversy was the threat that nationalization posed to important industrial and banking interests, the political debate was couched primarily in idealistic terms. As Tingsten, a prominent participant in the debate as editor of *Dagens Nyheter*, has written in his memoirs:

> The principal criticism of Social Democracy, or more correctly of its socialization intentions, . . . could also be seen as a defense of democracy. . . . My viewpoint . . . was that extensive socialization was not compatible with political freedom and hence with democracy. I did not deny that the Socialists believed in good

---

23 *Program*, p. 7.
24 *Program*, p. 7.
25 *Program*, p. 11.

faith that the preservation of freedom was possible under inclusive socialization, but I did maintain that they were deluding themselves. Free organizations, free debate, and a free press are not conceivable beyond a certain point of state control and, even more, of state ownership.[26]

A similar theme was developed by Tingsten and Eli Heckscher, a conservative economist, in a radio debate with representatives of the Social Democratic Party in June 1945. Tingsten declared: "Socialization means the state would own the means of production. A planned economy means the state would determine the use of productive resources. In reality the difference between them is minimal. . . . [It] is not possible to reconcile a planned economy or socialization with democracy. By democracy I do not mean merely majority rule but also, and possibly above all, freedom in a spiritual sense."[27] Heckscher's principal argument against the Socialist program was that "it would eliminate diversity. There would be no choice, no possibility to turn to groups in society when only one [group] has access to material resources— that one being the state. . . . Once the state begins to determine production there is no retreat."[28]

Leaders of the three nonsocialist parties shared essentially the same viewpoint. Their hostility to the Social Democratic government was based as much on a desire to dismantle price and trade regulations imposed during the war as on their opposition to the theoretical implications of extended socialization in accordance with the 27 points. The Liberals actively challenged the Socialist position with an alternative concept of "social liberalism" that envisaged the extension of existing welfare measures within the framework of decentralized public and private control over capital savings and production. "In the group I represent," Liberal chairman Ohlin declared in a Riksdag debate in October 1945, "we do not believe that a centrally-directed economy is desirable. . . . We believe that a more flexible . . . system, resting on competition . . . [and] private initiative, will lead to more rapid expansion . . . than a system that is centrally controlled."[29]

[26] Herbert Tingsten, *Mitt liv, III: Tidningen 1946–1952* (Stockholm: P. A. Norstedt & Söners Förlag, 1963), pp. 121–122.

[27] "Planhushållning?" Radio discussion among Eli Heckscher, Karin Koch, Herbert Tingsten and Arne Björnberg on June 12, 1945. Reprinted in *Röster i Radio*, 12 (July 1–7, 1945), 6–7, 22, 36, and *Röster i Radio*, 23 (July 8–14, 1945), 6, 36.

[28] "Planhushållning?"

[29] Swedish, Riksdagen, *Riksdagens protokoll vid lagtima riksmötet år 1945, höstsessionen, Andra kammaren*, 34, (1945), p. 43.

Among the major organized interests only the LO unequivocally supported the government's program. Although spokesman for private sectors of the economy professed their willingness to continue cooperation with the government's planning commission in maintaining price controls during the initial postwar period, they resolutely resisted the long-term implications of the 27 points. In a representative statement, Ernst Wehtje, Director of the Federation of Swedish Industries, said in January 1945:

> We business representatives have sometimes been criticized for not coming forward with a postwar program. The majority party has pointed with pride to its guidelines for postwar society. In rebuttal I would like to say that we employers . . . naturally think about these questions and draw up our plans for the future. But we are possibly not as inclined to . . . propagandize our work as [are] the visionaries responsible for the . . . 27 points. The proponents of that document talk glibly about how easy it will be to solve all our problems and . . . there are probably many who are beginning to believe them. But if they should actually try to put their plans into effect, they will probably discover that planning is made of the same material as that in the fable of the emperor's new clothes. We know that the problems which industry will meet in the postwar period will be difficult ones that will demand a multitude of . . . practical prerequisites to solve. One cannot solve them, however, through attractive plans on a drawing board.[30]

Against this background of general ideological debate, opposition criticism of the Socialist government was focused on a series of specific issues. The first was a six-year trade agreement with the Soviet Union, which the Social Democrats submitted to the Riksdag early in the summer of 1946. Fearing the consequences of economic dislocations in the West, Minister of Trade Gunnar Myrdal vigorously argued that credits of a billion crowns should be extended to the Soviet government for the purchase of Swedish industrial products. The government party reasoned that the agreement would serve to guarantee continued domestic productivity in case trade declined with Western nations.

Within parliament members of the opposition parties attached a number of reservations to the subsequent committee report affirming the government's proposition. Outside formal polit-

30 Speech by Ernst Wehtje, Director of the Federation of Swedish Industries, before the Örebro Engineering Club and Technical Association on January 26, 1945. Reprinted as a supplement to the *Svensk Papperstidning*, 2 (1945), 12–13.

ical channels Tingsten charged in *Dagens Nyheter* "that there was no reason to sell to Russia on credit because our industry already had a backlog of orders in Sweden and from abroad." In addition Tingsten maintained editorially that "the government was attempting to coerce industry with pressure and threats to agree to cooperate in fulfilling the terms of the agreement."[31]

The government secured parliamentary endorsement of the trade agreement in November. Largely because of the adverse criticism it had provoked, however, Myrdal resigned from the cabinet in April 1947.

A second issue of partisan attacks on the Social Democrats concerned Erlander's appointment as prime minister in 1946. In this case nonsocialist leaders demanded that membership in the cabinet be broadened to comprise a four-party coalition, but the Social Democrats refused. Finally, major disagreements arose during the 1947 sessions of parliament over the government's taxation policies and measures to combat inflation.

Although the Social Democrats successfully resisted opposition agitation to form a new national coalition or modify their immediate postwar economic measures, leaders of the majority party were acutely aware of their increasingly precarious margin in the Riksdag. The Socialist percentage of the national vote had declined from 46.6 percent in 1944 to 44.4 percent in the 1946 communal election, while the combined nonsocialist percentage had increased from 42.4 to 44.1. Communist strength had risen to 11.2 percent during the same period. As a result the Social Democrats could anticipate a gradual loss of seats in indirect elections to the upper house in the latter part of the decade.

The 1948 election to the lower house proved to be the major turning point in the opposition drive to restrain the Socialists from carrying out the socialization policies they had proposed in 1944. In a record turnout (82.7 percent of the eligible voters) a plurality of the electorate endorsed the nonsocialist parties. Together the Liberals, Conservatives, and Center received 47.5 percent of the national vote compared to 46.1 percent for the Social Democrats.

Even though the Socialist percentage increased in comparison to the 1946 election—the product of a significant Communist decline—the government party lost three mandates in the lower house. Nevertheless the Social Democrats were able to maintain control of cabinet office because of their absolute majority in the upper chamber and relative majority in the second.

[31] Tingsten, *Mitt liv, III,* p. 126.

From the nonsocialist point of view the 1948 election proved to be "both a triumph and a . . . miscalculation."[32] While the three opposition parties, particularly the Liberals, had scored major advances, they failed to achieve sufficient support to form an alternative ministry or persuade the Socialists to reconstitute a national coalition.

The nonsocialist advance did succeed, on the other hand, in persuading the Social Democrats to abandon the socialization plans contained in their 27-point program. Confronted with 110 bourgeois deputies in the lower house (only two less than the number of Socialists), the government party sought solace in the diminution of the Communist threat from the left and quietly shelved its nationalization proposals. Wigforss, the main architect of the 27-point program, resigned from the cabinet the following June.

The Social Democrats justified their retreat on the grounds that nationalization had not been necessary because the antici- pated depression in the West did not occur. An additional factor may have been that they were only half-heartedly committed to the postwar program in the first place. Nevertheless the sustained nonsocialist propaganda drive against socialization and the in- crease in opposition strength in 1948 had clearly played a major role in inducing the government to modify its policies.

THE SUPPLEMENTARY PENSION DISPUTE: 1957–1959

For nearly a decade after the conflict on nationalization abated, politics in Sweden followed a relatively moderate course. Wartime economic restrictions were gradually abolished, and expanding in- ternational trade stimulated an unprecedented growth of the do- mestic market. The major political event was the formation of the Socialist-Center coalition in 1951. The Liberals continued to reg- ister advances in electoral support, and after 1952 the Conserva- tives began to experience a perceptible upswing as well.

Partisan tempers flared again when a Royal Commission is- sued a majority opinion in February 1957 recommending a com- prehensive extension of Sweden's pension system. Supporting the proposal were the Social Democrats and the LO, while the three

[32] Tingsten, *Mitt liv, III*, p. 151.

nonsocialist parties and leading interest groups were arrayed in opposition. Once again Socialist and nonsocialist groups became deadlocked in an extended ideological controversy.

As a study of group conflict in postwar Sweden, the pension dispute displays important parallels with the 1945–1948 socialization debate. Once again the principal question was whether the Social Democrats would proceed with a controversial political initiative despite nonsocialist dissent. Most important interest associations joined in opposing the government's position in both controversies, and control of the national executive was ultimately at stake in each instance.

At the same time significant contrasts are discernible between the two disputes. By 1957 the Communists no longer posed an immediate threat on the left; the Social Democrats enjoyed a secure basis of parliamentary support through their coalition with the Center; and the nonsocialist parties, while united in resisting the pension proposal, were unable to agree on a single alternative with which to challenge it. Combined with other considerations noted below in context, these factors help explain why the result of the second endeavor by the nonsocialist parties to modify government policies proved different from the first.

The controversy did not involve the principle of old-age insurance itself. Since the passage of the first comprehensive pension program in 1913, Sweden's four democratic parties had been in fundamental agreement that all persons, regardless of income, should receive monthly minimum retirement benefits. As recently as 1946 the opposition parties had joined the Social Democrats in endorsing a general pension reform that significantly increased social security allowances.

Instead, the conflict centered on the issue of supplementary payments, relative to previous income levels, that would augment basic retirement allowances. The Social Democrats argued that supplementary pensions should be administered under state auspices and be made compulsory for all employed persons. Nonsocialist spokesmen maintained that management and labor should negotiate private agreements to institute a voluntary system of compliance. In these opposing perspectives was clearly revealed the persisting cleavage between collectivist and individualist orientations in modern Swedish politics.

Disagreement had become apparent as early as 1955 when a Royal Commission reiterated a 1950 commission recommendation that an inflation-proof supplementary pension should be implemented that would guarantee retirement benefits up to 36 percent of an individual's mean annual income.[33] In a minority opinion, Ernst Ahlberg, a Conservative Riksdag deputy and a member of the Royal Commission, offered a substitute proposal that advocated an increase in general pensions in place of supplementary payments.[34] When it became clear from nonsocialist criticism in parliament that the three parties would not accept the commission's majority suggestion, Minister of Social Welfare John Ericsson appointed a new pension commission in January 1956 to work out a possible compromise solution.

The commission was composed of representatives of the four democratic parties and delegates from the SAF, LO, and TCO. Working against an early deadline imposed by the cabinet, the commission succeeded in drawing up a compromise agreement to raise general pension levels but failed to achieve consensus on the supplementary pension issue itself. The Royal Commission presented three alternative proposals when it reported its findings to the cabinet in February 1957. One was a majority opinion, endorsed by the Socialist, LO, and TCO members, that reaffirmed compulsory pension supplements amounting to 50 percent of an employee's salary during his best 15 years of income. A second proposal—advocated by the Center party representative—called for voluntary supplementary pensions under state administration. The Liberal, Conservative, and SAF members advocated a strictly voluntary system over which the government would exercise no authority.

The inability of the Royal Commission to reach a compromise among the conflicting viewpoints reflected fundamentally divergent economic interests and political assessments among the four major parties. As parliamentary spokesmen for organized labor, the Social Democrats were initially moved to advocate compulsory legislation in response to explicit LO demands for supplementary pensions.[35] Politically they seized upon supple-

---

[33] Sweden, Justitiedepartementet, *Statens offentliga utredningar 1955:32, Allmän pensionsförsäkring. Förslag avg. av pensionsutredning* (Stockholm: Justitiedepartementet, 1955). The report is summarized and discussed in Åke Elmer, *Folkpensioneringen i Sverige* (Lund: CWK Gleerup Bokförlag, 1960), p. 112, and Björn Molin, *Tjänstepensionsfrågan* (Göteborg: Akademiforlaget, 1965), pp. 21–28 and 189–198. Both volumes have English summaries attached.

[34] Molin, pp. 20–21.

[35] The LO had advocated supplementary pensions to augment workers' retirement benefits since the early 1950s. In response to the LO initiative, Prime Minister Erlander had declared at the Social Democrats' twentieth party congress in May 1956 that "supplementary pensions are a reform in which the government is greatly interested." Quoted in Molin, pp. 40–41.

mentary pensions as a possible means to increase their electoral popularity among white-collar workers and therefore reverse their general postwar electoral decline.[36]

Among nonsocialist forces in parliament, economic interests and ideological considerations strongly influenced the negative position assumed by the Liberals, Conservatives, and Center. Major business and agrarian organizations had vigorously rejected compulsory supplementary pensions in favor of private contracts with labor and an increase in general pension levels. Furthermore, the nonsocialist leaders viewed mandatory supplementary payments with somewhat the same trepidation as they had the 27-point program. The creation of a large extrabudgetary fund under state control to finance the program would constitute, in their view, an equally serious threat to private interests as the nationalization of industries had posed in the mid-1940s.

The nonsocialist chairmen articulated attitudes that were widely shared among their parties' rank-and-file. Public opinion surveys conducted in 1956 indicated that an overwhelming majority of upper-class supporters for the two opposition parties were hostile toward the Socialist proposal to introduce compulsory supplementary pensions. A majority of working-class voters supported the plan, while salaried employees were ambivalent.[37]

In the case of the Liberals and Conservatives, tactical evaluations of prevailing political alignments also played a role in determining party attitudes. Encouraged by their recent electoral advances at the expense of the two government parties, the opposition leaders drew a conclusion that was diametrically opposed to that of the Social Democrats: by resisting compulsory legislation *they* would be the ones to gain additional support among marginal voters. Ohlin, in particular, was confident that a majority of white-collar workers favored a voluntary system over a mandatory arrangement. While the TCO representative on the Royal Commission had endorsed the majority opinion submitted in February, the TCO refused to commit itself officially to a choice between the proposals.

Hence, divergent party attitudes toward the supplementary pension issue converged along a spectrum similar to that in the nationalization controversy. In both instances differing organiza-

---

[36] In 1956 Socialist support had fallen to 44.6 percent, its lowest point since 1946.

[37] Särlvik, *The Role of Party Identification in Voters' Perception of Political Issues. A Study of Opinion Formation in Swedish Politics 1956–1961* (Göteborg: University of Göteborg, n.d.), p. 17. (Mimeographed.)

tion ties and special interest claims (combined with conflicting ideological commitments) placed the Socialists and nonsocialists in opposing camps. Tactically, however, the political alignment had shifted. Unlike the initial postwar period, the nonsocialist parties no longer constituted a single bloc even though all of them opposed the majority viewpoint toward compulsory legislation. While Center membership in the cabinet acted to restrain a unilateral Socialist initiative, it also served as an effective deterrent to a united nonsocialist offensive.

Parliamentary configurations dictated the first move in resolving the impasse. Confronted with the prospects of certain defeat in the face of a nonsocialist majority in the lower house, the Social Democrats refrained from introducing their version of the pension bill during the spring session of the Riksdag as they had originally intended. Instead, party leaders agreed on March 26 to a Liberal proposal to conduct a national referendum allowing the electorate to indicate its preference among the three alternative proposals.

Consistent with the earlier polarization of opinion within the Royal Commission, each of the parties and interest associations reaffirmed their respective support for one of the three alternatives. Endorsing the first proposal were the Social Democrats and the LO:

> 1. Employees have the legally secured right to supplementary pensions that will be determined according to earlier salaries and will retain their [relative] value. Others—e.g., employers—will have the opportunity to secure supplementary pension benefits to a certain upper limit, with this value to be guaranteed by the state.[38]

The Center and agrarian interest associations sponsored the second proposal:

> 2. Employees, employers, and others will have the voluntary opportunity to secure supplementary pensions to a certain upper limit, with this [relative] value to be guaranteed by the state.[39]

The Liberals and Conservatives joined the SAF and individual spokesmen for the TCO in affirming the third alternative:

---

[38] Olle Nyman and Hjalmar Sellberg, *Svenskt 1900-tal i dokumentens belysning* (Stockholm: Svenska Bokförlaget, 1959), p. 200.
[39] Nyman and Sellberg, p. 201.

3. Employees, employers, and others may voluntarily secure supplementary pension insurance. Revisions will be enacted in existing legislation that will enable supplementary pensions, without a guarantee by the state, to retain their [relative] value. Supplementary coverage will be arranged through collective pacts or individual or group agreements.[40]

The official neutrality of the TCO and the fact that the non-socialist parties presented competing proposals proved decisive in determining the electorate's response. When the consultative referendum was held on October 13, 1957, the Social Democrats obtained a relative majority (45.8 percent) for their proposal. The Liberal-Conservative plan for voluntary compliance received 35.3 percent support. Fifteen percent of the electorate endorsed the Center alternative.

White-collar workers, subject to conflicting pressures of long-term economic interests, which seemed to be promoted most effectively by the Socialist plan, and implicit ideological affinity with the Liberals, had been most divided of all occupational strata in their response. According to public opinion surveys, 40 percent of white-collar employees supported the Liberal-Conservative position while 28 percent favored the Socialists. A quarter of their number abstained from voting. In contrast nearly 70 percent of high-level employers and salaried employees voted for the Liberals and Conservatives, while 61 percent of industrial workers affirmed compulsory legislation. The third highest level of group cohesion was among the farmers, 49 percent of whom supported the Center.[41]

Although the Liberals and Conservatives drew encouragement from the fact that combined nonsocialist strength had totaled 50.3 percent in the referendum, the division of opinion among white-collar workers and their own relative majority prompted the Social Democrats to proceed with compulsory legislation. The Center, on the other hand, concluded from its increase in strength that the most advantageous course would be to withdraw from the coalition and assert a new party identity under its present name.

The government resigned on October 26. When the Center refused to join the Liberals and Conservative in a nonsocialist coalition because of the Socialist plurality in joint votes, the Social Democrats formed a minority cabinet on October 29.

[40] Nyman and Sellberg, p. 201.

[41] Sweden, Justitiedepartementet, *Statens offentliga utredningar 1959:10, Folkomröstningen 1957* (Stockholm: Justitiedepartementet, 1957), p. 27.

After consultations with opposition leaders once again failed to yield a compromise settlement,[42] the Socialists introduced a bill in February 1958 incorporating with minor modifications the basic principles of compulsory supplementary pensions contained in their referendum proposal. In response Ohlin initiated consultations with the Conservatives and Center to draft a joint nonsocialist alternative. Liberal efforts to reconcile opposition viewpoints failed when Hedlund declared that the Center was unwilling to deviate from its referendum commitment.[43]

A subtle shift in partisan positions occurred during the subsequent committee deliberations and the Riksdag debate on the government's proposition. While the Social Democrats remained adamant in supporting their original proposal, both the Liberals and Conservatives modified their respective attitudes. In an attempt to rally opposition forces to a "positive compromise solution,"[44] the Liberals now advocated supplementary pension legislation combined with the right for individuals to "contract out" of the system. Concomitantly the Conservatives moved closer to the Center policy of advocating a state-guaranteed pension fund while rejecting all legislation to regulate supplementary pension benefits.

This change of views within the nonsocialist bloc indicated a departure from earlier assessments of political tactics and public opinion. The Center party, no longer restrained by coalition membership, felt justified in pursuing a policy dictated solely by interest group considerations. Fearful that a purely negative attitude would result in further defections among white-collar workers, the Liberals sought to satisfy employee demands for legislation without entirely renouncing the freedom of choice important to employer interests. The Conservatives, who were less concerned with the ambivalence of middle-class white-collar workers as their major support came from business interests and high social strata, felt no compulsion to follow the Liberals' lead in seeking a compromise formula.

On the government side, the Social Democrats were determined to press for compulsory supplementary pensions largely because of labor demands for them and their positive assessment of the referendum results. Unlike their electoral losses in the immediate postwar period, the referendum had provided the Socialists with what they interpreted as a popular mandate. Therefore

[42] Molin, pp. 82–84.
[43] Molin, p. 87.
[44] A phrase used by Ohlin in a speech in the lower house on November 6, 1957. Quoted in Nyman and Sellberg, p. 205.

the Social Democrats reasoned that they could force the pension issue in parliament despite their minority status in the lower house. A defeat of the government's bill would provide the Socialists with sufficient cause to dissolve the second chamber and schedule new elections in the expectation that they would increase their support as advocates of a new social welfare initiative. Admittedly their strategy was a gamble. But given opposition disunity, evident in the inability of the nonsocialist parties to agree on a joint pension alternative and their failure to form a coalition the previous fall, the Socialists resolved that they could risk it.

A special joint committee recommended passage of the cabinet's proposition on April 23. After three days of intensive debate, the nonsocialist majority in the lower house rejected the bill 117–111. Consequently the Social Democrats announced on April 28 the dissolution of the second chamber and set a special election for June 1.

The election results confirmed Social Democratic hopes and the worst of Liberal fears. With an increase of 2.4 percent of the popular vote the Socialists reversed their earlier electoral decline and gained 5 mandates for a total of 111 seats. The Liberals, whose "positive compromise solution" had failed to satisfy either the salaried employees who favored compulsory legislation or those who supported private agreements between management and labor, lost 20 seats. The Conservatives and Center capitalized on persisting hostility to compulsory pensions among employers, high-level administrators, and farmers to register advances of 2.0 and 3.3 percent, respectively.

When the new Riksdag convened on June 18, the previous nonsocialist majority had thus been reduced to a minority of one. With Communist support the Social Democrats claimed 116 mandates compared to 115 for the nonsocialist parties. The government, however, was by no means assured of passage of its version of pension legislation. As the speaker in the lower house (a Social Democrat) was constitutionally deprived of his right to vote, the political alignment was in effect 115–115.

The Social Democrats initiated consultations with the Liberal Party after the communal elections in September in an effort to negotiate an agreement that would break the parliamentary deadlock. When the Liberals refused to compromise on Socialist terms, the government resubmitted its original proposal on March 13, 1959. It was assigned to a special committee composed of an equal number of Socialist and nonsocialist deputies.

A Liberal delegate and a member of the LO from Göteborg,

Ture Königson, decided the fate of the pension controversy. Königson declared on May 13, during the general parliamentary debate on the committee's report, that he could not support the committee's recommendation to reject the government's bill. He favored the Liberals' "positive compromise solution," but because the Conservatives and Center were unyielding in their opposition to compulsory legislation he conceded that the Liberal proposal had little prospect of leading to a common settlement among the parties. Hence Königson announced his determination not to vote, thus ensuring passage of the Socialist proposal, rather than reject supplementary pensions altogether.[45] When the Riksdag voted the following day, Königson abstained and the Socialist measure was passed 115–114.

IMPLICATIONS

When compared with the opposition success in the planned economy debate in the 1940s, the inability of the nonsocialist parties to restrain, or at least modify, executive policies in the supplementary pension controversy appears to be largely a function of the differing nature of the two conflicts. In terms of electoral response, the socialization debate involved primarily economic issues that were heavily charged with emotional overtones; opposition to the 27 points was effectively rationalized as an ideological defense of democracy. In contrast, the pension dispute was social as well as economic; the prospect of concrete welfare benefits apparently took precedence among key electoral strata over ideological resistance to the Socialist proposal as an infringement on individual freedom.

Politically, the difference in the context of the two conflicts suggests why the nonsocialist parties were united in one case and hopelessly divided in the second. They encountered relatively little difficulty in jointly opposing nationalization as an amorphous, vaguely defined program that was never spelled out in detail. Supplementary pensions, on the other hand, demanded a concretely formulated commitment to an alternative proposal. Differing interest claims and political assessments rendered nonsocialist consensus in the latter case impossible.

[45] Königson's decision was apparently attributed to his loyalty to organized labor. See Molin, pp. 103–113. Because of his breach of *party* loyalty, Königson was later expelled from the Liberal party. See Pär-Erik Back, "Det svenska partiväsendet," in Thomson (ed.), pp. 134–138.

As a result the Social Democratic victory on the supplementary pension question was achieved largely by default. Confronted with a continual shift in priorities and political alignments among the opposition parties, the Socialists were psychologically in a stronger position from 1957 to 1959 than they were during the nationalization debate, despite their objectively weaker base of parliamentary support in the later period. At first willing to explore the possibility of a compromise, the Social Democrats resolved to force the issue when the referendum indicated a relative majority in their favor. Their electoral advance in 1959 provided the final impetus to press for a partisan solution. In 1948 the Socialists were restrained from implementing nationalization measures by nonsocialist electoral advances; after 1958 the perceptible decline in opposition strength encouraged them to proceed with their initiative.

Thus the outcome of the two postwar conflicts suggests that the capacity of either the Socialists or the nonsocialists to exercise a decisive influence in controversial issues depends in the first instance on their respective electoral strength. A second factor of effective participation in political processes is the ability of parties and groups to promote or defend policies that are in accord with popular endorsement of democratic government and social welfare measures. Among bourgeois forces a third factor of importance is the extent of interest association support for nonsocialist political initiatives. When major organizations have been in basic agreement among themselves and with nonsocialist leaders—as in the planned economy debate—nonsocialist influence has been at a maximum. Conversely, ambivalent attitudes among members of one or more interest groups—for example, the TCO during the pension conflict—has tended to undermine nonsocialist effectiveness. Also relevant for nonsocialist prospects to play a positive role in conflict situations is the degree of their bloc cohesion. At least part of the success of the opposition propaganda campaign against economic planning after 1945 was due to the joint nonsocialist refutation of announced Socialist goals. Much of the failure of the opposition parties to influence the result of the supplementary pension issue, on the other hand, was attributed to their inability to formulate a common alternative to the government's program.

Despite the highly charged partisan exchanges that accompanied each of the conflicts, both revealed the underlying stability of the Swedish system. Just as the Social Democrats retreated in the face of concerted parliamentary and interest group criticism of their postwar program, the nonsocialist parties and interest associations abandoned their opposition to the new supplementary pension system after its implementation. Simultaneously both controversies marked important watersheds in the changing postwar political alignment. The first signaled a rising curve of nonsocialist electoral strength that induced the Social Democrats to share executive authority with the Center and pursue national policies of moderation through the mid-1950s. The second resulted in a shift in popular support to the advantage of the Socialists, enabling them to consolidate cabinet leadership and ultimately accelerate processes of socioeconomic transformation.

NINE
"THE COUNTRY SHALL BE BUILT WITH LAW"
Law and the judicial process

In the conclusion to his study of party politics in modern Sweden, Rustow writes: "Whatever its merits or defects the politics of compromise is firmly rooted in tradition. . . . The essence of that tradition is a strict and often meticulous regard for law and legal procedure, expressed in the old adage, *'Land skall med lag byggas'* —'Country shall be built with law.' "[1]

The development of legal principles in Sweden is inextricably intertwined with the evolution of a cohesive national political community. The "meticulous regard for "law" has not meant rigid subservience to established codes, but, rather, continuing efforts by public officials to adapt the legal foundation of the state to the changing character and needs of society. With the emergence of Sweden as a modernized state, judicial structures have been refined and elaborated into a complex yet functionally harmonious system of local, regional, and national courts. Serving as a distinctive feature of Swedish legal processes are independent ombudsmen with autonomous powers of investigation and supervision, whose rapidly expanding role is indicative of contemporary forces of sociopolitical transformation.

---

[1] Dankwart A. Rustow, *The Politics of Compromise* (Princeton, N.J.: Princeton University Press, 1955), pp. 236–237.

LAW AND MODERNIZATION

As Wallace Mendelson aptly points out, few studies have systematically explored the role of law in the development of nations.[2] Yet law has universally contributed an historical rationalization for " 'dominant [or emerging] institutions and accredited ways of life,' "[3] providing official sanctions for the attainment of national unity, industrialization, and the redistributive goals of contemporary welfare society. Following his assessment of the changing nature of law during phases of modernizing change in the United States, Great Britain, and Japan, Mendelson concludes: "Law no doubt is a stabilizing or conserving force. It is also—simultaneously—a crucial instrument of social change. Under a facade of formal symmetry, it must honor reasonable expectations born of the past, yet allow *lebensraum* [living-space] for the present and the future."[4]

The evolution of legal codes in Sweden substantially parallels the conserving-adaptive functions of law in other modern states. During the pre-Christian era of dynastical rivalry and Viking forays into the Baltic and North Sea regions, law was relegated largely to the personal realm. Disputes were regulated under the authority of the local *ting* (councils of freemen dating from the ninth century), and were usually settled through single combat. In isolated instances the administration of pagan law as acts of individual retribution persisted well into the Middle Ages, as graphically depicted by Töre's vengeful slaying of the herdsmen, who had raped and killed his daughter, in Bergman's film *The Virgin Spring*.

With the attainment of incipient national unity as a consequence of Christianization and the emergence of a Swedish nobility during the eleventh and twelfth centuries, new provincial codes were implemented that transferred legal authority from local bodies to the embryonic monarchical state. The earliest of these codes was the Västergötland Law which was adopted in the early part of the thirteenth century; it contained provisions for settling disputes among farmers as well as "the oldest decrees in existence which deal with the political constitution of the country."[5] Subsequent codes varied from one province to another, but they pro-

[2] Wallace Mendelson, "Law and the Development of Nations," *The Journal of Politics*, 32 (May 1970), 223–238.

[3] Mendelson, p. 223.

[4] Mendelson, p. 234.

[5] Ingvar Andersson, *A History of Sweden* (London: Weidenfeld and Nicolson, 1956), p. 39.

vided a common basis for a decentralized monarchy resting on powerful provincial *tings* dominated by the nobility, the richer peasants, and the church.

During the thirteenth and fourteenth centuries successive kings of the Folkung dynasty centralized monarchical rule, decreeing new laws and prompting the revision of provincial codes to guarantee "the preservation of the king's peace"[6] in much the same manner that Henry II had sought to replace feudal law with national law in the twelfth century in England. Under their influence Sweden's first constitution, the *landslag*, was promulgated in 1350. At the same time law served to restrain the arbitrary power of Swedish kings, who pledged in the medieval coronation oaths to respect the rights of the citizens to their life and property.

Law provided a particularly important unifying function during Sweden's successful bid for independence from Denmark and the consolidation of the Vasa dynasty in the sixteenth century. As the first king of the new national monarchy, Gustaf I initiated comprehensive administrative, legal, and political reforms, including the creation of a national treasury, the introduction of Roman law concepts into the judicial system, and the Swedish Reformation. His grandson, Gustaf II Adolf, established in 1614 Sweden's first court of appeal, the *Svea hovrätt*, which marked a significant step in the creation of uniform national judicial procedures.

Thus by the time of Sweden's entrance as a major European power into the Thirty Years War (1618–1648), the nation had achieved a degree of political integration comparable to that attained two hundred years earlier by Tudor England and Renaissance France. In each case legal codes and royal judicial structures provided authoritative supports for the maintenance of national unity. Throughout subsequent centuries new laws and constitutions were invoked to sanction the recurrent cycles of monarchical absolutism (1682–1718 and 1771–1809) and parliamentary supremacy (1719–1772). Concomitantly laws were affirmed by the Riksdag that contained harbingers of future sociopolitical change. Emerging as a consequence of factional strife between the "Caps" and the "Hats" during the Era of Liberty, Sweden's (and the world's) first law against government censorship in 1774 established important precedents for the Freedom of the Press Law of 1810. In 1734 Sweden adopted a new code of civil and criminal law that remains, at least in form, still in force.

The legal foundations of contemporary Swedish government

6 Andersson, p. 42. Compare Mendelson, pp. 229–230.

were established by the constitution of 1809, which prescribed a formal separation of executive and legislative power that ultimately gave way to the functional diversion of authority between the cabinet and the Riksdag under the prevailing rules of parliamentarism. From the judicial perspective the major contributions of the constitution were its provisions for an independent court system and the office of the ombudsman. Both remain essential characteristics of the Swedish legal system today.

As in the United States and much of Western Europe during the same period, law and judicial processes were modified in the nineteenth century in Sweden to make legitimate the gathering forces of industrialization. The abolition of guilds in 1846 and legal restrictions on free trade during the 1860s proved important stimuli for the growth of industry and commerce. Consistently law served to protect employer interests by upholding the freedom of contract and individual property rights. Employees were guaranteed the right of association, which provided the legal basis for the emergence of the Swedish trade union movement in the 1880s, but law tacitly favored stronger business interests by denying workers legal remedies in case of industrial conflict. Only with the collective agreements act of 1928 and the private Saltsjöbaden accord between the LO and the SAF a decade later was organized labor able to overcome its inferior status in relation to employer groups.

Sweden's entrance into the redistributive era of welfare politics occurred after precedents to provide workers' insurance had been established in Imperial Germany and Denmark, but significantly sooner than comparable efforts were undertaken in the United States, Great Britain, and France. National legislation introduced the nation's first industrial accident insurance program in 1901, family welfare subsidies in 1902, and old age pensions in 1913. Although the full maturation of the welfare state was to await the rise of the Social Democrats to political ascendancy, these early legislative acts were indicative of changing domestic attitudes concerning the nature of government responsibilities toward groups and individual citizens. No longer was the proper role of the state considered a limited one, restricted to maintaining private (especially economic) freedom. Instead, in response to demands primarily by the Social Democrats, "a fundamentally new view of the state [had emerged]. A leading idea is that the state should not only watch over its citizens' rights, but also actively promote their prosperity and social security."[7]

---

[7] Alfred Bexelius, "The Origin, Nature, and Functions of the Civil and Military Ombudsmen in Sweden," *The Annals of the American Academy of Political and Social Science*, 377 (May 1968), 14.

During the ensuing decades of cumulative welfare legislation, law, as in the United States from the mid-1930s onward, "was again crucial."[8] Swedish legal principles increasingly assumed a positive content, with statutory enactments and the development of wholly new fields of labor and family law complementing traditional criminal and civil codes as the basis for the contemporary judicial system. In the process law once more revealed its adaptive qualities, lending a modern definition to the supremacy of law contained in the ancient Swedish legal codes.

JUDICIAL AND LEGAL PRINCIPLES

Like the political system itself, judicial principles in Sweden are a product of indigenous traditions and doctrines imported from abroad. Elements of older Germanic law survive in a contemporary Swedish jurisprudence, yet many Roman law concepts have also been incorporated from the German and French legal traditions. During the past century Anglo-American practices have also exerted an influence on the development of Swedish law.

Hence Swedish legal principles may be described as a synthesis of Roman law and common law, occupying a halfway position between the systematic codification of legal tenets characteristic of the former and the "judge-made" law based on precedent associated with the latter. Much Swedish law is fixed in written form— for example, the Code of 1734 governing civil and criminal law (which has been wholly revised since its adoption), corporation law, labor law, and legislative status—but no comprehensive equivalent exists to the *Code civil* in France. At the same time many areas of litigation and judicial supervision are governed by practice rather than detailed legal documents, particularly in the fields of public and administrative law and in the functions performed by the ombudsmen.

Important features of Swedish law are the constitutional guarantees pertaining to civil liberties. An integral part of the constitution is the Freedom of the Press Act, which not only prohibits prior government censorship of any publication but also stipulates that private citizens may have free access to most official documents. In addition substantive individual rights are emumerated in Article 16 of the Instrument of Government, which has often been described as the Magna Charta of Swedish legal traditions because of its origins in the *landslag* of the fourteenth century. The article reads:

[8] Mendelson, p. 228.

The king shall strengthen and promote justice and truth, and shall prevent and prohibit wrongs and injustices. He shall neither destroy nor allow others to destroy anyone's life, honor, personal freedom, and security except through legal prosecution and conviction. Nor shall he deprive, or allow others to deprive, anyone of his property movable or real, without due process and judgment according to the procedures prescribed by Sweden's laws and statutes. The king shall not invade, or allow others to invade, anyone's peace in his home; banish anyone from one place to another; coerce, or allow others to coerce, anyone's conscience; or deprive any citizen of protection to practice his religion freely, as long as he does not disturb the public peace or create a general disturbance. The king shall allow everyone to be judged by the court to which he is legally subject.

As Robert Malmgren notes, Article 16 omits basic civil liberties found in many Western bills of rights, including the freedoms of assembly, association, and speech; freedom from ex post facto legislation; and the right of petition.[9] Such liberties are secured instead through statutes and well-established political tradition.

That many provisions for individual rights are subject to parliamentary enactment rather than constitutional enforcement points to another fundamental characteristic of Swedish legal principles: the law-making supremacy of the Riksdag. Even though the Instrument of Government allows for an independent Supreme Court and a Supreme Administrative Court, parliament exercises the ultimate authority, through constitutional amendment, to abolish the court system altogether. As this is an unreal prospect, Swedish courts enjoy in fact functional independence within the constitutional-statutory framework that defines their structure and competence. The principal empirical consequence of the legal supremacy of the Riksdag is that courts in Sweden, like those in Great Britain, possess no authority of judicial review. Proposed legislation concerning civil and criminal law must be submitted to a Law Council (*lagrådet*), which is composed of three members of the Supreme Court and one member of the Supreme Administration Court, for an advisory appraisal before it is formally introduced in the Riksdag. Other types of bills may also be referred to the Law Council at the cabinet's discretion. But opinions of the Law Council are not constitutionally binding, although they may exert a considerable effect on the ultimate

---

[9] Robert Malmgren, *Sveriges grundlagar och tillhörande författningar*, 8th ed. (Stockholm: P. A. Norstedt & Söners Förlag, 1964), p. 24.

decision by the parliament. As one student of Scandinavian politics has stated: "This means that Swedish citizens depend upon the Riksdag rather than upon the courts to maintain the constitutional guarantees. The remedy against abuse of legislative power, if such abuse should come in Sweden—though such an eventuality seems improbable—is found in the ballot box."[10]

COURT ORGANIZATION AND PROCEDURE

Sweden's contemporary court system dates from the judiciary act of 1734 which rationalized the existing local and appeals court structures. In 1789 the Supreme Court (*Högsta domstolen*) was established to assume appellate jurisdiction over inferior courts that had previously been exercised by the king and members of his advisory council. The Instrument of Government was amended in 1909 to create the Supreme Administrative Court (*Regeringsrätten*). During the twentieth century changes in the number of lesser courts and judicial procedures have been periodically implemented through statutory legislation and administrative decree.

Nearly 150 local courts (*underrätter*) exercise primary responsibility, measured by the number of cases, for administering Swedish justice. Of this figure 33 are classified as urban (*rådhusrätter*) and 115 as district (*häradsrätter*) courts. Presiding over judicial proceedings on the local level are chief magistrates (known as the *borgmästare* in the city courts and the *häradshövdning* in the district courts), who are trained jurists appointed by the king-in-council. They share their legal duties with associate and (in the larger cities) assistant judges, and are provided with a full-time professional staff. The number of associate judges ranges from 2 in most district courts to 73 in Stockholm.

Except in criminal libel cases, there are no jury trials in Sweden.[11] Instead a panel (*nämnd*) of at least 18 persons is elected by communal assemblies to serve six-year terms as lay judges in each of the urban and district courts. Larger cities may have 100 or more lay judges; Stockholm has 750. Their function is to preside over cases with the chief magistrate or one of his associates, hearing all evidence and directly participating in the

[10] Ben Arneson, *The Democratic Monarchies of Scandinavia* (New York: D. Van Nostrand Company, Inc., 1949), p. 168.

[11] In the case of criminal libel trials, a jury is chosen by lot from a panel of jurymen to determine the validity of a charge that "any printed matter is outside of protection afforded by the constitution. . . ." Arneson, p. 169.

court's decision. Each lay judge sits a minimum of 10 days a year in court and is usually reelected to office for consecutive terms, thus insuring continuity in the composition of the panels and the acquisition of considerable legal expertise among their members. In an overwhelming majority of cases the lay judges will concur in the chief magistrate's ruling; should they disagree a qualified majority (three out of four or seven out of nine) can vote to overrule him. Lay judges take part in all criminal and most civil law cases; a panel of three professional judges may decide civil suits of lesser importance.

Court proceedings are basically similar to those in the United States, with the presentation of evidence resting on the adversary system. Like court officials on the continent Swedish judges actively question witnesses and may call additional ones. All parties to a case are entitled to free counsel, provided by the state, if they are unable to attain legal advice on their own.

Over 95 percent of all litigation in Sweden is decided wholly on the local level. In 1966 urban and district courts ruled in 35,708 civil suits, with 61 percent of the cases involving judicial separation and divorce, and 113,284 criminal proceedings. The most prevalent types of criminal convictions were for public drunkenness (62,368) and theft (18,302). Sentences for acts of violence, in contrast, were relatively infrequent. Nearly 4000 persons were convicted for offenses against life and health—including 44 murders—and 1381 persons for resisting arrest.[12]

Six courts of appeal (*hovrätten*) comprise the intermediate echelon in the judicial system. The oldest is the Svea Court in Stockholm, founded in 1614; the newest are those in Sundsvall and Göteborg, established in 1948. The remaining courts of appeal are situated in Jönköping (1634), Malmö (1820), and Umeå (1936).

Like their professional counterparts in the local courts, judges in the courts of appeal are appointed by the king-in-council. There is no provision for lay judges. The courts of appeal are divided into two to ten chambers, each usually composed of five judges, that distribute the work of the court. Cases are decided by majority vote. In addition to their appellate function in reviewing cases appealed from the urban and district courts, the courts of appeal are responsible for administering the local court structure.

In 1966 the six courts of appeal agreed to hear 1602 civil

---

[12] *Statistisk årsbok 1968*, p. 306.

appeals and 3755 criminal appeals, which represented 4.4 percent and 3.3 percent of the civil and criminal cases, respectively, that had previously been decided on the local level. The courts also reviewed 2545 rulings from other types of courts such as military and specialized (for example, water rights) tribunals. They dismissed a total of 995 cases, ruled in 6854 instances, and postponed 2668 hearings to the following year.[13]

Assigned highest appellate jurisdiction over civil, criminal, and military cases is the Supreme Court in Stockholm. When the Court was created in 1779 the king was accorded the right to preside over its proceedings and to cast two votes. Swedish monarchs rarely took advantage of this prerogative, and in 1909 the king's membership on the Court was abolished. The king-in-council retains the right, however, to appoint its members. Composed today of 26 judges with the special title of *justitieråd*, the Supreme Court conducts its work in three chambers with seven justices in each chamber. As in the courts of appeal, decisions are reached by majority vote. The remaining members of the court serve on the Law Council.

The right to appeal decisions to the Supreme Court is shared by litigants in the courts of appeal, the ombudsmen, and the state prosecutor. In deciding whether to review cases the court utilizes procedures similar to the American practice of certiorari. Comparable to prevailing criteria in the United States, the usual grounds for granting an appeal are the judicial significance of a particular case and the continuing need to insure uniform application of the law. A special panel of three judges rules in most instances whether the court should accept an appeal. Only when a particular decision might depart from previous judgments must the justices meet as a body to deliberate the merits of a case.

Fewer than 1 percent of all civil criminal cases initially tried in the urban and district courts reach the Supreme Court for review. In 1966, for example, 323 civil and 640 criminal cases were appealed; an additional 299 appeals were granted in other areas of litigation. Out of 2435 cases and petitions that were filed during 1966 or were still pending from the previous year, the court reached a verdict on 1406, removed 41 from the case list, and postponed 895 until the following year.[14]

The legal counterpart to the Supreme Court for noncriminal or civil law suits (including controversies concerning the schools

13 *Statistisk årsbok 1968*, p. 300.
14 *Statistisk årsbok 1968*, p. 301.

and the church) is the Supreme Administrative Court. It consists of 17 judges, at least two thirds of whom must be professional jurists.[15] The remainder are recruited from the civil service. Cases are appealed to the Supreme Administrative Court through the administrative apparatus from local offices of the central boards and agencies or, in taxation matters, from the Fiscal Court (*Kammarrätten*).

Other legal structures of national significance are the Labor Court, which settles conflicts arising out of the interpretation and implementation of collective wage agreements; special water courts; and the office of the Chancellor of Justice. The Chancellor of Justice, whose position was established in 1713, is appointed by the cabinet to supervise the courts and administrative agencies on behalf of the national executive. Still sanctioned by the Instrument of Government is the Court of Impeachment (*Riksrätten*), which is authorized to try members of the cabinet on a motion of the Committee on the Constitution and would be composed of high-level judicial, military, and civil officials. The Court of Impeachment has not convened, however, since 1854.

All judges in Sweden, with the exception of a minority of the members of the Supreme Administrative Court and the representatives of the LO, SAF, and TCO on the Labor Court, must have completed a university legal education. Upon graduation judicial candidates are assigned by courts of appeal to preliminary service in the urban and district courts. Later they may become qualified clerks in a court of appeal. Promotions to assistant, associate, and presiding judgeships as well as the assignment of judges to specific courts are made by the king-in-council. Once an official has advanced to professional rank, he attains security of tenure and may be removed from office only through prescribed judicial procedures.[16] In case a judge is accused of misconduct in office, the Chancellor of Justice is charged with supervising his prosecution.

As members of one of Sweden's most venerated professions, judges enjoy high social status and popular confidence. By definition of the qualifications for appointment they are, as a group, well-educated and experienced jurists. At the beginning of 1970 all of the members of the Supreme Court, for example, possessed advanced legal degrees (one was a Doctor of Law) and had served an average of 29 years in the national court system.

[15] *RF*, art. 18.
[16] *RF*, art. 35.

THE OMBUDSMEN: CITIZENS' PROTECTORS

The best-known feature of the Swedish judicial system in Western legal and social science literature is the institution of the ombudsman (known officially as the *Justitieombudsman*). Elected by parliament with independent authority to insure the impartial administration of justice and implementation of public policy, the ombudsman has provided for the past 160 years an important guarantee for the protection of citizens' rights. The political significance of this function can be measured by both the increased work load of incumbents in Sweden and the widespread interest generated in the office abroad. In the twentieth century a number of countries, including Denmark, Norway, West Germany, New Zealand, and England, have established equivalent offices based on the Swedish model.[17]

Reaction against the absolutism of the late eighteenth century provided the immediate impetus for creating the position of ombudsman. Having deposed King Gustaf IV Adolf in the coup of 1809, the drafters of the new constitution were determined to prevent a possible reassertion of monarchical supremacy over the administration and parliament in the future. Dissatisfied with the power vested in the Chancellor of Justice, who was accountable to the executive, to investigate the nation's courts and administrative agencies, they incorporated into the Instrument of Government provisions for the ombudsman as a second control device. They justified their actions with the argument that "the courts and other officials would be less inclined to disregard the law in order to serve the wishes of the cabinet if the activities of the authorities were watched by a people's tribune who was independent of the government."[18]

From its inception the office proved an invaluable means to enforce judicial and administrative conformity with prevailing law.

---

[17] The jurisdiction of the ombudsmen in Denmark and Norway is roughly comparable to that of the Swedish ombudsmen, while the investigatory authority of the British and New Zealand ombudsmen is restricted to administrative procedures. The West German office deals exclusively with the military. For comparative data see Donald C. Rowat (ed.), *The Ombudsman* (London: George Allen & Unwin, Ltd., 1965) and Walter Gellhorn, *Ombudsmen and Others* (Cambridge, Mass.: Harvard University Press, 1966). A critical appraisal of the British ombudsman is contained in Douglas L. Capps, "The Citizen, Administration, and Politics in Post-Welfare Britain." in Hancock and Sjoberg (eds.), *Politics in the Post-Welfare State: Responses to the New Individualism* (New York: Columbia University Press, 1972).

[18] Bexelius, p. 11.

In the rural setting of early nineteenth-century Sweden "the activities of the [ombudsman] were primarily directed against unlawful constraints in personal liberties of various kinds. The annual reports describe a great number of actions against, for instance, undue constraints on liberty, or arrests insufficiently warranted, or false imprisonment."[19] With the growing complexity of administration as a consequence of modernization, one ombudsman no longer was able to manage the increased demands for investigation. Hence a second ombudsman for military questions (*Militieombudsman*) was created in 1915. The further expansion of the public administration during the modern era of welfare politics, which has been accompanied by a progressive broadening of the social context of the ombudsman's responsibilities, led in March 1968 to a second reorganization of the office. At that time the earlier distinction between an ombudsman for legal-administrative affairs and one for military supervision was abandoned and three ombudsmen were appointed, each with the title of *Justitieombudsman*.

Today, as under the original terms stipulated in the constitution, the ombudsmen are charged with general supervision of all judicial, administrative, and military personnel. Since 1957 communal authorities—though not the elected assemblies—have also been subject to their jurisdiction. The only public officials who are explicitly excluded from the ombudsmen's scrutiny are members of the cabinet (who are politically responsible to parliament) and the Chancellor of Justice.

Acting on the basis of written complaints from individual citizens, newspaper accounts, and their own annual investigation of case files throughout the country, the ombudsmen seek to determine whether public officials, "in the execution of their official duties, have, through partiality, favoritism, or other causes, committed any unlawful act or neglected to perform their official duties properly. Especially [the ombudsmen] shall take actions against faults causing general insecurity with regard to the rights of the citizens."[20] The functional responsibility for these supervisory tasks is distributed among the three ombudsmen as follows: the first is assigned responsibility for the judiciary, prosecutors, the police, and the military; the second for social welfare, including social insurance, building, planning, and the classification of documents for publicity; and the third for civil administration.

---

[19] Bexelius, p. 14.
[20] Bexelius, p. 11.

They are assisted by three deputy ombudsmen, one chief of staff, six chiefs of sections, four deputy chiefs, and a staff of 23 persons.[21] The courts and government agencies are required by the constitution and statutes to assist the ombudsmen in their investigations by providing them access to all documents, case records, and even secret minutes relating to a particular decision.

If evidence is found of illegal or improper conduct, the ombudsmen may order a legal prosecution against the offending official or admonish him for misconduct. When the ombudsmen discover that discrepancies or vagueness in the law are the cause of inconsistent behavior they may recommend statutory amendments or other action to the Riksdag or the king-in-council. Although most complaints are dismissed for lack of grounds to undertake official action, the ombudsmen initiate corrective steps in approximately 20 percent of the cases they review annually. The most frequent recourse is for the ombudsman to point out in writing to the public official—in from mild to harsh terms—how he might have erred in his judgment. Prosecutions are infrequent, numbering only about six a year. (See Table 21.)

Table 21   Activities of the Ombudsmen, 1961–1967[a]

Cases and Disposition	1961		1967	
	JO[b]	MO[c]	JO[b]	MO[c]
A. Pending and New Cases: Total	1320	777	2195	902
Pending at First of Year	240	78	337	132
New Cases	1080	699	1858	770
Complaints	983	72	1684	118
Submission by Government		21	2	8
Own Initiative	97	593	172	636
Internal Organization	NA	13	NA	8
B. Disposition				
Referred to Other Agencies	17		11	2
Dismissed	1576	271	2807	388
Prosecutions	7	6	6	6
Disciplinary Action			2	
Reported to King-in-Council	16	7	34	7
Admonition	208	220	288	241
Other		167		138
Postponed	278	113	447	129

[a]Adapted from *Statistisk årsbok 1968*, p. 302.
[b]Abbreviation for *Justitieombudsman* (judicial-administrative ombudsman).
[c]Abbreviation for *Militieombudsman* (military ombudsman).

21 Sweden, The Swedish Parliamentary Ombudsmen, *Annual Report for 1969* (summary in English) (Stockholm, 1970), p. 520. Hereafter referred to as *Annual Report*.

Contrary to misconceptions about the office, both in Sweden and abroad, the ombudsmen do not personally act to correct wrongs committed against individual citizens. That is, the competence of the ombudsmen "is limited to reasoned argument. [They] may not order an official to change a decision, nor can [they] intervene and reverse it."[22] As Alfred Bexelius, a recently retired ombudsman, has observed:

> When [the ombudsman] is said to be the citizens' protector, the citizens are thought of in the plural number. You might rather say that he is supposed to be the protector of the public. Accordingly he has to act more on a general, abstract level than on an individual, concrete level. Cynically expressed, the complaints and the observations that are made in individual cases are used not so much to help the aggrieved person but more to support actions that aim at improvements of general nature.[23]

In isolated cases, however, an ombudsman may actively assist a person who has suffered damages from a wrong decision by supporting his claim for appeal or compensation.

Attesting to the importance of the ombudsman office are the professional qualifications of the incumbents. Since the middle of the nineteenth century elections of successive ombudsmen have been eliminated as an area of partisan conflict, with all parties in the Riksdag endeavoring to select men of demonstrated experience and skill on a unanimous basis.[24] Bexelius, who retired after 14 years of service as ombudsman in 1970, is a case in point. After passing his bar examination in Stockholm in 1928, he served first as a clerk and then as a judge, until his appointment as president of one of the chambers in the Sundsvall Court of Appeals in 1948. Six years later Bexelius was named chairman of the Freedom of Commerce Board, an administrative council made up of nine members selected by the king-in-council to investigate trusts and monopolies. He was elected deputy ombudsman in 1949 and to his first terms as ombudsman in 1956.

---

[22] *Annual Report*, p. 520.

[23] Alfred Bexelius, "Democratic Control in Sweden," a lecture delivered at universities in the United States in May 1970, p. 9. (Mimeographed.)

[24] Nils Herlitz writes that after 1865 the election of the ombudsman became "to a decreasing degree an expression of the political viewpoint of a parliamentary majority; in general [the position] was filled by civil servants without pronounced partisan views." Herlitz, *Grunddragen av det svenska statskickets historia*, 5th ed. (Stockholm: Norstedts, 1959), p. 250.

LAW AND SOCIAL CHANGE

The increase in the number of cases that come to the ombudsmen's attention each year is indicative of the changing role of law in contemporary Swedish society. In the early part of the twentieth century the ombudsman reviewed an annual average of only 100 instances of alleged misconduct among public officials; by 1956 the number had risen to 550. In 1967, as indicated in Table 21, the judicial-administrative ombudsman alone received 1858 new cases.

The underlying cause for this spiraling trend is the growth of the welfare state. Collectivist action to attain full economic productivity and socioeconomic security has led to a proliferation of government agencies and statutory and administrative regulations. Accordingly the ombudsmen must supervise an increasingly complex legal-administrative structure, as well as act to help clarify the meaning of new legislation in its practical implementation. Simultaneously the necessity for compliance with the expanding domain of law has imposed unprecedented obligations on the state and individual citizens alike. "This creates a need for protection against . . . officials' neglect of their duties defined by law and . . . private sacrifices on behalf of such interests as, for instance, town and country planning, communications, and public health. The need for protection is apparent [in both cases.]"[25]

As an instrument of social change, law has therefore contributed to the intensified activity of Sweden's ombudsmen by extending the domain of their responsibilities. At the same time the dissemination of new forms of critical consciousness associated with the rise of radical liberalism and the New Left has added additional demands on their services. In one year—from 1968 to 1969—the number of cases filed with the ombudsmen increased 25 percent, rising to 3128. Of this total 2708 were complaints submitted by individual citizens and 393 were investigations undertaken by the ombudsmen on their own initiative.[26] In commenting on this acceleration, the ombudsmen observed in their annual report to parliament in 1969:

> In an "active society" pressure groups as well as socially committed individuals are inclined to try all means of influencing the

[25] Bexelius, "The Origin, Nature, and Functions of the Civil and Military Ombudsmen in Sweden," p. 14.
[26] *Annual Report*, p. 521.

social processes. It is not astonishing that they should also try lodging complaints with the ombudsmen. It is symptomatic that political youth leagues have written to the ombudsmen during 1969 much more often than in any previous year. As in 1968 private persons have also sent newspaper articles to the ombudsmen and asked for investigations to an extent hitherto unknown.[27]

The role of the ombudsmen in reconciling the diverse claims of the state, particular groups, and individuals in what Mendelson describes as "the endless sequence of acommodations that we call civilization"[28] is a crucial one. They offer no panacea for maintaining an equitable balance between opposing forces of collective and individual control in modern Swedish welfare society. Their only recourse is to prevailing law; they can displace neither those responsible for framing the law nor those responsible for enforcing and administering it. But as Bexelius has written: "The mere existence of an office, independent of the bureaucracy, to which anybody can carry his complaints, will act to sharpen the attention of the authorities in preparing their cases, and to counteract tendencies toward abuse of power and arbitrary decisions."[29]

[27] *Annual Report*, p. 522.
[28] Mendelson, p. 235.
[29] Bexelius, "The Origin, Nature, and Functions of the Civil and Military Ombudsmen in Sweden," p. 16.

TEN
ACTIVE NEUTRALITY AND REGIONAL COOPERATION
Sweden and Scandinavia in world affairs

Expressing the strategic, economic, and political interests of a small nation that has escaped armed conflict for nearly 160 years and is highly dependent on international trade, Sweden's foreign relations embrace dual traditions of military neutrality and regional cooperation. Continuity in form and consensus on substance are principal characteristics of both tenets of Swedish foreign policy. During the postwar period the practice of neutrality and the prospects of cooperation have undergone revision in response to new factors of domestic and international politics, raising important questions concerning the future of Sweden's role in world affairs.

NATIONAL IDENTITY AND POLICY FORMATION

Once a major European power with an empire that included Finland and most of the Baltic coastline, Sweden was reduced to her present national boundaries as a consequence of the Great Northern War in 1709–1721, the Russian conquest of Finland in 1808–1809, and the dissolution of the Swedish-Norwegian Union in 1905. Unlike seafaring nations on the western periphery of Europe, Sweden never acquired far-flung colonial possessions. The early loss of empire, combined with the geographic insularity

241

of the nation, resulted in a limited perspective on foreign relations. Throughout the formative decades of modern Swedish history, domestic leaders were primarily preoccupied with internal affairs, seeking in their relations with the stronger Baltic powers of Russia and Germany to avoid involvement in war.

The success of Sweden's policies during the nineteenth and twentieth centuries has decisively influenced the sense of national identity among contemporary decision makers in relation to the international system. The vindication of neutrality spared Sweden the ignominy of national defeat and diminished territories that contributed to the assertion of militant nationalism throughout much of continental Europe. In a positive sense, the uninterrupted legacy of peace since 1814 has engendered a shared determination among policy elites to minimize national risks and promote peace-keeping operations when conflicts occur elsewhere.

Underlying national perspectives on foreign affairs is a widely diffused consciousness of regional affinity with Denmark, Norway, and Finland. From the Viking era through the Kalmar Union to the dynastical conflicts of the Middle Ages, the four Nordic countries shared a common historical heritage. The revolutions and wars of the past century and a half affected each of the Scandinavian states differently, thus accentuating distinctive qualities of nationality and foreign policy orientations. Yet basic similarities in culture, religion, legal-political systems, patterns of international trade, and (with the exception of Finland) language provide a natural basis for regional identity and cooperation. Hence political elites in Sweden, like their counterparts throughout the rest of Scandinavia, are predisposed to appraise their foreign policy goals in light of the requirements of the region as a whole.

Because of the consensual norms governing international attitudes among Swedish leaders, "foreign policy . . . has by and large been lifted above party strife; that is to say, it has to a large extent become common to all parties."[1] Although the cabinet exercises the leading role in policy initiatives, most issues are resolved through four-party consultations in informal party leadership conferences and the Riksdag's Advisory Council on Foreign Affairs. As a result, substantive foreign policy debates rarely occur in parliament or during electoral campaigns. Occasionally party

---

[1] Elis Håstad, "Sweden's Attitude toward the United Nations," in Swedish Institute of International Affairs, *Sweden and the United Nations* (New York: Manhattan Publishing Company, 1956), p. 13.

spokesmen have differed on specific policy proposals, as when the Social Democrats attempted in the face of nonsocialist opposition to reduce annual increases in the rate of military expenditures in 1966, but such conflicts are seldom.

THE PRACTICE OF NEUTRALITY

Elite consensus on neutrality as a basic principle of Swedish foreign policy does not imply national passivity. From a military point of view, the objective of neutrality is "to keep Sweden out of the 'cold war' and to maintain that freedom of action which Sweden in its exposed position has good cause to safeguard. It is then a program for peacetime; but also a program for policy in a crisis. It is directed toward maintaining the right and the prospects of keeping the country out of a new conflict between the world powers."[2]

The goals of Swedish neutrality thus resemble those of the other European neutral states. Unlike that of Finland and Austria, however, Sweden's neutral status is not enforced or guaranteed by international treaties. Similar to the role of Switzerland in international politics, Swedish neutrality is sustained by the force of national tradition.

An essential support for Sweden's policy of neutrality is the maintenance of sufficient military strength to deter possible attack in wartime. "Success or failure in securing its own demands or in resisting the demands of other states is the test of the power position of any state," Annette Baker Fox has observed. "In the case of the small powers, it has historically been the latter, the capacity to resist great-power demands, which has been the more important in defining their power status."[3] Cognizant that such capacity includes a nation's ability to make armed invasion sufficiently costly to discourage a would-be aggressor, Sweden's leaders have thus invested throughout the twentieth century in a strong national defense. During World War I and again in 1936 Sweden initiated extensive armament programs, with the latter efforts presumably influencing Hitler's decision not to invade Sweden when Denmark and Norway were occupied in World War II.

Today Sweden spends 4.0 percent of her gross national

[2] Håstad, p. 5.
[3] Annette Baker Fox, *The Power of Small States* (Chicago: University of Chicago Press, 1959), p. 3.

product on defense—a lesser percentage than Great Britain, Portugal, and France but greater than the remaining countries in Western Europe as well as most of those in Eastern Europe—and possesses one of the best-equipped and largest standing armies (in relation to total population) of any European nation.[4] Armaments include a naval fleet of 114 vessels, 39 air force squadrons, Sidewinder and Falcon air-to-air missiles, and an assortment of Swedish-manufactured air-to-surface missiles, jet fighters, and turretless tanks. Air defense consists of a "fully computerized and automatic control and air surveillance system, with which all components of the Swedish air defence are coordinated."[5] In addition Sweden has constructed an elaborate network of underground harbors, weaponry depots, and radar stations, which are invulnerable to conventional and all but direct nuclear attacks, in the Stockholm archipelago. Although Sweden does not possess nuclear weapons, Swedish scientists and military officials have conducted extensive research since the late 1950s on problems of atomic defense that could be utilized to develop a national nuclear capability if future policy needs dictate such a choice.

All Swedish males are subject to conscription, and are required to serve at least nine months active duty in the armed forces. In 1970 Sweden claimed a standing military force of 82,000 men, which represented a military-population ratio of 1:98. (In comparison the ratio of standing military strength to general population was 1:129 in West Germany, 1:143 in Great Britain, and 1:100 in France. With its citizens-in-arms military system, Switzerland can mobilize the highest ratio in all of Europe —1:9.) In case of a national emergency, Sweden could mobilize 627,500 persons and an organized voluntary defense force of 1,000,000.[6]

Swedish neutrality dates from the changed military-political alignment in Europe following the Napoleonic wars. Confronting a new continental hegemony sanctioned by the Congress of Vienna (1814–1815) and dominated by the five major powers that comprised the Concert of Europe, Sweden's leaders withdrew from active participation in European affairs. Even during the Prussian-Austrian attack against Denmark in 1864 to gain control

[4] Institute for Strategic Studies, *The Military Balance 1970–1971* (London: Institute for Strategic Studies, 1970), p. 110.

[5] *The Military Balance*, pp. 35–36.

[6] *The Military Balance*, pp. 35–36 and 112, and Institute for Strategic Studies, *The Military Balance 1966–1967* (London: Institute for Strategic Studies, 1966), p. 40.

of the German provinces of Schleswig-Holstein, Sweden did not depart from a neutral stance. Neutrality became regionalized with the outbreak of World War I when Sweden and Norway agreed "that they would under no circumstances permit the war in Europe to precipitate any hostile acts between the two countries. The agreement, which was also accepted by Denmark, established— for all practical purposes—a neutral entente of the North."[7] Finland similarly adopted a foreign policy of neutrality following her declaration of independence from Russia in December 1917.

All four Nordic countries modified their neutral status in the early 1920s by joining the League of Nations. When it became clear that the League was incapable of maintaining international peace, Scandinavian leaders asserted in 1936 that they no longer considered themselves bound by the League's provisions concerning automatic sanctions against aggressor nations. Two years later the Scandinavian countries issued a joint declaration of neutrality, but were unable to agree on positive steps to coordinate their defense policies in case of war. As a result each of them was forced to confront the impending Europeen conflagration in national isolation. Finland was attacked by Russia during the Winter War of 1939–1940, concluded an armistice in 1940, and attacked Russia in turn as a co-belligerent with Germany in 1941. To diminish British influence in the North Sea and to safeguard iron ore shipments from northern Sweden, Nazi Germany invaded Denmark and Norway in 1940. Surrounded on two sides by the occupation forces of the Third Reich, Swedish authorities were compelled to modify their neutrality policies by acceding to German demands to transport soldiers across Swedish territory between Norway and Germany. The agreement was terminated in 1943, when Nazi military supremacy in Europe began to wane. Subsequently the Swedes openly supported their beleagured Scandinavian neighbors, providing them humanitarian aid and training refugees for future "police service" in Norway and Denmark.[8]

The end of World War II marked an important turning point in Scandinavian foreign policies. Initially the four states simultaneously reaffirmed their determination to avoid military alliances and endorsed collective security as the best means to manage international conflict. Thus Denmark and Norway joined the United Nations as charter members in 1945, while Sweden be-

---

[7] John H. Wuorinen, *Scandinavia* (Englewood Cliffs, N.J.: Prentice-Hall, Inc., 1965), p. 32.

[8] Nils Andrén, *Power-Balance and Non-Alignment* (Stockholm: Almqvist & Wiksell, 1967), pp. 32–33.

came a member in 1946. But the deepening chasm between East and West quickly dispelled early hopes among Scandinavian leaders that the United Nations would suffice to guarantee world peace. By 1947 Allied discord over occupation policies in Germany, tightened Stalinist control over Eastern Europe, and Western countermoves such as the proclamation of the Truman Doctrine unequivocally signaled the dissolution of the wartime coalition among the major powers. Caught squarely in the middle of the emerging polarization of Europe, the Scandinavian states were compelled to reevaluate their strategic position.

Two policy choices emerged in the intensive debate on foreign policy that ensued in Scandinavia. The Norwegian response was that the Nordic countries should align themselves with the West. In Sweden several Liberal and Conservative newspapers strongly supported the Norwegian attitude, but party leaders rejected such a move. Instead the Swedish government suggested in January 1948 an alternative plan that would have meant the abandonment of the nation's traditional policy of freedom from alliances: the creation of a Scandinavian defense community. According to the draft treaty, the Nordic countries would remain neutral in case of war but would come to the assistance of any Scandinavian nation that was attacked by a third state.[9] An essential aspect of the proposal was that a Scandinavian alliance must remain independent of any formal or informal ties with any of the major powers. Motivating Sweden's insistence on continued Scandinavian neutrality was the concern that regional militancy allegiance with the West might induce the Soviet Union to move against Finland.

Norway and Denmark proved receptive to the Swedish initiative, but Finland was enjoined from participating in exploratory talks because of Soviet opposition. Vulnerable to Soviet policy dictates under terms of the armistice agreement of 1946, which imposed heavy war indemnity obligations on Finland and legitimized the transfer of more than one tenth of Finland's prewar territory to the Soviet Union, Finnish leaders were in no position to jeopardize their already precarious relations with the Russians. Therefore consultations on the proposed Scandinavian alliance were limited to the three western Scandinavian states.

The urgency to reach a decision on the possible reorientation of Scandinavian foreign policies was underscored by the escalation of the Cold War. The Czech coup in February 1948 extended

9 Andrén, *Power-Balance and Non-Alignment*, pp. 57 and 69–70.

Stalinist domination in Eastern Europe, while the formation of the Brussels Treaty Organization a month later signaled the incipient consolidation of the Western bloc. Under pressure from Moscow, Finland agreed in April to sign a treaty of "friendship, cooperation, and mutual assistance" with the Soviet Union that pledged both signatories to consult on common military action in case of a threat to either state from Germany or any of Germany's allies. In addition Finland was required to resist with arms any attack against Finland or through Finland against the Soviet Union.[10]

In this atmosphere of growing tension representatives from Sweden, Norway, and Denmark met repeatedly throughout 1948 in an attempt to reach agreement on a common Scandinavian policy. But from the beginning the cleavage between Norwegian and Swedish views proved unbridgeable. The Norwegians insisted that a Scandinavian defense alliance would be too weak to maintain itself without military assistance from the West. Equally adamant the Swedes argued that "a Scandinavian alliance would be an acceptable solution of the Swedish security problem only if it would be free in relation to the great-power blocs. . . ."[11] The Norwegian-Swedish impasse was finally broken when the United States announced that priority in armaments would be accorded members of the North Atlantic Treaty Organization, which was in the process of formation. Norway decided it would accept the American conditions; Sweden resolved that it could not. Consequently the three Nordic countries announced the failure of their joint defense consultations in January 1949. Norway and Denmark then joined NATO, while Sweden retained her neutral status.

As a result of deliberate policy choice, dictated by the force of tradition and consideration of Finland's special relations with the Soviet Union, neutrality was therefore preserved as a fundamental principle of Swedish foreign policy into the postwar era. In subsequent decades Sweden has continued to pursue a policy of nonalignment, circumspectly avoiding any steps that might provoke Soviet retaliation against Finland. For their part Norway and Denmark have also sought to dampen the effect of the Cold War in Scandinavia by refusing to allow foreign troops or nuclear weapons to be stationed under NATO aegis on their soil.

Despite differences in the foreign policy alignments among

[10] Max Jakobsen, *Finnish Neutrality* (London: Hugh Evelyn, Ltd., 1968), pp. 33–44.

[11] Government message to parliament on February 9, 1949, reprinted in Andrén, *Power-Balance and Non-Alignment*, p. 68.

the Nordic countries, the four nations have largely succeeded, Sweden and Finland through neutrality, Norway and Denmark through low-key defense postures within the Atlantic alliance, in assuaging much of Russia's apprehension that Scandinavia posed a potential military threat to the Soviet Union. In 1955 Soviet leaders agreed to terminate their lease of the Porkkala peninsula in Finland and evacuate the naval base they had established there in 1944 (only 12 miles from the Finnish capital of Helsinki).[12] Finland remains susceptible to Soviet policy restraints, as indicated below, but not to the total exclusion of participation in regional Scandinavian cooperation.

INTERNATIONAL ACTIVISM

Defined historically as freedom from alliance, Swedish neutrality has assumed a second dimension that reflects a changing self-image among national decision makers. As former Prime Minister Erlander has said: "An exhaustive description of Swedish foreign policy . . . is not that it is [only] a system to reduce the strategic interest of the great powers to involve us in a possible war. Its aim, while paying regard to international solidarity, is just as much to preserve our national interests in peace time and, in addition, to put us in a position to contribute towards the peaceful development of the world."[13]

Implied in Erlander's statement is the justification of an activist form of neutrality. In more explicit terms, the government declared in a message to parliament in February 1949: "A usual misconception is . . . that a neutrality programme means a duty to 'spiritual neutrality'. . . . Neutrality as a political concept and as a concept of international law does not mean that a nation desists from the right of its citizens to participate in debates on international questions or to speak up on behalf of democracy and liberty."[14]

Although individual political spokesmen and journalists have seldom felt themselves constrained in passing judgment on international trends throughout modern Swedish history, the assertion of international activism as official government policy is basically a postwar phenomenon. Its cause lies in the rise of a new genera-

---

[12] Jakobsen, pp. 45–47.
[13] Quoted in Andrén, *Power-Balance and Non-Alignment*, p. 125.
[14] Andrén, *Power-Balance and Non-Alignment*, p. 71.

tion of leaders whose values were decisively influenced by the nation's witness of totalitarianism and war during the 1930s and 1940s. Acting out of idealism born of the conviction that Sweden —by virtue of its neutral status—can usefully promote international peace, officials have assumed an initiating role in postwar world affairs that contrast sharply with past reticence in Swedish foreign relations. "The traditional idea of Sweden's attitude to international events . . . as one of not having any foreign policy at all," Andrén comments, "seems to be definitely and absolutely obsolete."[15] Translated into specific policies, Sweden's new activism has taken various forms, ranging from strong support for United Nations peace-keeping operations and international economic cooperation to outspoken criticism of the domestic and foreign policies of other nations.

Within the United Nations Sweden has emerged as a leading advocate of collective security measures and international efforts to sustain the right of national self-determination. Thus Swedish representatives endorsed United Nations operations in South Korea in 1950, supported the resolution of the General Assembly in urging the withdrawal of Soviet troops from Hungary in 1956, and contributed volunteer soldiers and economic assistance to United Nations programs in the Middle East in 1956, the Congo in 1960, and Cyprus in 1963. Sweden has also repeatedly affirmed a positive role by the United Nations in exerting collective pressure to end colonization and apartheid practices in Africa. In 1967, for example, Sweden broke off diplomatic relations with Rhodesia, urged the British government in 1968 to intervene to countermand the Rhodesian declaration of independence, and "demanded that UN sanctions [against the Smith regime] should be made total and effective."[16]

As a neutral nation, Sweden, like the most eminent Swedish spokesman at the United Nations, former Secretary-General Dag Hammarskjöld, consistently opposed the subordination of the United Nations to narrow bloc interests. "In this respect Sweden shares the opinion expressed by British representatives at the Security Council that it is important to preserve the universal character of the United Nations and not to convert the Organization into an anti-communist alliance, because it is essential to keep the United Nations in reserve as a forum where both sides can meet

[15] Andrén, *Power-Balance and Non-Alignment*, p. 9.
[16] Sweden, Royal Ministry for Foreign Affairs, *Documents on Swedish Foreign Policy 1968* (Stockholm: Utrikesdepartementet, 1969), p. 105. Hereafter referred to as *Documents*.

and where from time to time agreements can be reached that will reduce international tensions."[17] Accordingly Sweden resisted the policy of the major powers during the first decade of the United Nations' existence to exclude states that were identified with either the Eastern or Western blocs and has espoused the membership of Mainland China since the early 1950s.

A corollary to Sweden's assertive stance in the United Nations is Swedish policy on questions of international disarmament. Highly critical of the postwar arms race, Sweden has utilized unilateral diplomatic initiatives and participation in international forums to advocate the cessation of nuclear tests and the attainment of effective controls over the use of nuclear energy. In 1961 Foreign Minister Undén proposed that the nonnuclear states jointly declare their willingness to honor a test-ban treaty in an attempt to induce the nuclear powers to negotiate such a settlement. After a treaty prohibiting nuclear tests in the atmosphere was signed in Moscow in 1963, Sweden, as a member of the Eighteen Nation Disarmament Commission in Geneva, proceeded to press for early agreement on even more comprehensive arms control measures.

Endorsing in principle a draft treaty on nuclear nonproliferation that was submitted to the Commission by the United States and the Soviet Union in 1967, Swedish Ambassador Alva Myrdal submitted a series of amendments that would have significantly strengthened the document. Specifically she moved that the major powers permit the International Atomic Energy Agency to supervise their peaceful uses of atomic energy and that "all transfers of fissionable material between states [be banned] unless the material was subject to international safeguards relating to peaceful uses."[18] Even though the United States, the Soviet Union, and Britain did not fully accept the Swedish provisions, Sweden hailed the final treaty as a contribution "towards international stability [that should] facilitate further measures aimed at calling a halt to the arms race without delay and at disarmament in the nuclear field."[19] In subsequent sessions of the United Nations General Assembly and the Disarmament Commission, Sweden has urged that such steps include a ban on underground tests, direct negotiations between the United States and the Soviet Union to restrict their development of intercontinental ballistic missiles, and inter-

[17] Håstad, p. 7.
[18] *Documents*, p. 89.
[19] *Documents*, p. 96.

national studies to determine the effects of biological and chemical weapons.[20]

Parallel with national efforts to support peace-keeping operations and nuclear disarmament under auspices of the United Nations, Sweden has channeled an increasing flow of economic assistance to developing countries through multilateral agencies. Between 1963 and 1967 Swedish foreign aid more than doubled in volume, rising from $23,300 million to $59,854 million. Of these totals multilateral assistance, which was allocated primarily to the United Nations Development Program, UNICEF, and the World Food Program, amounted to $16,100 million and $33,768 million in 1963 and 1967, respectively.[21] Direct development aid includes grants and credits to such countries as Ethiopia, India, Kenya, Pakistan, Tanzania, and Tunisia. In addition Sweden awarded 278 fellowships in 1967, most of them to Africans and Asians, for study at Swedish universities.[22] Replying to domestic agitation that Sweden was morally obligated to provide even greater amounts of economic assistance, Foreign Minister Nilsson announced in the Riksdag on May 23, 1968, that the government plans to increase foreign aid to 1 percent of the gross national product by the fiscal year 1974–1975.[23]

Sweden's international activism is also manifest in official criticism of domestic and foreign policies that, in the Swedish view, violate human rights and the independence of other states. In September 1967 Sweden joined the other Scandinavian countries in protesting to the Council of Europe that the military junta in Greece had transgressed the European Human Rights Convention through unlawful imprisonment and torture of opponents to the regime. The Commission invited the Nordic states and Holland "to present written memorials on the merits of the case,"[24] which were submitted in March 1968. Rather than yield to the pressure exerted principally by the Scandinavian members of the Council to modify its domestic policies, Greece withdrew from the Council of Europe in 1970.

Similarly Sweden rebuked the Soviet Union for its occupation of Czechoslovakia in August 1968. In a cabinet statement on August 21, the government asserted: "We have been following with the deepest sympathy the development towards greater free-

[20] *Documents*, p. 99.
[21] *Statistisk årsbok 1968*, p. 384.
[22] *Statistisk årsbok 1968*, p. 150.
[23] *Documents*, p. 219.
[24] *Documents*, p. 150.

dom in Czechoslovakia. We, too, have hoped for a happy outcome for this development, which could have also helped to bring the peoples of Eastern and Western Europe nearer together. It is now to be feared that the existing trend leading towards a *detente* will be halted and that the international situation will again deteriorate."[25] In a speech the same day, Foreign Minister Nilsson described the Soviet action as a "political tragedy" and a "shattering defeat for freedom and the forces of democracy." He added: "But even more profoundly it is a still greater defeat for the whole social system which the Communist movement for half of a century has claimed to be a higher stage in the development of humanity and superior to parliamentary democracy, which it has combated either openly or clandestinely."[26]

The most controversial aspect of Swedish international activism, from the American perspective, is the government's condemnation of United States military involvement in Southeast Asia. Initially Sweden had in effect supported Western policies in Southeast Asia, voting in 1957 in favor of admitting both South Vietnam and South Korea to the United Nations. Three years later Sweden established diplomatic relations with South Vietnam, appointing the Swedish ambassador in Bangkok to serve in a double capacity as envoy to Saigon. But with the escalation of the Vietnamese conflict and in response to a rising wave of protests against the war among Swedish youth and intellectuals, the government's attitude began to change. In December 1965 the Swedish ambassador to Peking undertook the first of a subsequent series of regular visits to North Vietnam, while Swedish officials established direct contracts with members of the National Liberation Front delegation in Algiers. In 1967 Sweden suspended relations with South Vietnam, choosing not to extend the dual accreditation of the new Swedish ambassador in Thailand to the South Vietnamese capital. At the same time the North Vietnamese ambassador to Moscow was invited to Stockholm for consultations at the Foreign Ministry. According to cabinet-level statements, the purpose of such moves was to mitigate the diplomatic isolation of North Vietnam and to facilitate indirect communications between Hanoi and Washington about possible means to arrange a peaceful settlement. As Nilsson informed members of the lower house of parliament in April 1968: "The principal aim of the steps we have taken has been to create a serviceable chan-

---

25 *Documents*, p. 179.
26 *Documents*, p. 180.

nel for conversations between the parties. We have believed that it was in their interest to be kept informed of each other's viewpoints through a neutral country."[27]

Publicly Sweden became increasingly vocal in its opposition to American policies, demanding an end to bombing raids over North Vietnam as a condition for peace negotiations. Underlying the Swedish attitude was the growing conviction that American support for the South Vietnamese government was based on fundamental misconceptions about the nature of the conflict. As Olof Palme, who was then Minister of Communications, declared in a speech on February 21, 1968:

> Democracy is a demanding form of government. It demands respect for others. A form of government cannot be forced upon a nation from outside. A people must be left to shape its own future.
>
> Democracy therefore presupposes a right to national self-determination.
>
> Democracy demands justice. A people cannot be won over by filling the pockets of the haves while the have-nots sink deeper down into destitution. Demands for social justice cannot be met by force and military means. . . .
>
> The fighting of the last few weeks has shown opinion all over the world that the Vietnam war is a revolt against those who are suppressing fundamental social and human rights. This revolt is a social movement, with its roots deep in the popular consciousness. If this revolt had not in essence had the support of the people the attacks on the towns all over South Vietnam could not have been carried out with such success. . . .
>
> On what grounds can we deny the Vietnamese people the right to choose their own regime? The mission of democracy cannot be to become the watchdog for other peoples. Such an interpretation would on the contrary mean the abuse of the fundamental ideas of democracy.[28]

When President Lyndon Johnson announced in October 1968 that air attacks against North Vietnam would cease, the Swedish government greeted the decision "with profound satisfaction." Nilsson said: "In view of the indications of the importance of a halt to the bombing that have been apparent in the past, we are convinced that a significant step has now been taken on the way to negotiations that can bring the Vietnam conflict to an

---

[27] *Documents,* p. 139.
[28] *Documents,* pp. 122–126.

end."[29] Given the fact that the United States had implicitly recognized North Vietnam and the NLF at the Paris peace talks, Sweden then established formal diplomatic relations with the Hanoi regime in January 1969. Simultaneously Sweden intensified its program of public and private humanitarian assistance to Vietnam. Beginning with an initial sum of $11,000 that was distributed among the three combatants in 1965, Swedish aid increased to $130,000 in 1968—more than half of which was allocated North Vietnam and the NLF.[30] At the twenty-fourth congress of the Social Democratic party in September 1969, Nilsson proclaimed the government's intention to provide the North Vietnamese $40 million in aid over a three-year period.[31]

The immediate effect of Sweden's activist Vietnam policy was a deterioration of official American-Swedish relations. Ambassador William Heath was recalled to Washington for five weeks in March 1968 in protest against Palme's participation in an antiwar demonstration in company with a North Vietnamese representative. When Heath resigned January 1969, the Nixon administration delayed a year before appointing his successor. Contributing to Washington's annoyance was the presence of over 275 American deserters in Sweden.

Following Nilsson's promise of expanded economic assistance to North Vietnam, the United States indicated that it contemplated financial reprisals against Sweden. Officials of the Export-Import Bank indicated that an application by the Scandinavian Airlines System for a loan to finance the purchase of new equipment might be denied, while American firms reputedly cancelled orders totaling $57 million from Swedish companies.[32]

Confronted with increasing concern among Swedish businessmen about the effects of such reprisals on the domestic economy, the new Swedish cabinet—headed by Palme—responded by adopting a more subdued course on the Vietnamese issue. Nilsson qualified his earlier remarks by saying that the projected increase in aid to North Vietnam would begin only after the end of hostilities. Moreover, he expressed hopes that the assistance program would be extended to South Vietnam as well.[33] Mollified by these reassurances, the United States relaxed its overt pressure on Sweden. The most important symbolic gesture of a gradual recon-

[29] *Documents*, p. 148.
[30] *Documents*, p. 135.
[31] *The New York Times*, October 14, 1969, p. 11.
[32] *The New York Times*, October 14, 1969, p. 11, and October 19, 1970.
[33] *The New York Times*, October 19, 1970.

ciliation was the appointment of a new ambassador, Jerome Holland, to Stockholm in January 1970.

Sweden's policy of international activism has thus achieved mixed results. In situations where arms, material, and technical expertise have contributed direct supports to international peace keeping and enforcement activities, Sweden has been able to play a positive role in international affairs. Likewise mediation efforts, such as the transmission of information between the United States and North Vietnam, have yielded discernible if limited effects on international relations. Attempts by Sweden to modify the behavior of the major powers, however, have proved futile. Nevertheless such actions as Sweden's denunciation of Soviet policies in Czechoslovakia and the war in Vietnam have demonstrated the nation's determination to assert an independent stand on world events that adds credence to its neutrality and expresses the hope that "the language of power"[34] will become less strident.

REGIONALISM, EFTA, AND THE EEC

Militarily neutral and politically activist in the international system, Sweden is concurrently a full participant in processes of regional cooperation. Factors of Scandinavian cultural and political affinity, noted above, have facilitated the progressive coordination of domestic policies that has occurred among the Nordic countries since the beginning of the twentieth century. Closely linked with other Western European nations through membership in the Council of Europe and the European Free Trade Association, Scandinavia confronted at the beginning of the 1970s a series of foreign policy choices that will inevitably affect the prospects of future regional cooperation.

The historical impetus for institutionalized forms of Scandinavian regionalism was provided by the dissolution of the Swedish-Norwegian Union in 1905. Although an idealistic vision of a common Nordic identity had emerged in the form of a pan-Scandinavian movement in the mid-nineteenth century,[35] Danish-Swedish antipathy and Norwegian resentment of Swedish domination within the Union perpetuated regional disunity. With the attainment of Norwegian independence a major obstacle to cooperation among the Scandinavian states was overcome. On the basis of

[34] Speech by Alva Myrdal at a university church service in Stockholm on January 19, 1968. Reprinted in *Documents*, p. 10.
[35] Wuorinen, p. 125.

national equality, Scandinavian leaders initiated multiple efforts to coordinate their domestic and foreign policies.

The first step in the process of regional cooperation was the creation of the Nordic Interparliamentary Union (NIPU) in 1907, which was established as an autonomous organization for regular consultations among members of the three legislative assemblies within the larger Interparliamentary Union. An important display of external unity was subsequently achieved when the Scandinavian monarchs met for the first time in 1914. A second regional forum was instituted in 1919 with the formation of the Norden Society. Composed of economic, cultural, business, and political leaders in each of the countries, the Norden Society is organized in national chapters whose purpose is to promote cultural exchanges and better understanding of the other Scandinavian states. By 1957 the Society claimed a membership of 120,000.[36] During the interwar period—with the addition of Finland and Iceland to the NIPU and the Norden Society—cooperation was intensified in a number of policy areas. The Scandinavian countries coordinated many of their legal and social policies, collaborated extensively within the League of Nations, and established in 1934 a Nordic Postal Union and special Delegations for the Promotion of Economic Cooperation.[37] Growing regional solidarity was also demonstrated by the peaceful settlement of two territorial disputes within Scandinavia: Sweden accepted the verdict of an international arbitration commission in 1921 that the Åland Islands, located just outside the Stockholm archipelago in the Baltic, rightfully belonged to Finland, while Norway conceded Danish claims to Greenland in 1933.

After World War II the Scandinavian states embarked on even more comprehensive programs of regional cooperation. As recipients of Marshall Plan assistance, Sweden, Norway, Denmark, and Iceland joined the Organization for European Economic Cooperation (OEEC) in 1947 to help further postwar economic recovery and the liberalization of trade. The following year Sweden, Norway, and Denmark formed a Joint Scandinavian Committee for Economic Cooperation to consider the feasibility of special tariff reductions within Scandinavia and agreement on a common external tariff on imports form non-Nordic countries.

---

[36] Stanley V. Anderson, *The Nordic Council* (Seattle, Wash.: University of Washington Press, 1967), p. 142.
[37] Wuorinen, p. 126.

Although consultations proved inconclusive, the committee established an important precedent for later negotiations. In 1949 all but Finland became members of the Council of Europe, thereby committing themselves in principle to the idea of broader European political unity.

Within Scandinavia itself regular consultations were instituted among cabinet officials and civil servants to extend the coordination of domestic policies and government services. Official organs were founded, for example, to investigate social problems, legal codes, cultural affairs, communications, and economic relations. Informal contacts among administrative personnel were expanded in such fields as railway travel, postal and telegraph services, broadcasting companies, customs inspection, public health, and factory inspection.[38]

The structural culmination of regional Scandinavian cooperation was achieved in 1952 with the creation of the Nordic Council. Proposed by former Danish Prime Minister Hans Hedtoft at a meeting of the NIPU in 1951, the Council agreement was quickly ratified by the parliaments of Sweden, Norway, Denmark, and Iceland. At first the Soviet Union opposed Finnish membership, but she relented in 1955. Designed to provide an institutionalized setting for the joint review of policy needs, the Nordic Council is composed of 69 representatives from the five Scandinavian parliaments, who are chosen among the major parties, and approximately 30 members of the various cabinets. Convened for a week-long session once a year, Council meetings rotate among the national capitals. The Council's purpose, according to Article I of the Statute, is to serve as "an organ for consultation . . . in matters involving joint action by any or all of the countries."[39] As a Danish observer has noted: "In principle no question is excepted as long as it may be of common interest to two or more member states."[40] Excluded by tacit agreement from Council deliberations are topics concerning national defense and political relations with non-Scandinavian states.[41]

The Nordic Council possesses no supranational powers. Its sole authority is to discuss issues and make recommendations to the governments of the five nations. In turn the governments are

[38] Frantz Wendt, *The Nordic Council and Co-Operation in Scandinavia* (Copenhagen: Munksgaard, 1959), pp. 39–40.
[39] Anderson, p. 151.
[40] Wendt, p. 107.
[41] Wuorinen, p. 127.

expected "to inform the Council of the action which has been taken on the recommendations of the Council."[42] Whether political authorities actually implement particular measures is contingent strictly on national priorities and internal decision-making processes in each of the member countries. Based on the principle of voluntary cooperation, the Council therefore "is a stable rather than a steadily growing union. Its integrative power is not high, and unification has not penetrated into high spill-over sectors."[43] As Stanley Anderson comments in his detailed assessment of Scandinavian regionalism: "The citizens of the five countries continue to look to the separate national governments for the solutions to problems, and the Nordic Council has not been able to establish its own constituency. . . . The conclusion remains that . . . the Council has not succeeded in systematic penetration of the governments, either as an external pressure group or as an integral part of government."[44]

Despite these caveats, the Nordic Council has contributed at least indirectly to intergovernmental collaboration. While "the executive chooses the topics and sets the pace" of policy decisions in each nation,[45] the accomplishments of Scandinavian cooperation —through the Nordic Council and the specialized organs that exist alongside the Council—have been significant. During the postwar period the five Scandinavian countries have established a common area for customs clearance, abolished the need for passports by Scandinavian citizens, extended national welfare benefits to temporary residents from the other Nordic states, and created a common Scandinavian labor market. In a five-nation treaty of cooperation, which was signed at the tenth session of the Nordic Council in Helsinki in 1962, Scandinavian leaders pledged themselves to continued efforts to achieve greater uniformity of laws and government services in the future.[46]

In contrast to the relative ease with which a great many social policies have been harmonized throughout the region, economic cooperation has posed a more difficult challenge to Nordic leaders. Differences in national economic interests, Swedish-Finnish neutrality, and Finland's special status in relation to the

[42] Article XI of the Council Statute. The statute is reprinted in Anderson, pp. 151–156.

[43] Amatai Etzioni, *Political Unification* (New York: Holt, Rinehart and Winston, Inc., 1965), p. 185.

[44] Anderson, pp. 119 and 124.

[45] Anderson, p. 124.

[46] For the complete text of the "Helsinki Agreement," see Anderson, pp. 174–181.

Soviet Union are the principal factors that have complicated successive attempts at economic collaboration. Although the Scandinavian states succeeded in achieving an interim formula in the 1960s to resolve most of these potentially divisive policy factors, negotiations in 1970 to expand the European Economic Community raised the prospect of renewed cleavage.

Official interest in reducing restrictions on regional trade dates from the 1930s, but only with the formation of the Joint Scandinavian Committee for Economic Cooperation in 1948 was a concerted effort made to appraise the feasibility of a common Nordic market. The exploratory talks among Sweden, Norway, and Denmark produced only the agreement that further studies were necessary. Throughout the 1950s various intergovernmental bodies and Nordic Council committees met to compile data and issue recommendations to the three governments. In 1956 Finland joined the deliberations. Iceland remained largely aloof from the consultations because its economy, which is principally dependent on the export of a single commodity (fish), was too weak for integration with the other Nordic countries.

Impeding consensus on implementing a common market were domestic and European wide economic considerations. In the first place, the Norwegians and Danes were apprehensive about the effects of industrial competition from Sweden if regional tariffs were abolished. Similarly Sweden and Norway were concerned that an influx of cheaper agricultural goods from Denmark would harm their own farmers. Second, simultaneous negotiations within the OEEC to create a European free-trade area overshadowed much of the debate on regional economic liberalization. At the sixth session of the Nordic Council in 1958, for example, "the acting Danish Prime Minister, Viggo Kampmann, subordinated his approval of a common Nordic market to his concern with the prompt institution of the broader West European free trade area —he hoped that successful negotiations for the latter would soon permit a favorable decision to be made within Scandinavia."[47] An additional extraregional factor inducing restraint was Finland's insistence that it would participate in Nordic economic integration only if a common market would expand trade with Eastern Europe.[48]

Events elsewhere in Europe decided the immediate fate of the proposed Scandinavian market. The formation of the Euro-

[47] Anderson, p. 133.
[48] Anderson, p. 133.

pean Economic Community (EEC)—composed of France, West Germany, Italy, and the Benelux countries—in 1958 and the subsequent failure of the OEEC negotiations on a free-trade area necessitated a new policy response. Plans for Nordic economic integration were abandoned as members of the "outer seven," including the three central Scandinavian states, Great Britain, Austria, Switzerland, and Portugal, established the European Free Trade Association (EFTA) in January 1960. As in the earlier decision to form the Nordic Council, Soviet objections prevented initial Finnish participation in the new organization. In 1961, however, Finland joined EFTA as an associate member.

Unlike the EEC, the EETA Convention did not provide for either a common market or supranational structures. Instead, only internal tariffs on industrial goods would be eliminated among the member states. Explicitly excluded were most agricultural products, and no common external tariff was contemplated for trade with third countries. Policy authority was vested in the EFTA Council, where each state was accorded one vote. Unanimity was required in all "legislative" decisions affecting changes in the "scope and substance of the Association."[49] A majority vote was permissible solely in a restricted range of administrative decisions concerning interpretations and the application of EFTA rules.

The immediate advantages of Scandinavian membership in EFTA proved considerable. Between 1959 and 1964 Sweden increased its exports to EFTA nations by 86 percent, while Finnish exports rose 76 percent. The percentages for Norway and Denmark were 76.2 and 71.8, respectively.[50] Especially striking was the rate of increase among the Scandinavian countries themselves. Whereas the growth of exports within EFTA as a whole rose 76 percent by 1964, intra-Nordic exports increased 110 percent.[51] In 1967 the value of exports among the Scandinavian nations ($2506 million) was more than half that of aggregate Nordic exports to other EFTA-member states ($4655 million).[52]

Parallel developments within the EEC, however, raised fundamental implications for long-term Scandinavian economic prospects. Absorbing from a quarter to a third of Nordic exports, including agricultural products from Denmark and iron, steel,

49 F. V. Meyer, *The European Free-Trade Association* (New York: Praeger, 1960), p. 65.
50 *EFTA Reporter*, 7 (April 11, 1966).
51 *EFTA Reporter*, 7 (April 11, 1966).
52 Nordic Council, *Yearbook of Nordic Statistics* (Stockholm: Nordic Council, 1969), p. 78.

manufactured goods, timber, and pulp from the other Scandinavian states, the EEC countries have traditionally provided a major market for Scandinavian sales abroad. Even though EFTA exports to EEC countries had increased 64.6 percent by 1964,[53] Scandinavian leaders faced the prospect that future trade would suffer as the Common Market gained internal cohesion. The primary reason was the trade-diverting effect of the EEC's common tariff on industrial and agricultural products from third countries. By 1964 the problem of trade diversion had become especially critical for Denmark. Since 1959 Danish agricultural exports to the EEC had declined nearly 8 million dollars, with Denmark recording a deficit in trade with EEC nations of $300 million in 1964.[54]

Accordingly political leaders in Scandinavia—like those in the other EFTA nations—emphasized from the outset of EFTA's existence the necessity of reaching an ultimate agreement on the creation of a broader European market. As the EEC nations had rejected earlier proposals for a free-trade area within OEEC, the only policy alternative seemed to be direct accommodation with the EEC. Following the British lead of July 1961, Denmark thus applied for admission to the Common Market in August 1961. Norway submitted its application a year later. In light of the overlapping membership between the EEC and NATO, Sweden adopted a more cautious approach. Declaring that direct membership in the EEC "would not be compatible with the Swedish policy of neutrality," Prime Minister Erlander announced in October 1961 that Sweden would apply only for associate membership status.[55] Finland's policy was one of "wait and see."

Following De Gaulle's veto of British membership in January 1963, the Nordic countries did not abandon aspirations for an eventual enlargement of the EEC. But as a short-term expedient measure they concentrated on strengthening EFTA to offset the economic disadvantages of the outer seven's exclusion from the Common Market. Once the primary objective of EFTA to abolish regional tariffs on industrial goods was achieved by the end of 1966—three years ahead of the original timetable—Scandinavian leaders then revived the dormant plan for a Nordic common market as the logical next step to enhance regional cooperation. The prime ministers of Sweden, Norway, Denmark, and Finland jointly announced in April 1968:

[53] *EFTA Bulletin*, 7 (April 11, 1966).
[54] *EFTA Bulletin*, 6 (September–October, 1965).
[55] Andrén, *Power-Balance and Non-Alignment*, p. 126.

> Through EFTA cooperation a basis has been created for a free Nordic market for industrial goods. This is an important part of the cooperation between the Nordic countries and has been of decisive importance for the very marked increase in Nordic trade in recent years. . . . [C]onsidering that more comprehensive Nordic economic cooperation would benefit the Nordic countries —for instance by furthering cooperation within EFTA and the other endeavors to achieve integration in Europe as well as by strengthening the trade policy position of the Nordic countries, [we] find that the time is now ripe to make a new advance in Nordic economic cooperation.[56]

Specifically the prime ministers agreed that further studies should be undertaken—leading to concrete proposals to the four governments—to consider the establishment of a Nordic customs union with a common external tariff; the extension of cooperation in agriculture and fisheries; and the creation of a common Nordic fund to facilitate regional structural rationalization and development projects.[57]

Motivating this step, as Minister without Portfolio Krister Wickman explained in the Swedish parliament, was the shared conviction among the four leaders that:

> This extended cooperation would promote economic growth in our Nordic area, making us increasingly able to adapt ourselves to the rapid changes in technology and market conditions that characterize [contemporary] developments. . . . If, with our high economic and technological standard, we formed a united front we should be able to increase our share of world trade to a level that far exceeds what our population warrants. In that respect no other area having 20–25 million people would be able to match itself with the Nordic area.[58]

Negotiations on the Scandinavian customs union—known as NORDEK—proceeded rapidly. Between October 1968 and November 1969 the four prime ministers met four times to review reports compiled by a four-nation Committee of Experts. At their session in Helsinki in February 1969, they resolved that a treaty should be formally drafted by July. The document, which was duly submitted to the governments on July 23, envisioned the

---

56 *Documents*, pp. 60–61.
57 *Documents*, pp. 59–64.
58 *Documents*, p. 203.

creation of five new regional structures including a ministerial council, a standing committee of government officials, a secretariat, an industrial consultative council, and a Nordic investment bank. Agreement was reached on a common tariff on industrial goods, iron and steel, chemicals, and textiles, but policy differences persisted with regard to agricultural cooperation and fishing industries. In the first instance Denmark stated "that the country would not make a decision on the customs union as a whole until the content and extent of agricultural trade had been determined"; in the second, Sweden insisted that fish from Norway and Denmark could not be sold in Sweden below a minimum price established by Sweden.[59] At their fourth meeting since the initial decision to proceed with the NORDEK proposal, the four prime ministers declared in Stockholm in November 1969 that they would personally head their respective negotiating teams in an attempt to achieve final consensus on the treaty by February 1970.

Once again international considerations, as in the discussions on a Nordic common market in the 1950s, intervened to force a postponement. Apparently because of Soviet reservations, the Finnish government induced Sweden, Norway, and Denmark in December 1969 to delay a decision on NORDEK until at least after Finland's national election in March 1970. Simultaneously, the EEC agreed at a Council of Ministers meeting at The Hague to open negotiations with Britain, Norway, and Denmark in July 1970 concerning their possible membership in the EEC.

Hence the NORDEK consultations were abruptly suspended. The Finnish election resulted in a defeat for the Socialist-dominated coalition cabinet and the formation of a caretaker government, thereby introducing a new element of political uncertainty in Scandinavian regional relations. In larger perspective the new round of negotiations at Brussels emerged as the decisive factor that would affect the future course of Nordic economic cooperation.

THE DILEMMA OF CHOICE

The prospect of an expanded EEC posed a significant challenge to Scandinavian, and especially Swedish, foreign policy interests. For Norway and Denmark, membership in the EEC would be wholly compatible with declared economic objectives and military align-

[59] *News of Norway*, 26 (August 4, 1969), 54–55.

ment with the Western bloc. In the case of Sweden and Finland, the attraction of the Common Market was tempered by the qualifying factor of each nation's policy of neutrality. Of additional concern to Swedish decision makers was their regard for Finland's more limited freedom of action. Given ambivalent Soviet attitudes toward the EEC, the likelihood of even associate membership by Finland in the Common Market appeared remote.

With Danish and Norwegian applications for full membership pending at EEC headquarters, Sweden sought in 1970 to secure an arrangement with the Common Market that would perpetuate regional Nordic economic cooperation. In a major policy declaration during an official visit to London in April 1970, Prime Minister Palme stated that Sweden "was eager to join the Common Market if her special political needs can be met." His announcement, which contrasted with Erlander's earlier rejection of direct Swedish membership, was coupled with an important condition. When asked about Finland's relations with the EEC, Palme said: "You can't be too logical. Any arrangement with the European Economic Community must take account of Finland. Human ingenuity should be sufficient."[60]

Palme's optimism masked a policy dilemma inherent in Sweden's conduct of foreign relations in the 1970s. Throughout the postwar period Swedish neutrality had proved complementary to simultaneous processes of regional cultural, political, and economic cooperation. Free from bloc allegiances and able to pursue activist international policies, Sweden had experienced considerable domestic benefits as a member of the Nordic Council and EFTA on the regional level. Given the inevitability of a regional economic realignment that would result from a decision to broaden the Common Market, national leaders confronted the possibility that these dual aspects of Swedish foreign policy might become contradictory. Their choice was between a modification of Swedish neutrality to conform with the requirements of membership in the Western European Economic Community or the reaffirmation of strict neutrality at the cost of regional solidarity.

[60] *The New York Times*, April 9, 1970, p. 11.

ELEVEN
THE POLITICS OF
POSTINDUSTRIAL CHANGE
Prospects for the future

During the postwar period Sweden has undergone substantial socioeconomic and political transformation. Continued industrialization, urbanization, and the extension of welfare services have blurred traditional demographic and class boundaries. In the absence of pronounced religious, cultural, and regional cleavages, Sweden has accordingly attained a degree of mass homogeneity that contrasts markedly with the social systems of most advanced nations outside of Scandinavia.

Social change combined with widespread endorsement of the welfare state have prompted a partial realignment of the Swedish multiparty system. The increase in middle-class white-collar workers has forced nonsocialist leaders to compete increasingly among the same groups for electoral support, while opposition to state-sponsored welfare services and indirect government intervention in the economy has elicited declining popular support. Thus nonsocialist leaders have abandoned much of their partisan rivalry and distinctive profiles of the past. Following the Center's resignation from the cabinet in 1957, leaders of the Liberal, Center, and Moderate Unity parties have cautiously promoted a common bloc identity through policy coordination in the Riksdag and during elections. While formal electoral cooperation has been limited largely to the two middle parties, the decline in overt intrabloc strife has enabled the nonsocialist bloc to mount a serious challenge to Socialist ascendancy in two elections (1966 and 1970).

Concurrently, persisting imperfections of the Swedish industrial-welfare state yielded in the mid-1960s the impetus for the New Left-radical liberal attack on the established system. Seeking the socialization of the economy on a decentralized model of workers' control, New Left spokesmen succeeded in displacing the older, more orthodox leadership of the Communist party in 1964. Hermansson and his supporters thereby transformed the renamed Left Party-Communists into the nation's principal structure of militant ideological criticism and electoral agitation. On a broader political-cultural front radical dissidents in the nonsocialist parties, the LO, voluntary associations, and the communications media have initiated an animated public debate on issues of social justice and individual rights. Their demands for reform range from the rejuvenation of party leadership, increased membership participation in group decisions, and greater equality for women and lower-class groups to enhanced freedom of personal behavior and life styles. In pressing such demands, Sweden's more outspoken new radicals have challenged many of the norms of the dominant culture. For traditional behavior patterns of social restraint they have substituted active commitment; in place of political compromise they espouse categorical political action.

Confronted with these multiple pressures of change, the Social Democrats nevertheless managed to retain control of the cabinet into their fourth decade of executive tenure. Their broad basis of mass support among blue-collar and lower-level white-collar workers and their strong ties with the LO assured them a secure and loyal following among more than 40 percent of the electorate. Despite the incipient emergence of a loosely united nonsocialist bloc the Socialists also benefitted from the historical image of bourgeois disunity and the failure of opposition leaders to agree on a common electoral program. Moreover, their ideological pragmatism and receptivity to group claims, advanced through pluralist participation in Royal Commissions, *remiss* procedures, and informal consultations such as the Harpsund sessions, enabled them to avoid antagonizing important nonsocialist electoral strata. In a more positive vein, the Social Democrats demonstrated superb strategic skill in seizing the political initiative at times of electoral decline and ideological renewal among their opponents. Both the supplementary pension controversy of the 1950s and the adoption of the party's new economic program of 1968 resulted in increased Socialist strength and an extension of their executive mandate.

Following the September 1970 election, the Social Democrats were reduced to minority status in parliament but were able to remain in office because of the promise of indirect Left Party-Communist support. A precedent exists for this pattern from the 1950s, when the Communists similarly sustained the Social Democrats in the lower chamber and in critical joint votes of both houses. In historical perspective, the alignment in the new unicameral legislature suggested at least a temporary regression to the era of minority parliamentarism. Like the Liberals during the 1920s, the Social Democrats occupied a position at the beginning of the 1970s as a "balancer" between forces of the left and the right. Lacking a parliamentary majority of their own but confronting a situation in which no other viable government was possible, the Social Democrats could anticipate relying alternately on the Left Party-Communists and some or all of the nonsocialist factions to advance their policy goals.[1]

Beyond the exigencies of short-term political expediency such a parliamentary situation is potentially unstable, for it poses the everpresent threat of a ministerial crisis should the Socialists' *ad hoc* majority dissolve in a vote of no confidence. For ideological and political reasons the Social Democrats cannot formalize cooperation with the Left Party-Communists, while the trend toward greater nonsocialist cohesion would appear to exclude the possibility of renewed collaboration with the Center party. In seeking to restore their majority status in future elections, the Socialists are therefore likely to concentrate on measures that will simultaneously reduce the electoral appeal of the Left Party-Communists, and possibly eliminate them from parliament under provisions of the 4 percent clause of the electoral law, and expand their support among white-collar workers at the expense of the nonsocialist parties. In implementing such a strategy, the Social Democrats can be expected to sponsor reforms designed to enhance individual educational and socioeconomic opportunities, increase group solidarity among their present and potential middle-class clientele, and extend social influence (short of nationalization) over productive processes.

The failure of these policies to elicit sufficient popular support would prepare the way for an eventual formation of a nonsocialist coalition. Whether the nonsocialist parties can in fact

---

[1] The analogy, of course, should not be exaggerated. The Social Democrats were in a far stronger parliamentary position at the beginning of the 1970s than the Liberals in the 1920s, and no potential coalition offered an alternative basis for cabinet formation.

displace the Socialists depends in part, however, on the ability of the bourgeois bloc to forge a viable alternative government program. Notwithstanding nonsocialist claims that a common program can follow rather than precede the formation of a coalition ministry, prior concensus on policy principles would presumably increase the credibility of their aspirations to national leadership. Throughout the 1960s Center chairman Hedlund's personal opposition to intensified contacts with the Moderate Unity party proved a major obstacle to three-party electoral cooperation. His retirement in July 1971, when he was succeeded by former party vice-chairman Thorbjörn Fälldin, may facilitate future agreement.

Underpinning flux in electoral alignments and the structure of the multiparty system is elite consensus on procedural norms of diffused participation and compromise in political decisions. Despite partisan controversy over successive economic and social issues during the postwar period, these shared values constitute a firm basis for the sustained stability of the political system. The willingness of political elites to seek mutual agreement on matters of fundamental common interest was revealed in two major structural reforms: the consolidation of local communes into larger, more efficient units of government and the introduction of unicameralism. The upshot of both innovations was a significant rationalization of Swedish government that has facilitated the effective implementation of local policies and the direct expression of popular political preferences on the national level.

Domestic change in Swedish politics has been accompanied by the assertion of activist neutrality and regional cooperation within the Nordic Council and EFTA. By 1970 the prospect of an expanded EEC revealed a potential conflict between these dual themes of foreign policy, with Swedish leaders facing the uncertain consequences of possible Danish and Norwegian membership in the Common Market for their own political and economic relations with Europe. Given Sweden's dependence on regional and international trade for national affluence and the survival of the industrial-welfare state, political and economic elites can hardly risk the negative option of retreating into national isolation. But neither are they willing to forego military neutrality. To resolve this dilemma Swedish leaders will probably seek association with the EEC or special arrangements with the Common Market to preserve preferential trade links that have already been established with the other Nordic states and EFTA. The feasibility of either formula will depend in the first instance on the willingness of the

EEC's Council of Ministers to accommodate Sweden's special interests.

Within the constraints on policy choice dictated by international economic imperatives, Sweden confronts the continuing challenge of postindustrial modernization. The domestic debates of the 1960s revealed a number of symptoms of transition to the "super-industrial" era that are not unique to Sweden.[2] As in other advanced nations, the emergence of new countercultures, the resurgence of ideological controversy, and sociopolitical reforms mark the emerging outlines of the postwelfare state.

VARIABLES OF POSTINDUSTRIAL CHANGE: A COMPARATIVE ASSESSMENT

Defined in the introduction to this volume as enhanced control by man over his physical, social, and individual environments, modernization involves comprehensive system transformation. Yet as Eisenstadt emphasizes:

> [T]he mere development of [continually changing structural forms, activities, and problems] does not in itself assure the development of an institutional structure capable of dealing in a relatively stable way with these continual changes and concomitantly of assuring the maintenance of a civil order. Thus the crucial problem that modernization creates in its wake is that of the ability of the emerging social structure to deal with such continual changes, or in other words, the problem of *sustained* development, i.e., the ability of developing an institutional structure capable of absorbing continually changing problems and demands.[3]

The difficulties of sustaining transformation are acute not only in transitional societies but increasingly in the modern nations as well. As societies attain postindustrial complexity, affluence, and redistributive potentialities, existing structural arrangements have revealed many limitations in their ability to manage transformation. The central problem of modernization, as stated by Eisenstadt, is therefore ever present, demanding new solutions with each manifestation of man's changing relations with nature,

[2] Alvin Toffler uses the term "super-industrial" era to characterize postindustrial society in his book *Future Shock* (New York: Random House, 1970).
[3] S. N. Eisenstadt, *Modernization: Protest and Change* (Englewood Cliffs, N.J.: Prentice-Hall, Inc., 1966), p. 43.

society, and his fellow citizens. The advanced nations of Western Europe and North America are likely to respond differently to such a need, with variations in system capabilities, the degree of elite-mass consensus on fundamental political principles, and elite perceptions of future policy requirements leading to a wide array of structured alternatives.[4]

As a microcosm of postindustrial change, Sweden provides a model of potential transformation that is relevant for assessing the future of politics in other industrial-urban states. The United States, Britain, West Germany, Norway, and Denmark serve as a logical basis of comparison, for all of them display broadly similar attributes of modernity. Selected socioeconomic data are presented for comparative purposes in Table 22.

Necessary system conditions to sustain economic and social modernization in Sweden are provided by the nation's advanced industrialization, wealth, cohesive social system, the relative stability of labor market relations, expanding educational opportunities, and the scope of government expenditures on welfare and other services. In contrast the United States is the world's most affluent nation with the highest per capita investment in education and scientific research[5] but ranks lower than Sweden in social cohesion, labor peace, and state-sponsored services. Both Denmark and Norway are less affluent and industrialized with a more restricted government role in the economy and society. They share with Sweden, however, similar patterns of socioeconomic cohesion. Britain and West Germany are somewhat more industrialized than Sweden, but both have lower per capita GNPs and expend less on public services. Particular restraints on coherent socioeconomic change in Britain are imposed by a more sharply drawn class system and a less disciplined labor movement than in Scandinavia and Germany. In aggregate terms no definable combination of system capabilities is a sufficient guarantee for postindustrial modernization. Among the highly industrialized nations some will undoubtedly encounter greater obstacles to sustained change

---

[4] The significance of varied system responses to postindustrial change for sociopolitical analysis is explored in "Epilogue" in M. Donald Hancock and Gideon Sjoberg (eds.), *Politics in the Post-Welfare State: Responses to the New Individualism* (New York: Columbia University Press, 1972).

[5] Brzezinski notes that "contemporary America spends more on science and devotes greater resources to research than any other society." He cites Organization for Economic Cooperation and Development data reporting that the United States spent $93.70 per capita on research in 1962 compared to $33.50 in Britain, $23.60 in France, and $20.10 in West Germany. Zbigniew Brzezinski, *Between Two Ages* (New York: The Viking Press, 1970), pp. 25–26.

Table 22   Comparative Indexes of Socioeconomic
Modernity

Category	Sweden	United States	Britain
GNP (million U.S. dollars)[a]	26,250	880,774	102,875
Per capita GNP (in U.S. dollars)[a]	3,315	4,379	1,861
Expenditure of General Government, Social Security, and Public Enterprise as a Percentage of GNP[b]	52.9	27.9	45.3
Employment in Industry as a Percentage of Working-Age Population[b]	28.1	19.2	35.2
Students Enrolled in Higher Education per 1000 Population[c]	1,232	3,423	562
Primary and Secondary School Population as a Percentage of Population Aged 5–19[b]	71	81	80

Category	West Germany	Norway	Denmark
GNP (million U.S. dollars)[a]	132,700	9,021	12,394
Per capita GNP (in U.S. dollars)[a]	2,206	2,362	2,545
Expenditure of General Government, Social Security, and Public Enterprise as a Percentage of GNP[b]	38.8	36.5	29.9
Employment in Industry as a Percentage of Working-Age Population[b]	31.9	23.7	24.2
Students Enrolled in Higher Education per 1000 Population[c]	1,153	586	1,188
Primary and Secondary School Population as a Percentage of Population Aged 5–19[b]	73	70	72

[a]United Nations, *Yearbook of National Accounts Statistics 1969, II, International Tables* (New York: United Nations, 1969).
[b]Bruce M. Russett, *et al., World Handbook of Political and Social Indicators* (New Haven, Conn.: Yale University Press, 1964).
[c]United Nations, *U.N. Statistical Yearbook 1969* (New York: United Nations, 1969).

because of social heterogeneity or regional diversity, but all of them have attained at least the economic capability to create, in U Thant's words, "the kind and scale of resources they decide to have."[6] Decisions to develop and invest system capabilities in

6 Quoted in Toffler, p. 16.

particular resources, however, are essentially political acts—especially in an age of rapid technological-scientific change and ecological decay. Accordingly political variables of postindustrial change assume particular significance in assessing the prospects of future transformation.

The first of these variables—prevailing elite-mass attitudes toward the political system and policy objectives—establishes the boundaries of conceivable innovation and structural reform. Consensus on constitutional principles and the legitimacy of concerted government action can facilitate systematic change, while pervasive attitudinal cleavages may impede or even prevent transformation. In the case of Sweden, Norway, and Denmark the former appears the norm. Social homogeneity and the peaceful attainment of modernizing goals in the past have produced consensual political cultures, with an overwhelming majority of Scandinavian citizens affirming parliamentarism and the need for activist government economic and social policies. Parties, interest groups, and the new radical dissidents differ on numerous questions, but open conflict is muted and sporadic.

Similarly popular consensus pervades the United States, Britain, and West Germany with respect to basic political principles and political processes, although the West Germans display less affective orientations toward established government institutions.[7] Yet major groups in all three countries are more divided in their attitudes toward many fundamental issues and policy objectives than the populace of the Nordic states. Attitudinal cleavages are evident, for example, in partisan controversies concerning the extension of welfare benefits and social influence over industry. Racial discrimination and the emergence of organized Black Power and Chicano movements constitute a particular cause of political-cultural fragmentation in the United States. Conflicts over military intervention in Southeast Asia and efforts to achieve a *detente* with the Soviet Union provide additional sources of political cleavages in the United States and West Germany, respectively.

On balance, therefore, consensual attitudes in Scandinavia are probably more conducive to political decisions to achieve postindustrial transformation than the more divided political cultures of the three other advanced nations. Especially in the United States and West Germany immediate issues of domestic and foreign policy take precedence in policy counsels and the public

---

[7] Gabriel Almond and Sidney Verba, *The Civic Culture* (Boston: Little, Brown and Company, 1965), p. 64.

imagination over long-range programs of economic and political reform.

Beyond the possible limits on policy innovation imposed by diffused political attitudes, specific elite perceptions of system change comprise a second political variable of postindustrial modernization. Throughout the modernization process elites have played the crucial role in tacitly endorsing and/or initiating economic, social, and political transformation. In the advanced countries the "content of the value orientations"[8] among political and group leaders continues to be a decisive element in determining the course of change. On the basis of their value systems and their authority to determine public policy, national elites may oppose transformation or they can promote it through efforts to achieve more extensive control over nature and productive resources. They may resort to oppressive measures to curtail individual freedom or they can implement structural reforms to increase individual participation in collective decisions.

Comparative analysis of elite perceptions of future change is difficult because of the paucity of relevant empirical data. A careful assessment would require different kinds of attitudinal surveys than have been conducted to date in national elite studies, namely an appraisal of the elites' emotive identity with the *status quo* and their prescriptive images of alternative structural arrangements. A key element in measuring elite responsiveness to forces of postindustrial modernization would thus be the degree to which established leaders accept the legitimacy of innovating groups (such as the New Left, radical liberals, and militant ethnic organizations) and the demands they raise to restructure modern society.

On the basis of indirect and admittedly impressionistic indexes, leaders in the United States, Britain, and Germany seem oriented more toward maintaining than transforming change. In the Anglo-American countries the legacy of classical liberalism has engendered shared elite values emphasizing procedural rights and libertarianism. A corresponding distrust of "utopian" ideologies to reshape the collectivity or promote redistributive policies effectively constrains elite willingness to initiate structural transformation. West German elites present a more complex case, but the effect of their behavior is much the same as in the United States and Britain. Compelled to concentrate on the primary task of creating a viable political system within the truncated boundaries of a divided nation, postwar leaders have invested much of

---

[8] Eisenstadt, pp. 156–157.

their energies in political and economic reconstruction. With the attainment of internal consolidation and consensus on economic-military integration with the West, the German leadership has become increasingly committed to the preservation of existing authority structures. A minority faction of younger Social Democrats espouses extensive domestic changes in economic and social relations;[9] whether they can succeed in influencing party policy is a question of time and their rise to positions of strategic importance. On the local level educational elites in Germany have sanctioned efforts to achieve transformation through, for example, university reform. Opposition among senior faculty members and ideological cleavages among policy innovators, however, have limited the effectiveness of such attempts.

Elites in Scandinavia display discernible national differences in their attitudes toward system change. In Norway and Denmark leaders remain preoccupied with the refinement of industrial-welfare society. So far spared the intensity of ideological attacks that have characterized much of the public debate in other advanced nations, leaders in both countries have yet to devise a strategy of postindustrial change. G. Lowell Field and John Higley have found in the case of Norway that elites manifest a high degree of complacency toward the established system. "They know of no important political issues requiring strong corrective actions. They are little impressed with their own powers of decision and evidently do not wish they had more. . . ."[10] Complacency similarly dominated elite perceptions of the domestic system in Sweden following the end of the early postwar debate on socialization, but the supplementary pension controversy and the Social Democratic policy response to the emergence of the New Left revealed the willingness of the political leadership to undertake subsequent transforming initiatives. The tradition of Social Democratic radical reformism, though tempered by moderation and an inclination toward compromise, provides a continuing stimulus for socioeconomic transformation in the 1970s.

In comparative perspective, therefore, Sweden faces relatively fewer obstacles to coherent postindustrial change than other industrial-welfare states. Although Sweden lacks the resources to

---

[9] "Juso-Sieg an der Saar?" *Der Spiegel*, 24 (October 5, 1970), 60, 62.

[10] G. Lowell Field and John Higley, "Elite Unity in a Developed Polity: The Case of Norway." Paper prepared for delivery at the International Political Science Association Congress in Munich, Germany, August 31–September 5, 1970, p. 18. (Mimeographed.)

equal American investments in advanced scientific-technological research, Swedish technicians can borrow from "technetronic"[11] discoveries in the United States to augment the nation's otherwise favorable inventory of system capabilities. Elite sponsorship of extensive socioeconomic reforms within the framework of a consensual political culture has already partially molded these capabilities into new structural patterns. The adoption of the supplementary pension system and the Socialists' new economic program, which have expanded the indirect influence of the state over productive processes, constitute a basis for the progressive rationalization of collective control over the physical and social environments. The extension of welfare services and educational opportunities, LO support for increased wages among blue-collar workers, and the reform of parliament can simultaneously promote egalitarianism in the Swedish postwelfare state.

COUNTERSYSTEM ALTERNATIVES

The *potential* for transformation in Sweden, however, cannot be equated with the *certainty* of transformation. The fallacy of projecting apparent trends into the future has been underscored in the introduction to this study and the collaborative volume on *Politics in the Post-Welfare State.* Just as discontinuities occurred in the political-ideological debate of the 1960s, processes of postindustrial change may assume unanticipated directions in years ahead. The failure of Swedish leaders to reach a satisfactory agreement with the EEC or the erection of new barriers to trade among the industrial nations could provoke a decline in production and mass unemployment. Accordingly, Sweden's present capabilities to sustain socioeconomic transformation might degenerate into a condition of regressive change. Regression could also take place if incipient antagonisms among various occupational groups excessively disturb social cohesion and labor peace. A strike by government employees in February 1971, which was called by the SR and SACO in opposition to Socialist efforts to promote egalitarian policies at the expense of white-collar strata, was interpreted in

---

[11] Technetronic is a neologism coined by Brzezinski to define the basic characteristics of modern (primarily American) society as one "that is shaped culturally, psychologically, socially, and economically by the impact of technology and electronics—particularly in the area of computers and communications." Brzezinski, p. 9.

some quarters as the harbinger of just such a trend.[12] Given the increased complexity of modern industrial society, the prospect is likely to increase in the future that work stoppages by strategically placed unions, even if they are small in size, can disrupt the entire national economy. Even more important, new cleavages between white-collar and industrial workers could signal the start of class warfare that would thwart any attempt by Swedish leaders to pursue coherent policies of postindustrial transformation.

Similarly, the potential for system transformation does not inevitably mean qualitative improvements in the status of individual citizens. The rapid expansion of secondary schools and university facilities, for instance, may lead to a deterioration in public education. Nor will group structures necessarily be reshaped to permit greater individual participation in collective decisions. As radical dissent and the LKAB strike discussed in this volume indicate, the tension between collective and individual claims for control persists in modern Swedish society. If established elites fail to sanction significant changes in authority relations, the result might be an intensification of critical consciousness and mass alienation. Under such circumstances it is not inconceivable that many young academicians and workers would refuse to be co-opted by the existing pluralist system, thereby deepening sociopolitical malaise and increasing the potential for revolutionary acts. As Eli Ginzberg disconcertingly ponders: "Will young people coming of age fit themselves into the elaborate organizational structure which they had no part in fashioning and in the leadership of which they have no say? What will happen if they balk?"[13]

One possible response to the struggle to redefine and restructure the role of the individual in Swedish postindustrial society is the increased dominance of the collectivity. A new political-bureaucratic meritocracy based on specialized knowledge and skills could insure individual compliance with group norms through the manipulation of information and social organizations. Technocrats would exercise a virtual monopoly over political decisions, while education would serve to cultivate a passive mentality among the nation's youth. In such a system the rewards of con-

[12] See " 'White Collar Strike' Forces Swedes to Question Welfare State's Future," *The New York Times*, February 26, 1971, p. 3. Some 6000 employees initially went on strike to demand an average increase of 22 percent in wages. The government responded with a massive lockout and, in an unprecedented step, imposed a temporary settlement through parliamentary legislation. All parties except the Left Party-Communists endorsed the government initiative.

[13] Eli Ginzberg, "Sweden: Some Unanswered Questions," *The Public Interest*, 18 (Fall 1970), 166.

formity, conferred in the form of security and social esteem, might well preclude the necessity of mass surveillance and political repression to enforce the collectivity's preeminence.

An alternative "countersystem" is a dynamic synthesis between the enhanced capabilities for transformation on both the collective and individual levels.[14] Such a synthesis would require the simultaneous rationalization of productive resources (for example, through automation and reliance on computer technology) and the decentralization of both public and private bureaucracies. Pluralist structures would be modified to accommodate consultative referenda on political decisions, greater individual choice in the selection of group leaders, and client participation in the administration of welfare services.[15] A primary objective of public education would be to encourage reflective, creative citizenship. Characteristic of this countersystem would be continual change as individuals and groups engage in a ceaseless dialogue to reformulate the goals of public policy in response to new and unforeseen consequences of postindustrial modernization.

Regressive change caused by economic dislocations or domestic cleavages, the collectivist and libertarian models of transformation outlined above, or a combination of both countersystems in some form of maintaining change are at present only theoretical alternatives. The actual course of future Swedish politics—as is true in other advanced nations—will depend on the choices that the national leadership and an enlightened public make during the contemporary era of transition.

[14] Sjoberg and colleagues define "countersystem" as a logical counterpart to existing reality. The purpose of countersystem analysis is to delineate conceivable future structural arrangements as a means to enhance the predictive capabilities of scientific inquiry. See Gideon Sjoberg and Leonard D. Cain, "Negative Values, Countersystem Models, and the Analysis of Social Systems," in Herman Turk and Richard Simpson (eds.), *The Sociologies of Talcott Parsons and George C. Homans* (Indianapolis, Ind.: Bobbs-Merrill, 1971); Gideon Sjoberg, M. Donald Hancock, and Orion White, Jr., *Politics in the Post-Welfare State: A Comparison of the United States and Sweden* (Bloomington, Ind.: Carnegie Seminar on Political and Administrative Development, 1967); and Orion White, Jr., and Gideon Sjoberg, "The Emerging 'New Politics' in America," in Hancock and Sjoberg.

[15] Elvander proposes such structural modifications and enhanced opportunities for individual participation as a basis for "broadened democracy" in "Democracy and Large Organizations," in Hancock and Sjoberg. Increased client participation in the administration of welfare services is an integral part of the "dialectical organization" sketched in Sjoberg, *et al.*, *Politics in the Post-Welfare State.*

BIBLIOGRAPHY

As one of the world's most thoroughly documented nations, Sweden offers rich research potential to the serious student of comparative politics. Comprehensive census, economic, and electoral data can be found in the annual *Statistisk årsbok för Sverige* (*Statistical Abstract of Sweden*), in reports of royal commissions (published in the *Statens offentliga utredningar* series), and in specialized studies issued periodically by the Central Statistical Office, the Ministry of Finance, the Ministry of Commerce, and other government ministries. A principal source for Scandinavia as a whole is the Nordic Council's annual *Yearbook of Nordic Statistics*. Brief but incisive treatments of domestic and international affairs are also available in English from the Swedish Institute in Stockholm. The Institute's data sheets and booklets can generally be obtained on request from the various Royal Swedish Consulates-General, the Swedish Embassy in Washington, D.C., and the Swedish Information Service (825 Third Avenue, New York, N.Y. 10022).

For bibliographical research, students with a knowledge of Swedish should consult *Sveriges statskalender, Vem är det?* and *Vem var det?*

The leading scholarly journals with articles on Sweden and the other Nordic states are *Scandinavian Political Studies* (published annually in the United States by Columbia University Press), *Statsvetenskaplig tidskrift,* and *Acta Sociologica*. A good but now dated overview of secondary literature on Scandinavian politics is Stein Rokkan and Henry Valen, "Parties, Elections, and Political Behavior in the Northern Countries: A Review of Recent Research," in Otto Stammer, ed., *Politische Forschung* (Cologne and Opladen: Westdeutscher Verlag, 1960).

Semipopular articles on current events appear regularly in the Federation of Swedish Industries' excellent English publication, *Sweden Now*. For day-to-day developments the Swedish press provides a lively and indispensable source of information. The leading daily newspapers, all of which identify with particular political parties, include the liberal *Dagens Nyheter*, *Expressen*, and *Göteborgs-Posten*; the social democratic *Aftonbladet*; the conservative *Svenska Dagbladet*; and the center *Skånska Dagbladet*.

Introduction

Almond, Gabriel. *Political Development*. Boston: Little, Brown and Company, 1970.

———, and James Coleman (eds.). *The Politics of the Developing Areas*. Princeton, N.J.: Princeton University Press, 1960.

———, and G. Bingham Powell. *Comparative Politics. A Developmental Approach*. Boston: Little, Brown and Company, 1966.

———, and Sidney Verba. *The Civic Culture*. Boston: Little, Brown and Company, 1965.

Apter, David E. *The Politics of Modernization*. Chicago: University of Chicago Press, 1965.

Aron, Raymond. *The Industrial Society*. New York: Simon and Schuster, 1968.

Bell, Daniel. *The End of Ideology*, rev. ed. New York: Collier Books, 1961.

Black, C. E. *The Dynamics of Modernization*. New York: Harper & Row, 1966.

Brzezinski, Zbigniew. *Between Two Ages. America's Role in the Technetronic Era*. New York: The Viking Press, 1970.

Dahrendorf, Ralf. *Class and Class Conflict in Industrial Society*. Stanford, Calif.: Stanford University Press, 1959.

Deutsch, Karl. "Social Mobilization and Political Development," *American Political Science Review*, 55 (1961), 493–514.

Eckstein, Harry. *Division and Cohesion in Democracy*. Princeton, N.J.: Princeton University Press, 1966.

Friedrich, Manfred. *Opposition ohne Alternative?* Cologne: Verlag Wissenschaft und Politik, 1963.

Halpern, Manfred. "A Redefinition of the Revolutionary Situation," *Journal of International Affairs*, 23 (1969), 54–75.

Hancock, M. Donald, and Gideon Sjoberg (eds.). *Politics in the Post-Welfare State: Responses to the New Individualism*. New York: Columbia University Press, 1972.

Huntington, Samuel. "The Change to Change: Modernization, Development, and Politics," *Comparative Politics*, 3 (April 1971), 283–322.

———. *Political Order in Changing Societies*. New Haven, Conn.: Yale University Press, 1968.

Kahn, Herman. *Toward the Year 2000*. New York: Macmillan, 1967.

Lipset, S. M. *Political Man*. New York: Anchor Books, 1963.

Rustow, Dankwart A. *A World of Nations*. Washington, D.C.: Brookings Institution, 1967.

Sjoberg, Gideon, and Leonard D. Cain. "Negative Values, Countersystem Models, and the Analysis of Social Systems," in Herman Turk and Richard Simpson (eds.). *The Sociologies of Talcott Parsons and George C. Homans*. Indianapolis, Ind.: Bobbs-Merrill, 1971.

———, M. Donald Hancock, and Orion White, Jr. *Politics in the Post-Welfare State: A Comparison of the United States and Sweden*. Bloomington, Ind.: Carnegie Seminar on Political and Administrative Development, 1967.

Tingsten, Herbert. *Från idéer till idyll.* Stockholm: P. A. Norstedt & Söner, 1966.

Chapter One

Andersson, Ingvar. *A History of Sweden.* London: Weidenfeld and Nicolson, 1956.

Andrén, Nils. *Government and Politics in the Nordic Countries.* Stockholm: Almqvist & Wiksell, 1964.

————. *Svensk statskunskap.* Stockholm: Bokförlaget Liber, 1963.

Arneson, Ben A. *The Democratic Monarchies of Scandinavia.* New York: D. Van Nostrand Company, Inc., 1949.

Brusewitz, Axel. *Kungamakt, herremakt, folkmakt.* Stockholm: Bokförlaget Prisma, 1951.

Bukdahl, Jørgen, et al. *Scandinavia, Past and Present.* 3 vols. Odense: Arnkrone, 1957.

Childs, Marquis W. *Sweden: The Middle Way.* New Haven, Conn.: Yale University Press, 1937.

Derry, Thomas Kingston. *A Short History of Norway.* London: George Allen & Unwin, 1957.

Friis, Henning (ed.). *Scandinavia between East and West.* Ithaca, N.Y.: Cornell University Press, 1950.

Gustafsson, Lars. *The Public Dialogue in Sweden.* Stockholm: P. A. Norstedt & Söner, 1964.

Håstad, Elis. *Sveriges historia under 1900-talet.* Stockholm: Bonniers Förlag, 1958.

Heckscher, Eli F. *An Economic History of Sweden.* Cambridge, Mass.: Harvard University Press, 1954.

Herlitz, Nils. *Grunddragen av det svenska statsskickets historia,* 5th ed. Stockholm: P. A. Norstedt & Söner, 1959.

————. *Sweden: A Modern Democracy on Ancient Foundations.* Minneapolis, Minn.: University of Minnesota Press, 1939.

Höjer, Karl. *Social Welfare in Sweden.* Stockholm: The Swedish Institute, 1949.

————. *Svensk socialpolitisk historia.* Stockholm: P. A. Norstedt & Söner, 1952.

Kälvesten, Anna-Lisa. *The Social Structure of Sweden.* Stockholm: The Swedish Institute, 1965.

Lauring, Palle. *A History of the Kingdom of Denmark,* trans. by David Hohnen. Copenhagen: Høst, 1960.

Lauwerys, Joseph A., et al. *Scandinavian Democracy.* Copenhagen: The Danish Institute, the Norwegian Office of Cultural Relations, and the Swedish Institute in cooperation with the American-Scandinavian Foundation, 1958.

Montgomery, Arthur. *How Sweden Overcame the Depression 1930–1933.* Stockholm: Bonniers Förlag, 1938.

Nordström, G. Hilding. *Sveriges socialdemokratiska arbetareparti under genomsbrottsåren, 1889–1894.* Stockholm: Kooperativa Förbundets Förlag, 1938.

Rosenthal, Albert H. *The Social Programs of Sweden. A Search for Security in a Free Society*. Minneapolis, Minn.: University of Minnesota Press, 1967.

Rustow, Dankwart A. *Politics of Compromise*. Princeton, N.J.: Princeton University Press, 1955.

Samuelsson, Kurt. *From Great Power to Welfare State*. London: George Allen & Unwin, 1968.

Tingsten, Herbert. *Den svenska socialdemokratiens idéutveckling*. 2 vols. Stockholm: Tiden, 1941.

Tomasson, Richard F. *Sweden: Prototype of Modern Society*. New York: Random House, 1970.

Verney, Douglas. *Parliamentary Reform in Sweden, 1866–1921*. Oxford: Clarendon Press, 1957.

Chapter Two

Almond, Gabriel, and Sidney Verba. *The Civic Culture*. Boston: Little, Brown and Company, 1965.

Anton, Thomas J. "Policy-Making and Political Culture in Sweden," *Scandinavian Political Studies*, 4. New York: Columbia University Press, 1969.

Austin, Paul Britten. *On Being Swedish*. Coral Gables, Fla.: University of Miami Press, 1968.

Bottomore, T. B. *Elites and Society*. New York: Basic Books, Inc., 1964.

Coleman, James (ed.). *Education and Political Development*. Princeton, N.J.: Princeton University Press, 1965.

Dawson, Richard, and Kenneth Prewitt. *Political Socialization*. Boston: Little, Brown and Company, 1969.

Hendin, Herbert. *Suicide and Scandinavia*. New York: Grune and Stratton, Inc., 1964.

Myrdal, Jan. *Confessions of a Disloyal European*. New York: Pantheon Books, 1968.

Särlvik, Bo. "Party Politics and Electoral Opinion Formation: A Study of Issues in Swedish Politics 1956–1960," *Scandinavian Political Studies*, 2. New York: Columbia University Press, 1967.

————. "Political Stability and Change in the Swedish Electorate," *Scandinavian Political Studies*, 1. New York: Columbia University Press, 1966.

————. "Socioeconomic Determinants of Voting Behavior in the Swedish Electorate," *Comparative Political Studies*, 2 (April 1969), 99–135.

Thoenes, Piet. *The Elite in the Welfare State*, trans. by J. E. Bingham. New York: The Free Press, 1966.

Tomasson, Richard F. *Sweden: Prototype of Modern Society*. New York: Random House, 1970.

Chapter Three

Ahlmark, Per. *Vår fattiga politik*. Stockholm: Bonniers Förlag, 1964.

————, *et al. Många liberaler*. Stockholm: Bonniers Förlag, 1966.

————, *et al. Mitt i 60-talet*. Stockholm: Bonniers Förlag, 1965.

Anners, Erik, and Gustaf Delin. *Framtidens politiska villkor*. Stockholm: Bokförlaget Medborgarskolan, n.d.

Dahl, Robert A. "Preface," in Dahl (ed.). *Political Oppositions in Western Democracies.* New Haven. Conn.: Yale University Press, 1966.

Eisenstadt, S. N. *Modernization: Protest and Change.* Englewood Cliffs, N.J.: Prentice-Hall, Inc., 1966.

Eliason, Torsten. *Är välfärd nog?* Stockholm: Rabén & Sjögren Bokförlag, 1963.

Gustafson, Alrik. *A History of Swedish Literature.* Minneapolis, Minn.: University of Minnesota Press, 1961.

Gyllensten, Lars. "Swedish Radicalism in the 1960s: An Experiment in Political and Cultural Debate," in M. Donald Hancock and Gideon Sjoberg (eds.). *Politics in the Post-Welfare State: Responses to the New Individualism.* New York: Columbia University Press, 1972.

Hermansson, C. H. *Vänsterns väg.* Stockholm: Rabén & Sjögren Bokförlag, 1965.

Linnarson, Lennart. "Statsrådet i Sverige 1809–1934," in *De nordiska ländernas statsråd.* Uppsala: Statsvetenskapliga Föreningen, 1935.

Linnér, Birgitta. *Society and Sex in Sweden.* Stockholm: The Swedish Institute, 1967.

Samuelsson, Kurt. *Är ideologierna döda.* Stockholm: Bokförlaget Aldus/ Bonniers, 1966.

Sköld, Lars, and Arne Halvarson. "Riksdagens sociala sammsättning under hundra år," in Arthur Thomson (ed.). *Samhälle och riksdag,* I. Stockholm: Almqvist & Wiksell, 1966.

Sparring, Åke. *Från Högland till Hermansson. Om revisionismen i Sveriges kommunistiska parti.* Stockholm: Bonniers Förlag, 1967.

——— (ed.). *Kommunismen i Norden.* Stockholm: Bokförlaget Aldus/ Bonniers, 1965.

Tingsten, Herbert. *Demokratiens problem,* rev. ed. Stockholm: Bokförlaget Aldus/Bonniers, 1960.

———. *Från idéer till idyll.* Stockholm: P. A. Norstedt & Söner, 1966.

———. *Strid kring idyllen.* Stockholm: P. A. Norstedt & Söner, 1966.

Chapter Four

Andrén, Nils. *Modern Swedish Government.* Stockholm: Almqvist & Wiksell, 1961.

Jonnergård, Gustaf. *Staten och kommunerna.* Södertälje: Svenska Landsbygdens Studieförbund, 1965.

Sweden, Justitiedepartementet. *Statens offentliga utredningar 1965:54. Författningsfrågan och det kommunala sambandet.* Stockholm: Justitiedepartementet, 1965.

———. *Statens offentliga utredningar 1963:16. Författningsutredningen: VI, Sveriges statsskick, Del 1. Lagförslag.* Stockholm: Justitiedepartementet, 1963.

———. *Statens offentliga utredningar 1967:26. Partiell författningsreform.* Stockholm: Justitiedepartementet, 1967.

Chapter Five

Andrén, Nils. *Modern Swedish Government.* Stockholm: Almqvist & Wiksell, 1961.

————. "Sweden: State Support for Political Parties," *Scandinavian Political Studies*, 3. New York: Columbia University Press, 1968.

Anners, Erik. "Conservatism in Sweden," in M. Donald Hancock and Gideon Sjoberg (eds.). *Politics in the Post-Welfare State: Responses to the New Individualism*. New York: Columbia University Press, 1972.

Back, Pär-Erik. "Det svenska partiväsendet," in Arthur Thomson (ed.). *Samhälle och riksdag*, II. Stockholm: Almqvist & Wiksell. 1966.

Fusilier, Raymond. *Le Parti Socialiste Suedois*. Paris: Les Éditions Ouvrières, 1960.

Håstad, Elis. *Partierna i regering och riksdag*. Stockholm: Bonniers Förlag, 1938.

Inghe, Gunnar, and Maj-Britt Inghe. *Den öfardiga välfärden*. Stockholm: Tiden, 1967.

Mittensamverkan 68. Gemensamt politiskt handlingsprogram för centerpartiet och folkpartiet. Stockholm: Bokförlaget Folk & Samhälle, 1968.

Ohlin, Bertil. *Liberal utmaning*. Stockholm: Bokförlaget Folk och Samhälle, 1963.

Palme, Olof. *Politik är att vilja*. Stockholm: Bokförlaget Prisma, 1968.

Rustow, Dankwart A. "Scandinavia: Working Multiparty Systems," in Sigmund Neumann (ed.). *Modern Political Parties*. Chicago: University of Chicago Press, 1956.

————. *The Politics of Compromise: A Study of Parties and Cabinet Government in Sweden*. Princeton, N.J.: Princeton University Press, 1955.

Rydenfelt, Sven. *Kommunismen i Sverige*. Lund: C. W. K. Gleerup Bokförlag, 1954.

Stjernquist, Nils. "Sweden: Stability or Deadlock?" in Robert A. Dahl (ed.). *Political Oppositions in Western Democracies*. New Haven, Conn.: Yale University Press, 1966.

Sveriges socialdemokratiska arbetareparti. *Program för aktiv näringspolitik. Näringspolitiska kommitténs slutrapport*. Stockholm: Sveriges socialdemokratiska arbetareparti, 1968. (Mimeographed.)

Tomasson, Richard. "The Extraordinary Success of the Swedish Social Democrats," *The Journal of Politics*, 31 (August 1969), 772–798.

Wieslander, Hans (ed.). *De politiska partiernas program*. Stockholm: Bokförlaget Prisma, 1964.

Chapter Six

Almond, Gabriel, and G. Bingham Powell. *Comparative Politics. A Developmental Approach*. Boston: Little, Brown and Company, 1966.

Eckstein, Harry. *Pressure Group Politics*. Stanford, Calif.: Stanford University Press, 1960.

Elvander, Nils. *Intresseorganisationerna i dagens Sverige*. Lund: C. W. K. Gleerup Bokförlag, 1966.

————. "Organisationera och statsmakterna," *Industriförbundets tidskrift*, 8 (October 1963), 424–429.

Foyer, Lars. "Former för kontakt och samverkan mellan staten och organisationerna," in Sweden, Justitiedepartementet. *Statens offentliga utredningar 1961:21. Författningsutredningen: V, Organisationer, beslutsteknik, valsystem*. Stockholm: Justitiedepartementet, 1961.

Heckscher, Gunnar. "Interest Groups in Sweden: Their Political Role," in

Henry W. Ehrmann (ed.). *Interest Groups on Four Continents*. Pittsburgh, Pa.: University of Pittsburgh Press, 1958.
————. "Pluralist Democracy. The Swedish Experience," *Social Research*, 15 (December 1948), 417–461.
Huntford, Roland. "Why Did They Strike?" *Sweden Now*, 4 (June 1970), 36–38.
Jenkins, David. "Mixed Economy," *Sweden Now*, 3 (November 1969), 52–53, 100, 102.
Korpi, Walter. "Varför strejkar arbetarna?" *Tiden*, 62 (February 1970), 69–72.
Rokkan, Stein. "Norway: Numerical Democracy and Corporate Pluralism," in Robert A. Dahl (ed.). *Political Oppositions in Western Democracies*. New Haven, Conn.: Yale University Press, 1966.
Samuelsson, Kurt. "The Ironminers Walkout—Signal of Change?" *Viewpoint*. New York: Swedish Information Service, January 28, 1970. (Mimeographed.)
Wieslander, Hans. "Organisationerna i det moderna samhället," in Pär-Erik Back (ed.). *Modern Demokrati*, 2d ed. Lund: C. W. K. Gleerup Bokförlag, 1965.

Chapter Seven

Amilon, Ingvar. "Partiledarkonferenserna—en studie i parlamentarisk praxis," *Statsvetenskaplig tidskrift*, 66 (1963), 278–286.
Andrén, Nils. "Interpellationer och enkla frågor," in Arthur Thomson (ed.). *Samhälle och riksdag*, II. Stockholm: Almqvist & Wiksell, 1966.
————. *Modern Swedish Government*. Stockholm: Almqvist & Wiksell, 1961.
Fusilier, Raymond. *Les Monarchies Parlementaires*. Paris: Les Éditions Ouvrières, 1960.
Håstad, Elis. *The Parliament of Sweden*. London: The Hansard Society, 1957.
Heckscher, Gunnar. *The Swedish Constitution, 1809–1959*. Stockholm: The Swedish Institute, 1959.
Herlitz, Nils. *Grunddragen av det svenska statskickets historia*, 5th ed. Stockholm: Svenska Bokförlaget/P. A. Norstedt & Söner, 1959.
Malmgren, Robert. *Sveriges grundlagar och tillhörande författningar*, 8th ed. Stockholm: P. A. Norstedt & Söner, 1964.
Nyman, Olle. *Parlamentarismen i Sverige*. Stockholm: Medborgarskolans Bokförlag, 1961.
————. *Svensk parlamentarism 1932–1936*. Stockholm: Almqvist & Wiksell, 1947.
Ruin, Olof. *Mellan samlingsregering och tvåpartisystem. Den svenska regeringsfrågan 1945–1960*. Stockholm: Bonniers Förlag, 1968.
————. "Patterns of Government Composition in Multi-party Systems: The Case of Sweden," *Scandinavian Political Studies*, 4. New York: Columbia University Press, 1969.
Rokkan, Stein. *Citizens, Elections, Parties*. Oslo: Universitetsforlaget, 1970.
Stjernquist, Nils. "Riksdagens arbete och arbetsformer," in Arthur Thomson (ed.). *Samhälle och riksdag*, IV. Stockholm: Almqvist & Wiksell, 1966.

Chapter Eight

Andrén, Nils, *et al. Svensk statsförvaltning i omdaning.* Stockholm: Almqvist & Wiksell, 1965.

Heckscher, Gunnar. *Staten och organisationerna.* Stockholm: Kooperativa Förbundets Bokförlag, 1961.

————. *Svensk statförvaltning i arbete.* Stockholm: Studieförbundet Näringsliv och Samhälle, 1952.

Lewin, Leif. *Planhushållningsdebatten.* Stockholm: Almqvist & Wiksell, 1967.

Meijer, Hans. "Bureaucracy and Policy Formation in Sweden," *Scandinavian Political Studies,* 4. New York: Columbia University Press, 1969.

————. *Kommitépolitik och kommitéarbete.* Lund: C. W. K. Gleerup Bokförlag, 1956.

Molin, Björn. *Tjänstepensionsfrågan.* Göteborg: Akademieförlaget, 1965.

Ortmark, Åke. *Maktspelet i Sverige.* Stockholm: Wahlström & Widstrand, 1967.

Rustow, Dankwart A. *The Politics of Compromise: A Study of Parties and Cabinet Government in Sweden.* Princeton, N.J.: Princeton University Press, 1955.

Stjernquist, Nils. "Sweden: Stability or Deadlock?" in Robert A. Dahl (ed.). *Political Oppositions in Western Democracies.* New Haven, Conn.: Yale University Press, 1966.

Sweden, Justitiedepartementet. *Statens offentliga utredningar 1959:10. Folkomröstningen 1957.* Stockholm: Justitiedepartementet, 1957.

Tingsten, Herbert. *Mitt Liv, III: Tidningen, 1946–1952.* Stockholm: P. A. Norstedt & Söner, 1963.

Chapter Nine

Andersson, Ingvar. *A History of Sweden.* London: Weidenfeld and Nicolson, 1956.

Bexelius, Alfred. "The Origin, Nature, and Functions of the Civil and Military Ombudsmen in Sweden," *The Annals of the American Academy of Political and Social Science,* 377 (May 1968), 10–19.

Gellhorn, Walter. *Ombudsmen and Others.* Cambridge, Mass.: Harvard University Press, 1966.

Mendelson, Wallace. "Law and the Development of Nations," *The Journal of Politics,* 32 (May 1970), 223–238.

Rowat, Donald C. (ed.). *The Ombudsman.* London: George Allen & Unwin, 1965.

Chapter Ten

Abrahamsen, Samuel. *Sweden's Foreign Policy.* Washington, D.C.: Brookings Institution, 1957.

Anderson, Stanley V. *The Nordic Council.* Seattle, Wash.: University of Washington Press, 1967.

Andrén, Nils. *Power-Balance and Non-Alignment.* Stockholm: Almqvist & Wiksell, 1967.

————, and Åke Landquist. *Svensk utrikespolitik efter 1945.* Stockholm: Almqvist & Wiksell, 1965.

Etzioni, Amatai. *Political Unification.* New York: Holt, Rinehart and Winston, Inc., 1965.

Fox, Annette Baker. *The Power of Small States.* Chicago: University of Chicago Press, 1959.

Håstad, Elis. "Sweden's Attitude toward the United Nations," in Swedish Institute of International Affairs. *Sweden and the United Nations.* New York: Manhattan Publishing Company, 1956.

Institute for Strategic Studies. *The Military Balance 1970–1971.* London: Institute for Strategic Studies, 1970.

Jakobsen, Max. *Finnish Neutrality.* London: Hugh Evelyn, Ltd., 1968.

Lindberg, Folke, and John Kolehmainen. *The Scandinavian Countries in International Affairs. A Selected Bibliography.* Minneapolis, Minn.: University of Minnesota Press, 1953.

Lindgren, Raymond. *Norway-Sweden: Union, Disunion, Reunion.* Princeton, N.J.: Princeton University Press, 1959.

Scott, Franklin D. *The United States and Scandinavia.* Cambridge, Mass.: Harvard University Press, 1950.

Sweden, Royal Ministry for Foreign Affairs. *Documents on Swedish Foreign Policy 1968.* Stockholm: Utrikesdepartementet, 1969.

Tingsten, Herbert. *The Debate on the Foreign Policy of Sweden, 1918–1939,* trans. by Joan Bulman. New York: Oxford University Press, 1950.

Wendt, Frantz. *The Nordic Council and Co-Operation in Scandinavia.* Copenhagen: Munksgaard, 1959.

Wuorinen, John H. *Scandinavia.* Englewood Cliffs, N.J.: Prentice-Hall, 1965.

Chapter Eleven

Brzezinski, Zbigniew. *Between Two Ages. America's Role in the Technetronic Era.* New York: The Viking Press, 1970.

Dahl, Robert A. *After the Revolution?* New Haven, Conn.: Yale University Press, 1970.

————. "Epilogue" in Dahl (ed.). *Political Oppositions in Western Democracies.* New Haven, Conn.: Yale University Press, 1966.

Eisenstadt, S. N. *Modernization: Protest and Change.* Englewood Cliffs, N.J.: Prentice-Hall, Inc., 1966.

"Epilogue," in M. Donald Hancock and Gideon Sjoberg (eds.). *Politics in the Post-Welfare State: Responses to the New Individualism.* New York: Columbia University Press, 1972.

Ginzberg, Eli. "Sweden: Some Unanswered Questions," *The Public Interest,* 18 (Fall 1970), 158–166.

Gouldner, Alvin W. *The Coming Crisis of Western Sociology.* New York: Basic Books, Inc., 1970.

Myrdal, Gunnar. *Beyond the Welfare State.* London: Gerard Duckworth & Co., Ltd., 1960.

Sjoberg, Gideon, and Leonard D. Cain. "Negative Values, Countersystem Models, and the Analysis of Social Systems," in Herman Turk and Richard Simpson (eds.). *The Sociologies of Talcott Parsons and George C. Homans.* Indianapolis, Ind.: Bobbs-Merrill, 1971.

————, M. Donald Hancock, and Orion White, Jr. *Politics in the Post-*

Welfare State: A Comparison of the United States and Sweden. Bloomington, Ind.: Carnegie Seminar on Political and Administrative Development, 1967.

Slater, Philip. *The Pursuit of Loneliness.* Boston: Beacon Press, 1970.

Toffler, Alvin. *Future Shock.* New York: Random House, 1970.

White, Orion, Jr. "The Dialectical Organization—An Alternative to Bureaucracy," *Public Administration Review*, 29 (January–February 1969), 32–42.

INDEX